THE CENTENNIAL EDITION

OF THE WORKS OF

SIDNEY LANIER

GENERAL EDITOR

CHARLES R. ANDERSON

I. POEMS
Edited by CHARLES R. ANDERSON

II. THE SCIENCE OF ENGLISH VERSE and ESSAYS ON MUSIC
Edited by PAULL F. BAUM

III. SHAKSPERE AND HIS FORERUNNERS
Edited by KEMP MALONE

IV. THE ENGLISH NOVEL and ESSAYS ON LITERATURE
Edited by CLARENCE GOHDES and KEMP MALONE

V. TIGER-LILIES and SOUTHERN PROSE
Edited by GARLAND GREEVER

VI. FLORIDA and MISCELLANEOUS PROSE
Edited by PHILIP GRAHAM

VII-X. LETTERS
Edited by CHARLES R. ANDERSON and AUBREY H. STARKE

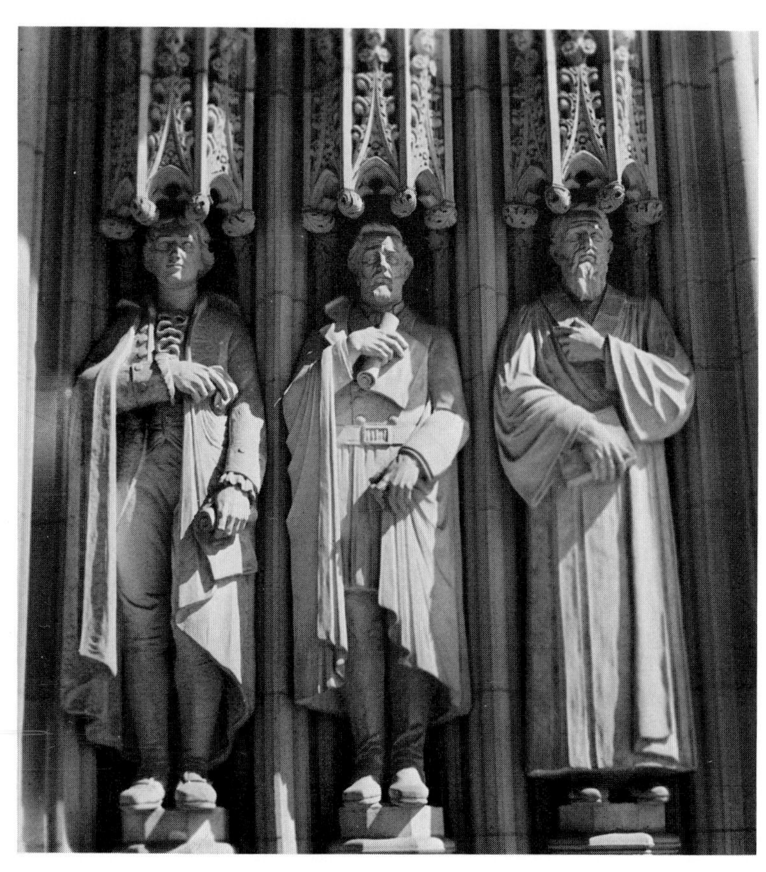

Symbolic Figures of Jefferson, Lee, and Lanier

Duke University Chapel, 1932

CENTENNIAL EDITION

VOLUME V

SIDNEY LANIER

TIGER-LILIES

AND

SOUTHERN PROSE

EDITED BY

GARLAND GREEVER

ASSISTED BY

CECIL ABERNETHY

BALTIMORE

THE JOHNS HOPKINS PRESS

1945

Second Printing, 1963

PRINTED IN THE UNITED STATES OF AMERICA

CONTENTS

INTRODUCTION

THE PURPOSE Lanier had held in his last year at Oglethorpe to prepare himself for college teaching, though thwarted by the war, may have been what deterred him for his first two years as a soldier from literary efforts. On May 12, 1863, however—just midway the conflict—his father wrote Clifford Lanier that the "annals & . . . episodes" of the struggle would in the future employ many pens, "whether historical, philosophical, dramatic or comic," and advised both sons to "take notes of many things you see or hear of." [1] Whether or not in response to this stimulus, Lanier on the Lower James turned to authorship in the months following. On January 18, 1864, he declared his "whole soul" was "merging itself into this business of writing, especially of writing poetry."

Prose fiction also attracted him strongly. While on furlough in late October and early November, 1863, he probably spoke to R. S. Lanier of intending a venture in it. For soon after returning to Virginia he told his father (letter of December 7) that he was meditating his novel "in the long night-guards" at Fort Boykin and that, fascinated by "the multiplicity of scenes and incidents" crowding upon him, he could hardly find time to write, or at any rate to copy, the introductory chapter or formulate much of the plot. On January 4, 1864, though hurried meanwhile into a campaign in North Carolina, he reported, "I have made a rough draft of two Chapters of my novel: and have about finished my conception of the plot." A fortnight later he sent the two chapters to his father for criticism. On February 6 Clifford, on his way back from North Carolina, announced that "Brother Sid" had written "three more chapters."

Virginia Hankins, testifying afterward that Lanier began *Tiger-Lilies* "in the leisure of camp-life at Fort Boykin," recalled also the "joyous ardor" with which he read the "first pages" aloud at Bacon's Castle.[2] On March 14, 1864, he exulted to his father, "Some very grand projects begin to present themselves to me, in connection with the novel. . . . Not only grand, but feasible." Soon, however, General Butler moved with Federal fleet and army from Fortress Monroe against

[1] Unless otherwise marked, letters referred to in this Introduction are printed or cited in the present edition, vols. VII-X, or may be found in (a) the Charles D. Lanier Collection or (b) the Clifford A. Lanier Collection, both at Johns Hopkins University. Other MSS mentioned without being assigned elsewhere are in the Charles D. Lanier Collection. (Usually the giving of an exact date in the Introduction implies a letter of that date.)

[2] *Southern Bivouac*, II, 760-761 (May, 1887).

Petersburg, and for more than a year Lanier added nothing to the five chapters he had written.

Partly recovering from physical collapse at the end of the war, he found time while a tutor at the Fulton plantation, near Macon, for various literary endeavors. Letters to Clifford show that by the end of September he had at least four more chapters of his novel on paper and " a whole host of others " in his head. Illness drove him to Point Clear, Alabama, where his pen must have been idle. At the Exchange Hotel in Montgomery, in 1866 and early 1867, it became very active again. On March 3, 1867, the novel was " finished and within a day's work of being ready for the press." [3]

Almost precisely two years after Appomattox Lanier set off with the manuscript for New York. There, as he wrote Clifford on June 15, he underwent "many rebuffs" and "much weariness and waiting." Nevertheless, as his letter of May 17 to Gertrude Lanier announced, "the best firm of Publishers in New York"—inferentially Hurd & Houghton of 459 Broome Street—made him " propositions," not necessarily written or specific but looking to him, we assume, to finance publication. He was ultimately to borrow the money for this purpose from his Northern kinsman J. F. D. Lanier.[4] First, however, letting alternatives be explored, he entrusted the manuscript to a broker, Edward G. Parker, superintendent of the American Bureau for Literary Reference, 132 Nassau Street, and returned to the South. Parker obtained an offer from Blelock & Company, 453 Broome Street, to include *Tiger-Lilies* in a "Library of Select Novels by Southern Authors." Before July 12 Lanier declined to publish on the terms proposed.[5]

[3] Evidence of Lanier's chronological progress on his task is fairly ample, though confusing or even contradictory about some details. On May 12, 1866, Lanier hoped to finish the novel " ere long." On May 27 Clifford bore witness that he was "writing nearly a chapter every day." On June 22 R. S. Lanier criticized the first two chapters of Book II. By July 1 Lanier had evolved some ten chapters and counted on having about ten others to do. On July 13 he was beginning " to see the end of the novel " and was thinking of publishing it with Clifford's *Thorn-Fruit* in one volume. On Oct. 9 R. S. Lanier could have no better tidings than " that Sid's only 'doctor' " was " doctor Resolve-to-finish-his-book." Five days later Lanier explained, " I get on slowly with the book: but, I believe, surely." About Feb. 15, 1867, he had finished *Tiger-Lilies* but needed " two weeks, at longest," to copy and arrange the MS.

[4] See notes 42 and 48, Letters of 1867.

[5] By these terms Lanier would pay for the plates at "a little less than $5 a page double column, 128 pages in all"; Blelock would bear the other expenses and print initially 3,000 copies, in paper covers; author and publisher would share the net profits equally. The broker, on his part, would have a fee of $50 if the offer were accepted, otherwise nothing.

By July 24 he entered into a contract with Hurd & Houghton whereby he was to pay $400 down and $400 on publication for an edition of 1,000 copies and to underwrite alterations in press, advertising, and the supplying of copies for review, while the company was to receive 10% on the retail price from sales. Under this arrangement the novel was published, apparently at the end of November, 1867. The actual number of volumes issued was 962. The price was $1.75. Lanier was excused from paying half the second instalment of $400.

By New Year's Day, 1868, Lanier was entitled to $1.05 apiece on the 515 copies sold, less the extra expenses that had accumulated.[6] The publishers remitted a balance of $227.48 and began to talk of a second edition of 500 copies, which should cost the author only 48 or 50 cents each. Unfortunately, of the 174 copies still on hand 59 remained unsold after another year (in the latter half of 1868 only seven had been disposed of), and the novelist had in pocket a mere $96.33 more.

To salvage what he might Lanier, at an unspecified date, drafted an offer (still extant, but bearing no address) to transfer ownership of copyright and copper plates for $500. If he circularized publishers with this, he found no takers.

It seems likely that both Blelock and Hurd & Houghton thought *Tiger-Lilies* would find its chief market in the South and were disposed to leave sales largely to the author's exertions. The copies Lanier individually purchased seem to have been turned over to local dealers, at least some of whom deducted for themselves 20% of the proceeds.[7] The total sales, Lanier wrote Clifford afterward (October 14, 1874), were 800; this estimate slightly exceeds the possible sales under the Hurd & Houghton reports. The chances are that *Tiger-Lilies* cost Lanier $200 to $275 in excess of what he got back. The deficit does not include the expense of his trip to New York.

That, after a brisk beginning, sales fell off so disastrously may have been due in part to the material depression and political dismay which just then paralyzed the South, in part to the inertia of the publishers. It is probable, though, that even under favorable auspices *Tiger-Lilies* would not have sold widely. As conditions were, no second issue was called for.

Later in 1867 Blelock brought out Clifford Lanier's *Thorn-Fruit* as No. 3 in his Library, pricing it at fifty cents a copy.

The Parker correspondence is in the Charles D. Lanier Collection, Johns Hopkins University.

[6] Representative expenses: $11.52 for alterations in the MS, $80 for 100 copies purchased by Lanier, $138.40 for 173 copies for review, $41.53 for advertising. (Data in this paragraph and the one preceding are from the Hurd & Houghton correspondence, reports of sales, etc., in the Charles D. Lanier Collection.)

[7] See Clifford A. Lanier's letter, Jan. 2, 1867 (1868).

The critical response was like the monetary—encouraging but short-lived. Kinsmen and friends made discriminating comments. Clifford, at the author's elbow through most of the writing, in effect characterized the novel then as he was to long afterward, "It is not thought-out, but poured-out, like the lead fused in a ladle for bullets by a hunter." [8] R. S. Lanier thought the masque-ball chapter the best and was impressed with the war-flower image, but raised questions to be touched upon later in this Introduction. Virginia Hankins found vagueness and immaturity with an *embarras de richesses*; she protested Lanier's sentiment that the only real wretchedness "is the suffering of one's own transgressions." [9] Salem Dutcher commended the artistic merits of the novel. In a letter to Lanier, January 4, 1868, Edward B. Peck made a shrewd and well-balanced analysis.

Three Southern men of letters—one beginning, one midway, and one ending his career—took cognizance of the novel, the first two privately. Joel Chandler Harris, for a few months a typesetter in Macon, had apparently met or seen Lanier, regarded him as "a good, modest young man, charming in manner," deemed him "the most accomplished flute player in America," and detected in his music "something weird and mysterious, ravishing and entrancing" which was not to be described though a passage in *Tiger-Lilies* "comes near telling it." He pronounced the novel "original and good," [10] and on June 29, 1868, recommended having another "ready for the Fall trade." Paul Hamilton Hayne, in letters of September 7 and December 5, 1868, and October 30, 1869, was amazed that such "brilliant talent" should have been shown by a sick man and besought Lanier not to let his first work be his last. William Gilmore Simms enjoyed the novel and anonymously reviewed it in the Charleston *Courier* (mentioned below).[11]

Most newspaper notices are doubtless lost. Scattered ones remain in files, in clippings [12] which frequently omit date and source, or as reprints in other papers. The principal Southern notices found are those in the Macon *Daily Telegraph* of (December?) 17, 1867, the *Georgia*

[8] Letter to W. M. Baskervill, Sept. 21, 1896. MS, Duke University Library.

[9] For her debate with Lanier on this topic see her letters of Jan. 27, 1868, and Mar., 1869, his letter conjecturally dated Apr., 1869, and below, p. 47.

[10] Robert L. Wiggins, *The Life of Joel Chandler Harris* (Nashville, 1918), pp. 70-71 and 80.

[11] Simms is identified as author of the review in Hurd & Houghton's letter to Lanier, Feb. 27, 1868. (Simms' copy of *Tiger-Lilies*, with sundry passages marked, is in the possession of the present editor.)

[12] These are in the Charles D. Lanier Collection, Johns Hopkins University. The one from the Milledgeville *Era*, mentioned in the next sentence, lists the price of *Tiger-Lilies* as $1.50.

Journal and Messenger (Macon) of December 18, 1867,[13] the Milledgeville *Era* (date unknown), and the Charleston *Courier* of February 4, 1868 (Simms' article).[14] The principal Northern notices are those in the New York *Evening Mail* and the February 25, 1868, issue of the Syracuse *Courier and Union* (the paper with which Lanier's friend Milton H. Northrup was connected).[15]

Reviews by four magazines have been preserved: the *Home Monthly* (Baltimore; the clipping is undated); the *Round Table* (New York), December 14, 1867; *Peterson's Magazine* (Philadelphia), March, 1868; and the *Atlantic Monthly* (Boston), March, 1868.[16]

Two other discussions survive. The first, a manuscript critique signed I. (J.?) K. M., appears to be the report of Parker's reader. The other forms part of the sketch of Lanier in James Wood Davidson's volume *Living Writers of the South* (New York, 1869).

Most reviewers below the Potomac showed awareness that Lanier was one of their own, and the Milledgeville *Era* commended the presentation of the "heroic struggle" of "the glorious army of Virginia." The *Round Table*, though lauding the absence of "sectional rancor," thought it detected "sympathies with the rebellion"; the *Atlantic Monthly* waxed sarcastic that the villain was a Northerner; and Parker's reader, sure that "the art, music, and metaphysics" made Boston the place to publish, felt equally certain that "the Confederate sentiments would . . . keep the book from that market." All in all, however, the sectional stops were but lightly sounded.

Essentially the critics were in fair accord with each other. Nearly all thought the plot flaccid and the movement sluggish; some remarked that the narrative improved in Book II. Many were baffled or smothered

[13] The weekly issue. Presumably it duplicates the column in the issue (lost) of Dec. 15 which Lanier mentioned in a letter of Dec. 16, 1867.

[14] In addition the Macon (*Journal and*?) *Messenger* had a preliminary notice (reproduced in the Montgomery *Weekly Mail* of Dec. 11, 1867); the Montgomery *Weekly Mail* itself contained notices on Dec. 11, 1867, and Jan. 1, 1868; an unidentified paper (in Savannah?) carried a paragraph; and the New Orleans *Picayune* of Mar. 19, 1868, referred to the novel in commenting on "Little Ella." Also the Macon *Daily Telegraph* mentioned *Tiger-Lilies* in discussing Clifford Lanier's *Thorn-Fruit* (see letter of Jan. 28, 1868), and the Milledgeville *Federal Union* had a notice (see letter of Sept. 3, 1868), but neither of these notices has been found.

[15] The New York *Evening Mail* notice was reprinted in the *Georgia Journal and Messenger* on Dec. 18, 1867, and in the Montgomery *Weekly Mail* on Dec. 25, 1867. Apparently the *Courier and Union* review was written by Mrs. Mary E. Tucker (see Lanier's letter of Mar. 8, 1868).

We know, further, that the Galesburg *Press*, New York *Tribune*, and Cincinnati *Commercial* carried notices.

[16] Evidence exists that in addition there were reviews in the *Legal Intelligencer* (Philadelphia) and *Southern Society* (Baltimore), the latter before Jan. 26, 1868.

by the jumble of the contents, by the disquisitions, by the digressions, by the oddity or strain of phrasing or fancy, by the literary allusions, by the music and musical talk, by the intrusions of the author, by what Peck called the "tropical luxuriousness of beauties." Most sensed a lack of popular appeal. But despite their adverse comments, Lanier did not much overstate when he said that few "were not on the whole favorable."[17] Most emphasized the poetic quality of his work and the freshness of imagery and tone. Some observed the fidelity with which he reflected aspects of Southern life—especially mountain life—and presented scenes from camp, battlefield, and prison. Some adduced passages of workmanlike skill, esthetic charm, or moral impressiveness. Virtually all hailed Lanier for powers exceptional if unseasoned—for "great capacity, needing very severe training," as he summarized it (letter of June 15, 1867)—and discerned greater achievements ahead. "The South," affirmed Parker's reader, "has not produced a writer since the war, who promises as well as the author of this novel." "His errors," said the critic for the *Round Table*, "seem to us to be entirely errors of youth and in the right direction. . . . we hope to have from his pen a better novel than *Tiger-Lilies*—a better one, in fact, than any Southern writer has hitherto blest us with."

Lanier himself, though stoutly defending *Tiger-Lilies* against sundry criticisms, and though confident he and Clifford could "attain at least a rank as high as any hitherto attained by American authors," did not appraise his work extravagantly, even at the time (June 15, 1867). By May 17, 1869, he could speak of it as "a foolish book . . . of a foolish boy," adding, "Ah, how I have outgrown Tiger Lilies . . . !" He thought of rewriting it, but never did.

He had begun it, as the early letters to his father show, before fashioning "a consistent plot." Apparently he did not name it until it was completed; even Virginia Hankins, who had heard him read the initial chapters, found the title mystifying (January 27, 1868). But upon the New York *Evening Mail's* declaring he had been "dreamy" and "careless," he on January 14, 1868, wished to replace those adjectives with the words "all deliberate." He had in truth cherished definite intentions about what should go into the novel and how he should put it together.

To begin with, he purposely employed sundry elements, concepts, themes, and interests. Some of these we cannot get at except by divining as we read. But to some he gave explicit clues or brief

[17] See his letter to Northrup, Mar. 8, 1868. The most sweepingly condemnatory review, that in *Peterson's Magazine*, contained less than a complete grammatical sentence: "One of those novels, the chief wonder of which is, that they ever got published at all."

formulations in a manuscript preface, in the printed preface, in his correspondence, or in memoranda in his Ledger.

First, beauty. The preface existing in longhand begins, "Beautiful Things . . . float through my soul, in vague and cloudy forms . . . [and demand] that they be moulded into visible and suitable shapes." [18] The published preface announces that he withheld meretricious and melodramatic appeal because of "a love, strong as it is humble, for what is beautiful in God's Nature and in Man's Art." That a concern with beauty permeates the novel cannot escape notice.

Second, love. The manuscript preface shows that love—God's love and that love of which man at his highest is capable[19]—was early decided upon as the theme of the novel. The first motto following this draft—the only motto published—is the stanza from *In Memoriam* on giving earthly love his dues. Of the numerous references to love in the novel the passage on page 26, below, is best known.

Third, art. With love Lanier binds art. The draft of the preface closes, "God loves, and therefore He creates. We are made in His image, and all men are Authors." To this assurance he appends the warning, "*What* we love and *what* we create,—are seven words which stretch one way to Heaven and one way to Hell." The warning rightly intimates that the proper and the wrong use of art will have heed in the narrative. It also aids us in understanding certain characters. Philip Sterling and Rübetsahl exemplify wholesome, altruistic, heavenward-bent art. Cranston represents art diabolically distorted. Nowhere in the novel as published is Cranston's role so pointedly revealed as in the manuscript draft of the passage about the "chief-guest to a complimentary dinner" (page 37, below), where he is labeled "an Artist spoilt by . . . selfishness" and the explanation follows, "The essence, the one life, of art is Love, which is unselfishness." In consonance with Lanier's credo that art shall never be defeatist the published preface exhorts novelists to provide "more sunshine and less night," "more household sweetness and less Bohemian despair."

Fourth, music. On this particular art Lanier intended from the beginning to say much.[20] He fills the novel with the subject, of course

[18] Ledger, p. 46. (The Ledger—Henry W. Lanier Collection, Johns Hopkins University—is a commonplace book, repository of ideas for future development, and literary practice field; Lanier began it soon after the war.) The passage just quoted suggests at least a measure of improvisation, as does the second motto (set down on the same page): "It shall be called Bottom's dream, because it hath no bottom!" Note also Lanier's argument, below, against a rigid artistic pattern.

[19] On p. 260, below, Lanier defines it as "not a sentimentality; . . . [but] that grand overmastering passion for all that is noble in human life, and for all that is beautiful in natural organism."

[20] See the *Charles Auchester* passage in the letter of Apr. 12, 1864, to Mary Day.

interweaving love, as on page 31, below: "Music means harmony, harmony means love, and love means—God!"

Fifth, metaphysics. On August 6, 1867, Lanier informed Virginia Clay that his novel contained "some popularized metaphysical discussions." He did not intend that their popular cast should make them less earnest. As he wrote Virginia Hankins on May 17, 1869, he held that "philosophy and . . . lofty sentiments," so far from looking to "intellectual repose" as an end, should lead to "the most intense intellectual *activity*."

Sixth, personal experience. When he wrote Northrup (May 12, 1866) of perhaps getting his wartime adventures into print, he may have been thinking of Book II of *Tiger-Lilies.* In fact he levied upon both his civil and his military life for the novel.

Finally, the spirit and the meaning back of actualities. His published preface closes with the acknowledgment that his "chief difficulty had been to avoid enriching reality at the expense of truth."

Likewise he had from the outset, or acquired in process, definite ideas about the technique of fiction. On December 16, 1867, he set down the phrases "the whole plan of the book" and "what was written in illustration of a very elaborate and deliberate theory of mine about plots of novels." Characteristically, he longed for "some channel thro' which to put forth this same theory." A private channel he had already found. On July 4, 1866, R. S. Lanier questioned whether a novelist should pose his opinions directly, remarked that readers are bored by "chapters of 'moralizings' or what not," and thought a test for materials should be whether they "add something towards a development of plot." Lanier replied nine days later that "Authorities and precedents without number" exist for an author's speaking in his own person rather than through his characters and that the nature of the medium further justifies the practice—"A Novel is nothing more than a *Drama with the Stage-directions indefinitely amplified and extended*." He thus was writing under the theory that prose fiction should be loose and comprehensive rather than closely knit and restrictive.

About style as such the little he had to say concerned his particular pitfalls. As early as January 18, 1864, he noticed in himself "a tendency to the diffuse Style" through pressing metaphors so far that they became conceits. As late as when the book was in press (September 12? 1867) he perceived that all his prose was redundant and that he had not eradicated his deep-rooted "tendency to a profusion of metaphors."

About style as conjoined with content his ideas underwent evolution. On July 13, 1866, he admitted that the earlier portions of his narrative are in a "descriptive" style, "interspersed with much *high talk*." But he declared "the last part"—presumably beginning with Book II, Chapter III—is "almost exclusively" in the "dramatic" style. His final verdict was for the more objective method and for presenting rather than expounding or describing. On September 17(?), 1867, he wrote Mary Day, "I am better pleased with the later chapters of my book than with any others." The later, we trust, were not the very last.

Why, feeling thus, did he not recast the earlier chapters? The letter of July 13, 1866, contains words that possibly explain:

> Indeed, the book . . . represents in its change of style almost precisely the change of tone which has gradually been taking place in *me*, all the time. . . . I seem to see portions of my old self, otherwise forgotten, here preserved. If the book should possess no other merit, it will perhaps be valuable, to others even, on this very account: being the genuine and almost spontaneous utterance of a developing mind.[21]

Thus far attention has been focused on the making of *Tiger-Lilies*, its contemporary reception, and Lanier's own stated intentions and judgments regarding it. The novel must now be looked at through modern eyes, with respect first to its general character and later to particular qualities and aspects which call for analysis.

Modern eyes, candor must concede, seldom scan its pages. Even students of American fiction often ignore its very existence.

Examined for its general character, it proves to consist of three books, of fifteen, thirteen, and three chapters respectively, the first two books being about equal in length, and each of them more than six times longer than the third. It has also a preface, which decries the murders, sensuality, and pessimism of much contemporary fiction,[22] finds in the love of nature and art an impetus to wholesome living, and exalts truth above fact as the stuff of literature.

Tiger-Lilies is not homogeneous in either matter or form. As a narrative it succeeds in spots, is a failure as a whole. Nobody ever read it through for the fiction's sake. It bears, indeed, one mark of unity: it presents a "framed" story through beginning and ending with identical

[21] Lanier's letter of Oct. 14, 1866, to his father has this further statement about the novel: "I'm certain it is much improved, since you saw it: it is as if the first part were written by a boy and the last part by a man: and I think I'll let it stay so, if only as a true and faithful representation of growth." But on Sept. 12(?), 1867, Lanier wrote Mary Day, with especial regard to his redundancy: "I have grown so much in the last six months that I would write quite differently in another book."

[22] The passage seems to have been affected by an anonymous article, "Recent Novels: Their Moral and Religious Teaching," originally published in the *Quarterly Review* (London) and probably seen by Lanier as a reprint in *Scott's Magazine* (Atlanta), III, 108-118 (Feb., 1867).

exclamations and prayers. Midway, however, the story becomes virtually a new one.[23] By and large, Book I is nebulous and talk-laden romance in the mountains of Tennessee, with the scene of one chapter in Germany. Book II depicts, semi-realistically, life and conditions on the Lower James and in Federal prisons before returning to the Tennessee highlands and romance. Book III, with falling Richmond and Petersburg as its locale, accelerates the romance and brings the tale to a perfunctory and incredible close.

Certain incidents are sinewy and believable. Especially so are the deer hunt in Book I, and in Book II Cain's ruse for routing the marauders, his reaction (both emotional and verbal) to his brother's recreancy, Gorm's return to what had been home, the charge of the Confederate battleline, the prison scenes, and in general the life and talk of soldiers. These convince because of their closeness to reality. But the intervening atmosphere is remote and the movement sluggish.[24] Outside of Book II the narrative nowhere really marches.

The characterization likewise is weak in the aggregate, though in several minor instances and two or three major ones original and promising. Percymmon, crass exponent of Trade, is a man of straw dangling in a void. The prisoners, on the contrary, if sometimes extravagantly limned, speak and act as a rule with homely verity. In the main plot are four categories of leading persons—cultured summer visitors, transcendental German exiles (with anguished memories), illiterate mountaineers, and villains. Their flesh and blood values vary in inverse ratio to their social standing. Only now and again do the visitors acquire any measure of vitality. The Germans are still more tenuously connected with a recognizable world. The mountaineer Cain is unique in that he strides through three books as a human being. Gorm, mountaineer and villain, and the only prominent character in Book II who apparently was not thought of till Book I was finished, is not given a sympathetic role—Lanier could not condone evasion of public duty—but has the understanding and even the sympathy due one who suffers because of the draft. Cranston, villain and representative

[23] Little in Book I prepares a reader for the martial character of Book II. Faint foreshadowings are the end of Chapter III, the hint about Flemington's talent for command (see p. 79, below), and the casual words "after Paul had gone to the wars" (p. 29, below). The MS, however, is at times prognostic, as in the sentence, "The Yankee uniform is blue, Mr. Confed!" (Fragment B, p. 119)

[24] An example of static thought and erratic method is the beginning of Book I. The first paragraph is filled with ejaculated benisons by Paul Rübetsahl, of whom a reader expects to be told forthwith. Instead, the next four paragraphs are given to a digression, the rest of the chapter descants on Percymmon the grocer and "the tie betwixt mess-pork and poetry," attention then shifts to new persons and incidents, and not till the end of Chapter II does Rübetsahl again appear.

of Bohemianism and Trade, attains self-realization, ceases to be a mere abstraction, and, like Gorm, comes partly alive.

Permeating the volume are Lanier's pet theories and opinions. Seemingly our literature affords *Tiger-Lilies* no rival, except possibly Emerson's *Nature*, as a first book fairly a-bristle with the ideas which the author was to amplify and expound through the rest of his life. Besides ideas already noted, the following are typical: nature as beneficent and divine; heat, motion, and other natural forces as interrelated with all life (and, for Lanier, as an inexhaustible source for figures of speech); nature becoming (especially under the influence of science) the friend and fellow citizen of man; the wedding and interdependence of soul and matter; science as intimately connected with art and promotive of its achievements; music as the art of today; and music as an uplifting power (the climax of the philosophy of Books I and II, as shown in their last chapters).

Finally, the mood and effect of the volume are exuberant amateurism. That the author was a young man may be seen in the humor, in the intricacy of some of the craftsmanship, and in the lyrical strain.

The humor is abundant and somewhat varied, though frequently of a kind that has not worn well. Often it turns to far-fetched puns and practical jokes involving physical discomfort. Again, it pokes fun at somebody or something—through respectful gibes, as at John Sterling during the deer hunt; through burlesque, as of Mrs. Parven at the ball; through obvious satire, as of Percymmon; or once at least (in touches regarding the war-flower) through irony so detached and mordant as to bring "A Modest Proposal" to mind. Yet again, and somewhere between its boisterous and its intellectual aspects, it is sheer glad-hearted response to the world's geniality, perhaps reveling in quirk of phrase or fancy, perhaps simply a-tingle with inner satisfaction.

The craftsmanship is too often indirect or oversubtle. In his poetry Lanier could deliberately scaffold his meaning about with ingenious carpentry.[25] In his prose likewise he again and again could abandon forthrightness. With a native aptitude for detecting similarities, he filled—and overfilled—his works with comparisons, which he tended to expand into "anaconda conceits"[26] or even into allegories. The image of the war-flower at the beginning of Book II makes that chapter the best known in the novel.[27] But the figure may be deemed more

[25] See his letter of Jan. 4, 1864, to his father. Apropos of his bent for tropes, etc. (discussed in the following sentences of this paragraph), we may observe that as early as Feb. 21, 1861, his father found in his writings "a rich fund of imagery" and "inexhaustible conceit," that is, "subtlety of thought."

[26] This phrase of Lanier's may be read in its context on p. 297, below.

[27] The image may derive from Tennyson's phrase "the blood-red blossom of

clever than appropriate; a flower is too frail to symbolize adequately the destructiveness of war, especially when the comparison is sustained and elaborated.

The poetry springs from a young man's awareness of the immanence of beauty. Lanier saw loveliness everywhere. In presenting it to readers he pressed comparisons into service. Some of these, as has been indicated, show artifice. Some are so protracted as to stifle narrative. But the best have a spontaneity and an unexpectedness hardly short of breathtaking. A reader is reminded of the early poems of Keats. There was perception if not prophecy in the words of Parker's reader, "The metaphors and similes, the rich fancy of the writer will make publishers and public forgive much."

Of the matters connected with the novel and the elements in it which require somewhat careful analysis the first is the significance of the title.

That title baffled most contemporary critics and has been ignored by most subsequent scholars. Though denoting a definite flower, it obviously has symbolic purport. An attempt to fathom the symbolism requires a glance at a number of passages, two of them in the novel, the rest in works composed about the same time. Perhaps all the passages relate, if only obliquely, to tiger-lilies, though the first three mention the members of the compound (the tiger and the lily) separately.

In the novel Lanier speaks of "lithe Temptation" as a "swift tropical tiger" leaping upon a man who stoops to pluck a flower in the jungle. In "Retrospects and Prospects" he connects a water-lily with music. In "Nature-Metaphors" he quotes the *Gita-Govinda* on love as a tiger which springs upon a woman whose "face is like a water-lily."[28] From these passages it is to be surmised that he thought of a lily as innocence or love or the beloved person, and of a tiger as a ferocious force—if love, then love sundered from its gentler nature.

But he speaks of tiger-lilies as well as of tigers and lilies. Once in the novel he has tiger-lilies typify "the enchanting virtues" into which Nature, penitent, may convert her "boisterous sins."[29] The dichotomy, be it observed, is in Nature alone; the flowers represent, not two forces, but one—and that one virtuous.

In the remaining citations tiger-lilies stand for duality. They gather into themselves two opposing forces. What they embody is not harmony, but conflict.

war" in the seventh line from the close of *Maud.* (Lanier's phrase is "the blood-red flower of war.") *Maud* glorifies conflict, however; *Tiger-Lilies* condemns it.

[28] The passages are on pp. 165, 292-293, and 313, below.

[29] See p. 87, below.

"Retrospects and Prospects" has Nature juxtaposing "tiger-hates" and "lily-loves."[80] In an apostrophe to music an earlier draft of the essay brings the warring elements together into a single entity: "Thou beautiful Fury, thou fierce Flower, thou Tiger-Lily of matter as Love is of spirit." Finally, "The Three Waterfalls," written before Lanier's novel was completed and published three or four months ahead of it, has the narrator behold love floating, like a divinity, up through the depths of the beloved's eyes:

He came up slowly, in the likeness of a lily, and rested on the quiet eye, as on a quiet lake, one second—then, in a flash, he had become a spotted tiger, with tense muscles and still, gleaming eye, in the attitude of springing: and then the tiger wavered out of sight, and the lily reäppeared, quietly hovering, daintily undulating. Upon this lily my soul descended. O, love, thou tiger, I said to myself—O, love, thou lily, I love thee best in thy lily form: and so, upon this infinite petal of thee let me float over life forever!

The passage seems to bear definitely on the meaning of Lanier's title. It was fresh in his mind when he named his novel, it has the animal and the flower unmistakably symbolizing the two aspects of love, and it couches the narrator's preference for the mild and wholesome aspect over the cruel and bestial.

The conclusion may therefore be reached that the title symbolizes, however obscurely, Lanier's two concepts—the duality of love and the power of the lily phase (love etherealized) to exalt and transfigure the tiger phase (hate or selfish love).

These concepts may be traced in at least three domains of the actual narrative.

First, that of love between the sexes. Cranston descends with Ottilie into sensual love, thereafter fails to achieve the bliss of pure love (the hand of Felix Sterling), but partly etherealizes himself. Ottilie falls victim to love the tiger, exemplified by Cranston, but obtains salvation through love the lily, exemplified by Philip Sterling.

Next, that of the conflict between love and trade. Cranston and Percymmon, mercantile in origin, would exploit mankind. The characters unblighted by mercenary forces are altruists.

Last, that of love's role amid mortal dissension. Lanier glimpses malice and savagery (the plunder, prison, and revenge scenes), but does not let them degrade such characters as Philip. Love etherealized is to man both inspiration and stay.

The symbolism here investigated may owe not a little to *Hein-*

[80] P. 284, below. The two remaining citations in this paragraph are to pp. 293 and 220-221, below.

rich von Ofterdingen. That it does is more likely because Lanier in this period was reading Novalis and responding to his influence.

In *Heinrich von Ofterdingen,* a philosophic and allegorical novel on the perfecting of love, a German youth has beheld the blue flower, typifying the highest the heart may desire. The flower seems to be the face of a girl, and in several girls Heinrich afterward recognizes it. To pluck it is beyond him until he shall educate and spiritualize himself unto worthiness. Whether his attainment of perfect love is to take place on this earth or only in the other world we are not told; for the novel was to be in two parts, Expectation (*Erwartung*) and Fulfillment (*Erfüllung*), and the first alone was completed.

Lanier resembles Novalis in that he shrouds his theme in figurative language, has the flower stand for love, and maintains that love in its spiritual character shall transform and redeem all life. He differs from Novalis in that, whereas the blue flower represents love in its ideal state, tiger-lilies represent it in both its debased and its exalted form.

Lanier's German indebtedness extended past his title into his novel itself. He had become interested in German literature, especially romanticism, while still at college. During the war he prodded further into the language, did some reading in German authors, made some translations from German poets.[31]

The German prose romance of the late eighteenth and early nineteenth century is a baffling genre. It is not primarily story. Though it rhapsodizes endlessly about art (especially music and poetry), it seeks rather than shuns incoherence and digression. Though it lauds the natural, it fills itself with shadowy characters, unreal happenings, and metaphysical conversations. Though it would bring men comprehensive

[31] His knowledge had definite boundaries. He was far from being thoroughly acquainted with German literature, and of his hold on the language the MS of *Tiger-Lilies* (end of first chapter) states, "The Author unhesitatingly admits . . . that he does *not* understand either French, German, Italian, or Spanish, save to a very limited extent."

Ignorance of the tongue, however, was not a fatal handicap. German romanticism had been well introduced into this country before Lanier was born. Carlyle and Emerson had provided exegesis, Carlyle had made translations (including from Jean Paul the novels *Schmelzle's Journey to Flaetz* and *Life of Quintus Fixlein,* from Goethe the novel *Wilhelm Meister,* and from Novalis considerable fragments, these last being inserted into the essay on Novalis), and other translators and anthologists had been industrious. (In *Tiger-Lilies* the quotations from Novalis's *Lehrlinge zu Sais* are all taken from Carlyle's essay.)

Moreover Americans had writers of their own who aped and echoed the Germans. Of the flamboyant annuals of the twenties and thirties Fred Lewis Pattee exclaims (*Cambridge History of American Literature,* II, 369), "Never before such a gushing of sentiment, of mawkish pathos, of crude terror effects, and vague German mysticism."

and ultimate truth, it involves itself in allegory and presents nothing in plain terms.

All this was congenial to Lanier. Three writers of German romance—two of them Germans, one an American—had exceptional influence upon *Tiger-Lilies.*

The first was Novalis. His general thinking and his spirit were of a kind to appeal to Lanier.[32] Concern here, however, must be with the further impact of *Heinrich von Ofterdingen* upon *Tiger-Lilies.*

That impact comes through a long fairy tale interconnected with the story of Heinrich and filled with symbolism. In a castle in the north a king (the Divine Principle) and his daughter (Peace) lie in enchantment and await the release which is to come from the earth. About a mundane household typifying the "struggle for the reinstatement of poetry" are gathered a father (Artistic Sense), a mother (Heart), a boy (Love), a girl (Poetry), a nurse (Imagination), a clerk (Rationalism), and others. To make himself master of the household, the clerk captures the father and burns the mother to death, but the girl ingeniously overcomes him and with the boy heads a procession which ultimately includes mankind regenerated. Love releases and weds Peace, and the two become rulers of the new golden epoch, with Imagination and Artistic Sense as their representatives on earth.[33]

The part of *Tiger-Lilies* restricted to the household and guests at Thalberg, and to the pertinent development in their fortunes, differs from this part of *Heinrich von Ofterdingen* in that the scale of its story is personal rather than universal. It does not incarnate the Divine Principle or Peace. It does not portray a triumphal procession of humanity.

We may, however, at least think of Thalberg as a household for promoting the restoration of the arts, and of the people associated with it as personifications of various forces. John Sterling then embodies Artistic Sense, and his wife Heart. Sundry characters taken from

[32] His interest in the physical sciences, his yearning to reconcile all the sciences under one vast philosophical system, and his belief that "the division of Philosopher and Poet is only apparent, and to the disadvantage of both," may largely account for similar attitudes of Lanier. His reflection "Philosophy can bake no bread; but she can procure for us God, Freedom, Immortality. Which is then more practical, Philosophy or Economy?" has a counterpart in Lanier's questions to Percymmon (p. 9, below): "Hast thou studied the intimate inter-balance of the prices of cheese and of salvation? . . . And knowest thou the tie betwixt mess-pork and poetry?" And his words "The true Poet is all-knowing; he is an actual world in miniature" express a prime tenet of Lanier's. (All three Novalis quotations are from the *Fragments.*)

[33] See the more detailed summary and interpretation in Robert M. Wernaer, *Romanticism and the Romantic School in Germany* (New York, 1910), pp. 283-286.

Novalis appear in duplicate, as his flower, when transplanted, symbolizes two qualities instead of one. Thus Cranston and Percymmon represent two levels of Rationalism and of Materialism or Trade; Philip Sterling and his transcendental self Rübetsahl represent two manifestations of Poetry; Felix Sterling and Ottilie represent, the one ideal and passionless Love, the other a more earthly and betrayable Love. Cranston (Rationalism and Materialism) destroys both Artistic Sense and Heart by his course though not with his own hand.[34] Though he also destroys Rübetsahl's household by seducing Ottilie and threatens Philip's through becoming infatuated with Felix, Ottilie is redeemed by the pure devotion of Philip and the vainly sought Felix gravitates to Rübetsahl. Thus Rationalism-Materialism fails of espousing high spiritual qualities, American Poetry marries German Love, and German Poetry marries American Love.[35]

That Lanier deliberately put into his novel such complex shadowing is too much to say. At least he inserted not a little symbolism which neatly conforms with the Novalis pattern.

Regarding the second writer of German romance to affect *Tiger-Lilies* the *Atlantic Monthly* reviewer said, "Mr. Lanier has taken more Jean Paul than is good for him." Starke declares, "The obvious master—if Lanier had one—is Jean Paul Richter." [36] The Jean Paul elements tend, however, to become diffused; the German's swift poetry, his large philosophy, his preoccupation with the arts, his capacious sympathy and tolerance, his interplay of sentiment and humor, his talks with the reader, his heterogeneousness, and his wilful grotesqueries of thought and style show, but show uncertainly, through *Tiger-Lilies*.[37]

The third influence for German romance was the American author of *Hyperion*. Longfellow, like Lanier, was in Carlyle's debt. His romance makes sundry references to Novalis, and its hero resembles Heinrich

[34] There is no resurrection, as of Heart in Novalis or in Lanier's poem "Tournament."

[35] In respect to having Philip represent Poetry and Felix Love this interpretation reverses Novalis. Possibly Novalis's symbolism should be taken over without change. But Felix and, more still, Ottilie fit the role of Love better than that of Poetry, and Lanier's view is that Rationalism debauches Poetry and Love alike.

[36] *Sidney Lanier*, p. 106. (Probably Jean Paul's shapeless novel *Flower, Fruit, and Thorn Pieces* determined the title and influenced the content of Clifford Lanier's *Thorn-Fruit.*)

[37] They always bear something of the stamp of Carlyle, through whose two essays Lanier came to know Jean Paul. Richter's extravagance may perhaps be seen in the portrait of Percymmon, the metaphysical account of John Briggs' death (p. 135, below), and the crotchets of the ball-and-chain dancer at Fortress Monroe (pp. 141-142, below).

Blended with evidence of the German's craftsmanship are sometimes other hallmarks; for example, the Shandean accent (Richter admired Sterne) and the Thackerayan aside.

in pursuing an ideal because of the death of a sweetheart. It emulates Jean Paul—to whom it devotes much of a solid chapter—in being nearly plotless, discursive, and somewhat like an annotated travelogue fraught with literary essays and legendary lore.[38]

Hyperion and *Tiger-Lilies*, besides their likeness in certain details,[39] parallel each other in various general respects. Both are the work of young men. Both illustrate the impingement of a foreign force on an America whose thinking is still provincial. Both employ puns, rough jocosity, a structure receptive to diverse matter, prolix discussions of the arts, transcendentalism of mood and outlook, and the same large conception of what life should be.

As German romance they contrast with each other geographically, artistically, and historically. *Hyperion* has its setting in Europe, *Tiger-Lilies* (except for one unconvincingly localized episode) in America; *Hyperion* transports Americans and Englishmen to Germany, *Tiger-Lilies* Germans to America. *Hyperion*, scant of story, is true to the art form of German romance; *Tiger-Lilies*, ampler in story in even Books I and III, veers from romance toward realism in Book II. *Hyperion*, issued in 1839 when German romance had freshness of influence in America, bears importantly on our literary trends; *Tiger-Lilies*, published twenty-eight years later, was outmoded before it was written.

Many proper names in *Tiger-Lilies* reflect—sometimes dubiously and indirectly—the influence of German romance. "Thalberg" (valley-mountain), as explained in a manuscript note (end of Book I, Chapter IV), is "Montvale" Germanized. "John Sterling," doubtless due in part to the first name of Lanier's grandfather, may also owe something to the English poet-clergyman whose biographer was Carlyle. "Felix" may be reminiscent of Mendelssohn. The "Paul" of "Paul Rübetsahl," perhaps ultimately from "Jean Paul," is immediately from "Paul Flemming," the hero of *Hyperion*. "Rübetsahl" transliterates into Eng-

[38] Lanier was unquestionably acquainted with *Hyperion* just after the war; from it he culled a tentative motto for the first two chapters of *Tiger-Lilies* written after Appomattox (Chapters VI and VII). Almost certainly he was acquainted with *Hyperion* before he began his novel at all; on July 6, 1863, Virginia Hankins, whom he had recently met and was introducing to books he cherished, was reading it. (For the privilege of seeing entries in a transcript of *Ma Ruche*, an irregular diary which Miss Hankins kept for at least a few months, the editor thanks her nephew, Mr. Richard P. Hankins of Richmond.)

(The motto Lanier considered using closes a seduction scene in *Hyperion*. The two chapters to which it was attached in the MS of *Tiger-Lilies* prepare and present a seduction scene.)

[39] Examples: (1) *Hyperion* has "lofty souls . . . build themselves nests under the very eaves of the stars" (II, vi), while *Tiger-Lilies* begins and ends with nests built "upon the strongest bough of the great tree Ygdrasil"; (2) *Hyperion* declares, "Nature is a revelation of God; Art a revelation of man" (III, v), while the preface of *Tiger-Lilies* proclaims fealty to "God's Nature and . . . Man's Art."

lish the form " Rübezahl " from German legend (designating a mountain spirit) and from Longfellow's novel.[40] " Flemington " seems to be adapted from Longfellow's " Flemming." " Ottilie " we may suppose taken from Goethe's *Wahlverwandschaften* (*Elective Affinities*).

Though German romance wanes in Book II, it never entirely vanishes. With Chapter XIII it re-establishes its sway, and John Sterling's music-room lecture and the destruction of Thalberg form the structural climax of the book. German romance continues, almost undisputedly, its control through Book III, thus dominating the end, as it dominates the beginning, of Lanier's narrative.

This fact must not go unheeded. Though to a twentieth century reader the war chapters are the most vital in the volume, in function they are only an interlude. German romance is what Lanier started to write and what he came back to after finishing the digressions the genre permitted.

The novel contains autobiographical elements. For a reckoning with these the three books must be examined separately. R. S. Lanier must have had Book I in mind when he categorically declared that " out of material . . . picked up " in weeklong " camp hunts " in the mountains near Montvale " with . . . friends including some of the ' natives ' from the coves " the young author " essayed " his novel.[41]

Certainly Lanier was familiar with the Tennessee locale. Into his narrative he introduces the resort his grandfather had operated, Montvale Springs, and prominent natural objects like Chilhowee mountain, the Little Tennessee river, and that stretch of the main Tennessee which was then called the Holston. As certainly he was acquainted with such outdoor activities as hunting and with the social diversions of summer visitors. Amid mountain solitudes he had plunged into philosophical discussions with his father.[42]

Some of the characters coming from lower country into the mountains may be recognized. Philip Sterling is Lanier himself.[43] Rübetsahl is the

[40] In Lanier's MS the first paragraph has " Paul Gellert "—presumably from Christian Fürchtegott Gellert—but cancels the surname and substitutes " Rübetsahl."

[41] Letter of Sept. 25, 1883, to the Rev. J. A. Fisher.

[42] For Lanier's hunting see his father's letter, above; his own letters of Oct. 11, 1859, Dec. 21, 1873, and (to Clifford) Jan. 31, 1874; and Clifford's " Some Reminiscences of Sidney Lanier " (the *Christian Advocate*, Apr. 20, 1899). For life at Montvale Springs see Lanier's letter of the summer of 1860 to Samuel L. Knox. For his discussions with his father see his letter of Dec. 6, 1860.

[43] Even down to Lanier's nickname Sir Philip (from Sir Philip Sidney) and to his inability to sing (see p. 91, below, and compare *Mid-Continent*, VI, 85, May, 1895: " He [Lanier] could not sing, but his whistle was wonderful "). The references in the next sentence are to *Thorn-Fruit*, p. 21, and to Starke, p. 92.

Ideal which Clifford found combined with the Real in Sidney's nature; in Starke's phrase he is Lanier's "transcendental ego." John Sterling is a fictionizing of R. S. Lanier, the inconspicuous Mrs. Sterling of the novelist's mother, Felix Sterling of his sister, and Walter (presently rechristened Mark) Sterling of his brother.[44] "The mighty hunter . . . the Grand Tycoon" is William Lanier, brother to Sidney's grandfather.[45] Mrs. Parven and her Beck suggest, however regrettably, Mrs. Hankins and Virginia, and Mr. Parven suggests "General" Hankins.[46] Other characters may have prototypes less surely identified.[47]

Book II through most of its length lets the story emerge from dense

[44] Walter—perhaps the name derives from Sir Walter Scott—or Mark appears in only Chapters III to V of the MS; he is absent from the printed volume. Without him, be it noted, the Sterling household exactly matches that in *Heinrich von Ofterdingen.* Can Clifford have been sacrificed to symbolic convenience?

Felix resembles Wilhelmina Clopton Lanier, Clifford's wife, in that her face on a bending neck is like a flower on a curving stem (see the poem "To Wilhelmina Clopton," vol. I of the present edition, and p. 71, below). She resembles Mary Day in her special love for music. Lanier apparently testifies in his letters of Sept. 8(?) and 10(?), 1867, that he put Mary's eyes but not her essential self into *Tiger-Lilies.* While writing his novel he was singularly reticent to Mary about it (see his letter of Apr. 12, 1864, and hers of Dec. 17, 1866).

[45] Opinion expressed to the editor by Wilhelmina Lanier Tilley (Clifford's daughter) and supported by Lanier's letters of Dec. 4, 1861, July 4, 1873, and (to Clifford) Jan. 31, 1874; see also R. S. Lanier's letter to Sidney, Nov. 15, 1865. (The Deputy Tycoon may have been Clifford Anderson, brother of Mrs. R. S. Lanier. This "six-footer uncle" was slightly wounded in battle—apparently not at Gettysburg—and doubtless bore "deep scars" from the death of his first two children.)

[46] Parven is represented in Book I by his gum-coat only. Mrs. Parven may owe her avoirdupois to Lanier's grandmother (see letter of July 1, 1866). Beck Parven's first name may come from that of Virginia Hankins' friend Rebecca (Reba or Beck) Alexander. Conjecturally, Lanier planned to dedicate his novel to Virginia (see his letter of Aug. 21, 1867), but omitted the compliment on becoming engaged to Mary Day.

[47] To the topographical features, the customs, and the persons identified above, Miss Nathalia Wright of the Lamar Memorial Library of Maryville College contributes interesting regional additions in her unpublished study *The East Tennessee Background of Sidney Lanier's Tiger-Lilies*, which she has generously placed at the editor's disposal. By comparing evidence from geographical landmarks, contemporary newspapers, county records, and the like with the fictitious account Miss Wright clarifies Lanier's use of the actual. She demonstrates, for example, that he brings into his narrative numerous areas and objects of the countryside, but for artistic reasons reduces distances and exaggerates altitudes; that he selects a real site for the imaginary Thalberg; that he adopts or adapts names from families of the locale; and that he parallels and perhaps directly appropriates incidents striking in themselves and illustrative of the change in conditions as the war dragged on.

Teutonic mists and changes autobiography of discussion and atmosphere to autobiography of action. For the book, though restricted to the period of Butler's advance (the spring of 1864), embodies a rough equivalent of much that Lanier as a soldier underwent on the Lower James and in prison.

The specific happening that seems authentic appears much more frequently than in Book I. The locale is that in which Lanier served; the place names of the narrative—Burwell's Bay, Newport News, Smithfield, Ivor, Petersburg, etc.—are the ones which stud his letters. The landmarks may be recognized; the Parven home is a shrunken Bacon's Castle, and the prisons—Fortress Monroe and Point Lookout—are those in which Lanier had been pent.

The characters of Book I virtually all remain or reappear in Book II. Fortunately, they undergo a sea-change. The Parvens are less burlesqued; Philip and his confreres become more real; Cain Smallin is limned, if no more starkly, yet more completely. Several of the new characters have about them a look of verity: the men in Federal prisons, Major M— (for whose portrait Major Milligan probably sat, or rode), and, conspicuously, Gorm Smallin.

Book III, tenuous in itself, is tenuous in autobiography. It somewhat mirrors, however, Lanier's earlier haunts around Petersburg and mentions "terrible Battery No. 5," which he elsewhere characterizes as "terrible." [48]

Much as *Tiger-Lilies* tells us of Lanier's course and milieu in the period it covers, its statements by no means always square with other evidence. Lanier suppresses certain facts. He takes liberties with certain facts. He goes contrary to certain facts.[49]

[48] See pp. 185 and 274, below.

[49] Examples: (1) Suppression of facts: In Book I, Chapter III, the MS has the words, "I, here in Virginia scribble, between guard-hours." In the printed text this becomes, "I scribble," thus depriving readers of any clue to the time and conditions of Lanier's beginning to compose. In what is now the last paragraph of Chapter II the MS announces, "The Author, I . . . am just twenty-two!" (possibly anticipating by a month or so). In the text of 1867 the statement is omitted. In a letter of May 28, 1869, Lanier reveals that at Fortress Monroe he was "under custody of some foolish negro soldiers." In the novel he mentions no such guards. In the novel he is silent about his blockade-running, though perhaps he adverts to what he had learned about selling confiscated goods (see Book III, Chapter II, and Samuel G. French, *Two Wars: An Autobiography*, Nashville, 1901, p. 157).

(2) Alteration of facts: In Book I, Chapter III, the MS facetiously remarks that persons going to Thalberg uninvited would receive "an ungracious welcome at the hands of John Sterling." In the published volume Sterling "would welcome . . . every one,—so big, so big was his heart!" (Here a reader trusts it was the MS which did the altering.) In the same chapter the MS, after asserting that the Deputy Tycoon had been "'touched off' at Charleston,"

For these departures from strict fact there were plenty of reasons. For one thing, an artist often finds that literal actuality is not malleable enough for esthetic ends. For another, Lanier wished his readers to see through German romance, darkly. For yet another, he was at pains "to avoid enriching reality at the expense of truth." For another, he shrank from too painful memories; though showing the physical destructiveness of war, he dodged most of the psychological reactions of Philip to imprisonment. Finally, in unfolding his narrative he could not have escaped the influence of his father and brother. R. S. Lanier proffered counsel at two or more stages, once at least with effect (see pp. xxxv-xxxvi, below). Clifford, besides being at Lanier's side through most of the composition, was himself engaged at Montgomery upon a closely parallel work, a novel turning upon the life of the two brothers and their associates on the Lower James in the spring of 1864.[50] Though Lanier probably drafted his story with little outside suggestion or interference, the atmosphere in which he wrought was not exclusively his. Into *Tiger-Lilies* he wove, along with "portions" of his "old self," substantial if less tangible portions of R. S. Lanier and Clifford.

As war fiction *Tiger-Lilies* fell in with a current trend. The novel dealing with the conflict of 1861-65 began to appear in 1862 and

replaced "Charleston" with "Gettysburg." The print both changes the battlefield and resurrects the dead man by substituting "the Deputy beareth scar of Gettysburg." In the preceding chapter the MS gives Philip (Lanier) a "straight firm chin" but switches to a "curving, somewhat indecisive chin." The published version makes the chin adjectiveless.

Sometimes a reader is left doubting whether Lanier sticks to the facts. Was Lanier, like Philip, in the Tennessee mountains on Sept. 30, 1860 (see p. 10, below)? Presumably not. On the Lower James "one of the last days of April, '64" (p. 98, below)? Almost certainly so. In a Petersburg hotel the night of May 6, 1864 (p. 129, below)? Evidence is wanting. Regarding Cain Smallin's ruse Henry Wysham Lanier, in *Selections from Sidney Lanier: Prose and Verse* (New York [1916]), p. 165, testifies, "This episode was based on a personal experience of Lanier's during the war." A reader would like to know in what exact way Lanier shared in the exploit.

(3) Reversal of facts: Book I has Mrs. Parven and Beck visit Montvale in 1860 and move in the Sterlings' circle; Lanier actually first met the Hankins family at Bacon's Castle in 1863. The novel has Philip taken prisoner in the fighting near Petersburg; Lanier himself was captured months afterward off Wilmington. The novel has Philip escape from prison; Lanier was exchanged. The novel lets Philip enter Richmond as the city falls; at that time Lanier was ill in Macon. The MS of the novel makes Felix Sterling older than Mark because she must be of marriageable age; Gertrude Lanier was actually younger than her brother Clifford (the two originals).

[50] Through chance, intuition, or a deliberate division of the field the brothers escaped flagrant duplication of each other. Perhaps Sidney neglected such experiences as blockade running because Clifford was making them his province.

reached a floodtide of popularity in 1866-68. When penned by Northerners, it laid little stress on martial glory but conducted a crusade against the arrogance, brutality, and degeneracy of the South. When written by Southerners, it was cognizant of the hypocrisy, venality, and vandalism of Yankees but mostly pictured gray cavaliers in chivalrous combat. Wherever authored, it did not dwell on realities or on the effect of the struggle on plain soldiers and common civilians. With all its melodramatic elements, it was stereotyped in cast, in plot, and in depiction of background.[51]

Tiger-Lilies, as has been shown, is not primarily a war novel. Had Lanier set out to make it such, it should surpass everything in the field except *Miss Ravenel's Conversion*. His purpose being what it was, German romance had first claim and the blue flower somewhat stifled the war flower. But the latter blossom, however stunted, is what we have here to examine.

Tiger-Lilies makes use of several conventions of war fiction in the South and of others of war fiction in the whole country. It savors the life of a cultivated household. It marshals youth accustomed to the genteel manner. It admits wandering ladies, not indeed to battlefields, but to to the downfall of the Confederate capital. It pictures (in the Smallins) the house divided. It has a man from the North (Cranston) in love with a girl from the South (Felix). But it tempers these materials with a moderation foreign to most war novels. The youths are not too baronially exalted. Femininity is kept from the front until

[51] Best of the Northern war novels is John William De Forest's *Miss Ravenel's Conversion from Secession to Loyalty*, published in New York in 1867. Never widely read, it possesses such understanding, forthrightness, and satirical deftness as make it, though not free from partisanship, the most solid realistic achievement of the time. Best known of the Southern war novels is John Esten Cooke's *Surry of Eagle's-Nest*, brought out in New York in 1866. It is in part high Scott romance (with a Brontë sauce of gloomy men and mad women), in part a gentleman-reporter's spirited account of campaigns in the Shenandoah. Neither De Forest nor Cooke influenced *Tiger-Lilies*.

Macaria; or, Altars of Sacrifice by Augusta J. Evans was issued in Richmond in 1864. In this novel the proud, artistic, self-renouncing heroine and the poor, stubborn, Brontë-esque hero pursue a course of alternate schism and reunion until he dies in battle, his head pillowed on her lap. A review (Jan. 24, 1865) by J. C. Harris remarked upon salient qualities and themes—characters preoccupied with "the doctrines of the mystics," classical allusions, "aesthetics of politics and religion," dislike of "manufactures," dismay at "the 'gross utilitarianism' [Harris called it improvement] of the age" (Robert L. Wiggins, *The Life of Joel Chandler Harris*, Nashville, 1918, pp. 61-62). Clifford's subsequent recollections make it evident that Lanier procured a copy of *Macaria* soon, perhaps immediately, after it came from the press; the copy was in the portable library captured by Federal raiders. *Tiger-Lilies* exhibits qualities and opinions similar to those listed by Harris, and for Alfred Aubrey borrows the surname of Miss Evans's hero, Russell Aubrey.

the hurried last scenes. Brother is pitted against brother naturally and effectively. Between Northern man and Southern girl is raised no barrier of sectionalism.

The novel differs from nearly all rivals in its closeness to the actualities of warfare. Though it is not fully or consistently realistic, even in Book II, it has a preserving salt of realism. It catches the accent of soldier talk, the trials of the infantry, the hilarities and the hazards of scouting, the scarcity of food and clothing in the South in 1864, the loneliness of isolated civilians, the demoralizing effects of captivity, the moods of battle (individual madness in a melee, the let-down after the crisis, the composite psychology of a military charge), and other aspects of the time and milieu.

Yet it escapes the perturbation and the seething immediacy of many war novels. Its mood is emotion recollected in tranquillity. In it Lanier writes of mountains after he has left them, of scouting and imprisonment after they are past.

It carries no illusions about armed strife. Though appreciative of the self-sacrifices and heroisms, it is equally sensible of the "frauds and corruptions and thefts." It perceives that "a rich man's war" may be "a poor man's fight." So convinced has its author become, by the year following Appomattox, that conflict is futile that he takes his stand as an unqualified pacifist: "If war was ever right, then Christ was always wrong." [52]

It is uniquely non-partisan. It neither proclaims nor intimates that this section or cause is superior to that. It is neither defiant nor abject at the outcome of the conflict. Nowhere does it boast. Nowhere does it apologize.

Finally, it radiates good will. Three aspects of the mood are worth observing.

Good will toward the North. Amid the miseries of Reconstruction, indeed, Lanier tentatively put into his novel mockery if not denunciation of Sumner and Thaddeus Stevens; in the published volume, however, he suppressed the passage.[53] With respect to the war itself he gives never a sign of even temporary rancor; in the manuscript a chapter written in 1864 contains the words, "By as much as we love, by so much are we Gods!" [54]

Good will toward the Negro. Lanier himself had been in the custody of Negro soldiers at Fortress Monroe and Point Lookout; the inhabitants of the Lower James, his friends among them, had been harried by Negro raiders; and in the novel he shows a Negro threatening to take

[52] For the quotations in this paragraph see, respectively, pp. 94, 166, 95, below.
[53] See pp. xxxv-xxxvi, below, and the letter of July 13, 1866, to R. S. Lanier.
[54] P. 26, below.

liberties toward a white woman. Yet *Tiger-Lilies* manifests no animosity whatever toward the black race.

Good will despite personal suffering. In the conflict Lanier lost his health, his monetary security, his prospects for the future. After the conflict he saw the South devastated by conquerors and subjected to tyrannies. But his philosophy forbade him to cherish grievances. "The climate of a large and loving heart," he declared, "is too warm" for the "frigid plant" of bitterness.[55]

The announced theme of *Tiger-Lilies* is love. That Lanier truly adheres to this theme, and exemplifies it, is a feat without parallel among the war novels of the era.

As portrayal of the mountaineer *Tiger-Lilies* relates itself to literary tendencies of the day and shows Lanier in rapport with the indigenous in American life.[56]

Literature was in transition from romantic to realistic writing, though the trend toward simpler style and more earthy subject matter was neither abrupt nor sure. Authors keen of perception were often indulgent of fancy; in drawing upon the commonplace they too frequently made over the world they described; they exploited better than they represented. A character they were fond of portraying was the Pike County man or, more succinctly, the Pike; this shiftless, ungrammatical, expectorating, but often astute provincial had the merit of being autochthonous and, by the same token, suited to burlesque. A theme they prized was local color; brash or shamefaced writers had toyed with it years before, and about the time *Tiger-Lilies* appeared Bret Harte and men of his stripe came trailing clouds of sentimentalism, melodrama, exaggerated dialect, and regional idiosyncrasy.

Lanier felt the attraction of both the character and the theme. He was acquiring firsthand knowledge of a Middle Georgia cousin of the Pike from at least the year when he dropped out of college to be

general delivery clerk in the Macon post-office. At this period he exhibited considerable power of mimicry and sense of humor, frequently regaling the dinner table and the family evenings by his descriptions of the funny or eccentric characters applying at the post-office for letters or newspapers.[57]

He was also meeting the cracker in print, in the pages of William Tappan Thompson and presumably in those of Augustus Baldwin Longstreet. In days to come he was to extend practical literary

[55] Letter to Mary Day Lanier, Jan. 1, 1875.

[56] On the latter point see Orpheus C. Kerr's review of the *Poems* (note 15, Letters of 1877).

[57] "Notes Biographical of Sidney Lanier from the Recollections of Clifford Lanier" (typed MS), Clifford A. Lanier Collection, Johns Hopkins University.

assistance to Richard Malcolm Johnston and was himself to enshrine the cracker in dialect verse.[58]

He encountered another kinsman of the Pike in the Montvale Springs area. The contrast between mountain men and women and their summer visitors caused him to draft in his College Notebook an imaginary conversation in which his " sister " was scandalized because a girl from the " backwoods of Tennessee; and oh! so shockingly green! " had gone into Smyrrke Drigoods' store " and actually asked for—stockings!!!!!!! " If he met the mountain folk in print, it must have been in the boisterous sketches and tales of " Sut Lovengood " (George Washington Harris), which, however, scarcely distinguished mountaineers from bumpkins in general.[59]

Thus Lanier had a new locale and an unspoiled type to present.[60] Though delighted with both, he limited his use of them because of other purposes. It must not be forgotten that upon Southern mountain life he grafted German romance, that he was solicitous lest external facts should obscure truth, and that he inwove not a little allegory into his treatment of the locale; for he held with John Sterling that matter is an instrument for the expression of soul, and with Philip that dreams on the heights must lead to work in the world.

Tiger-Lilies shows that he enjoyed mountain speech. He does not render it, to be sure, with entire consistency. He perhaps segregates it less rigorously than he might from other patois, as that of Georgia crackers in his subsequent poems. He may have mixed what his ears told him with what his eyes found in printed works like Thompson's. But he is artistic and reasonably faithful in his use of the vernacular.[61]

[58] For the service to Johnston see note 40, Letters of 1881. For Lanier's possible precedence in the metrical presentation of the Pike County type see note 136, Letters of 1874.

[59] Miss Nathalia Wright (see note 47, above) thinks Lanier may have known Harris " as a public figure in Knoxville in the late 1850's." Harris, she declares, " owned and operated a farm in Blount County . . . some fifteen miles from Montvale."

[60] It was chiefly through a sprinkling of place names and a considerable use of mountain dialect that Lovengood may be said to have brought local color to the Tennessee mountains. " Charles Egbert Craddock," usually credited with literary discovery of the region, began to publish about a decade after *Tiger-Lilies* was issued. Local color, indeed, did not reach the Appalachians elsewhere until the year *Tiger-Lilies* came from the press (1867). In that year Rebecca Harding Davis's novel *Waiting for the Verdict* was appearing serially. (It achieved book form in 1868.) Some of its scenes reported convincingly the wartime fighting and the physical setting in the Kentucky mountains.

[61] Besides the mountain and the prison talk, *Tiger-Lilies* contains snatches of three dialects—Gretchen's Germanized English, Chilhowee's Indian gibberish, and the vocalization of Negroes. The first two are rather amateurish; the third, so far as it goes, has the right ring.

The pungency of colloquialisms and the pith of idioms are in his lines, and for simple eloquence unfalteringly sustained Cain's rebuke to Gorm is the noblest passage in the volume.

In portraying his mountaineers he at times resorts to artifice. Cain's talk about the elephants, in Book I, Chapter II, has a forced, almost a freakish, note. Gorm's gaucherie and gluttony at the restaurant, in Book II, Chapter XI, accord with that stock device of the local colorists, the outlandish character in incongruous surroundings. Cain is foisted upon a squad of gentlemen for effect rather than from need.

But Lanier does not set the mountain folk, and above all the Smallins, before us as mere Pike County curiosities. He does not make them shiftless, taciturn, and queer, as their kind came to be represented. He portrays them as individuals. Cain, with the resinous smell of the mountains about him, is the most vital character in the novel. Gorm, repulsive and grotesque at first, becomes less abnormal as he returns to the haunts from which he was conscripted against his interests and his desire. When he stands by the ashes of his home and the grave of his wife he changes into a human being.[62]

In the movement toward maturing realism *Tiger-Lilies* has its place. It is not one of the first works to delineate the Pike or employ local color. It is, however, one of the very first to exhibit these tendencies, not in sketches or stories, but in a novel. It may be classed with the earlier ventures through its emphasis on regionalism, through its riotous farce, through its artistic unripeness, and through its sharing in the sudden expansion and rapid development in the use of dialect. It differs from the earlier ventures in here and there merging its melodrama into drama, in levying somewhat extensively upon the actual, and in advancing as far as it does toward realism. More nearly than these tentative, pioneer works it spans the major aspects of the movement as a whole.

It owes more than may be supposed to the mountaineer. In Book I the folk element appears near the beginning and does more than anything else to lift the narrative from unreality. In Book II Gorm's disloyalty and Cain's reaction to it supply the one absorbing theme of the plot. In Book III Cain has the spotlight in the single lively episode. Whenever present the mountaineers at least share, and not infrequently they dominate, the interest. Without them the novel would lose sadly in flavor and in force.

[62] Regarding the portrait of Gorm, Edward B. Peck wrote Lanier (letter of Jan. 4, 1868, Charles D. Lanier Coll., Johns Hopkins University), "It is well done—the more so that your feelings and sympathies would not lead you to see his side of the matter—it is a touch of the Shakespearean faculty of nestling into a man's brain and thinking from thence and not from your own."

Until recently the only text of *Tiger-Lilies* known to scholarship was that of the published edition (1867). This text remains unique for the published preface and for considerable segments of the novel. The manuscript used by the printer in setting it up has vanished.

At length portions of still earlier manuscript came to light. They comprise three fragments of consecutive narrative and certain miscellanea, all in Lanier's handwriting.[63]

Fragment A contains the first five chapters of Book I. It is written in ink on pages—six by eighteen inches—from a ledger. The opening page presents a false start of two paragraphs succeeded by a blank in which Lanier afterward scribbled directions for a reader: "*Inside*: and don't criticize the grease and dirt!" After a new start on a fresh page the narrative proceeds continuously, though numerous cancellations, interlinings, and marginal inserts suggest that the author is feeling his way into the subject.

Beyond much question Fragment A is that part of the manuscript which Lanier inscribed in the Fort Boykin area. The quality of the content and the appearance of the document confirm this conjecture. The time-darkened pages underwent more romance than that which was penned upon them. In April, 1864, a Federal regiment raided Fort Boykin, sacked the post, and almost captured the little garrison. On May 28, however, Lanier reassured his father, "I did *not* lose my flute, *nor* the Novel, having taken the precaution to secure them . . . about my person, in my haversack—." A corroborative crease shows that the long manuscript pages were folded in half. On leaving the Lower James the young author entrusted the holograph to Virginia Hankins for safekeeping. A glimpse of its history is afforded by the words of her letter of January 27, 1868, to Lanier "the rough manuscript first chapters and I, having had many hair-breadth 'scapes together from Yankee raids & vandalisms."

Fragment B takes up the story where A leaves off and carries it through half the eighth chapter of Book II. Preliminary, however, to its organic beginning—that is, to Book I, Chapter VI—it has an aside or interchapter (epitomized in note 71, below). It gives evidence that Lanier was now striking a surer literary stride, for it differs less than A from the text of 1867, though more than C.

[63] Fragments A and C were discovered in 1936 by Mr. Cecil E. Abernethy. They were in the possession of Wilhelmina Lanier Tilley and had belonged to her father, Clifford A. Lanier. Fragment B and the miscellanea were found when inventory was taken of materials available for the present edition. They were in Lanier's Ledger, owned by his son Henry W. Lanier, Fragment B (headed "Ye Novel") occupying pp. 106-236, a discarded preface appearing on p. 46, and four other miscellanea at intervals (see note 64). All these MSS are now at Johns Hopkins University.

Fragment C begins with the ninth chapter of Book II and extends midway through Chapter XII. It is accompanied by three extra sheets (two for Chapter XI, one for Chapter XII) which virtually duplicate passages of the fragment itself. It is written on letter paper, some of the pages folded and some not, but all writing surfaces measuring eight by ten inches.

In bulk the fragments differ among themselves: B is approximately twice as long as the other two combined, and A is about a third longer than C. Collectively, they form an early—very possibly the earliest—draft of almost four-fifths of the novel. Their omissions are the preface, the battle scene (in Book II, Chapter VIII), the second half of the Point Lookout prison scene (in Book II, Chapter XII), the destruction of Thalberg (Book II, Chapter XIII), and the scenes at the close of the war (Book III entire).

The miscellanea consist of a discarded preface, previously cited and summarized (see p. xiii, above), and four short passages.[64] The four passages all express ideas related to the villains of the narrative—the first three to Cranston, the fourth to Gorm Smallin. All the passages except the third are metaphorical.[65]

In large content the text of 1867 does not differ glaringly from the manuscript. But it differs in particulars.

Here and there the print introduces—not always to advantage—ideas and philosophizing passages not present in the manuscript.[66] Sometimes—and again not always advantageously—the print, without intruding new ideas, elaborates and rearranges old ones.[67] Some-

[64] Ledger, pp. 10, 13, 17, and 67. The first is an early draft of the "complimentary dinner" passage (p. 37, below), the second of the "begetting" passage (p. 36, below), and the fourth of the passage on Temptation the tropical tiger (p. 165, below); the third, which glances at the devil's power as continuing in the life to come and at sin as being divinely sanctioned, has no parallel in the published volume. (The text of 1867 alters the import of the first and second passages.)

[65] The three fragments and the miscellanea complete the tally of MS definitely known. Further jottings in the Ledger which are akin in idea or imagery to passages in *Tiger-Lilies*, and parts of the Ledger's philosophical essays which are paralleled in the novel (especially in John Sterling's utterances), may not have been written for use in fiction.

[66] An example confronts us on the initial page of Book I, Chapter I, where, between the first and second paragraphs of the MS, the print inserts four paragraphs on an author's need and means of sustenance. The intrusion changes coherence to baffling incoherence.

[67] Thus the MS of Book I, Chapter XV (Ledger, p. 174), offers from the lips of two speakers two consecutive generalizations on art's changing uses of nature:

"'. . . Our poets,—may they live forever!—have humanized all Nature: they have, like lesser Gods, given to all Natural forms that they shall suffer and love.

times the published text phrases ideas too figuratively,[68] or if a trope has already been employed, adds a different and more complex figurativeness.[69]

But if the text of 1867 elaborates, embellishes, and obscures, it in turn telescopes and condenses, to the improvement of the art.[70] Moreover it omits not a little material found in the manuscript.[71] And in what it says about political trends and leadership it strikes an odd compromise. The manuscript had opened Book II with a satirical condemnation of war as seen in the passionate sentimentality of the South (Chapter II) and the calculating vindictiveness of "Messrs. T. Stevens and C. Sumner" (Chapter I). On July 4, 1866, R. S. Lanier had protested both chapters, declaring that the picture of

Hurrah for Matter, wild, mysterious, spirit-hiding matter, say I! The poets of the 19th Century have conquered the rocks and the storms, and made out of them, not slaves but friends!'

"'And that's true,' said Felix, 'not only of poetry, but of music, and all Art.'"

The same ideas—that poetry and the other arts have humanized nature—appear in print (pp. 89-90, below, from "Our poets, God bless 'em!" to "said Felix Sterling"), but details make them intricate and the transition from one to the other is no longer lucid.

[68] Thus for the MS statement (Ledger, p. 113) that the elder Cranston "provided John with letters of ample credit, and turned him loose upon Germany" it substitutes (p. 38, below) "he hung a golden chain about the neck of his young lion-cub, and turned him loose upon Germany."

[69] Thus the miscellanea (Ledger, p. 10) interpret in one paragraph the character of young Cranston and his role in the story:

"John Cranston was thoroughly selfish. He thought that he had been invited into the world, as to a complimentary dinner: and, forgetting even the customary forms of politeness, reached out his hand for every dainty, regardless that any neighbor was starving. . . . He was an Artist spoilt by . . . selfishness. The essence, the one life, of art is Love, which is unselfishness: and the love of self is a contradiction in terms. But he was a strong-souled man."

The corresponding sketch in the published text (from the second line on p. 37, below, through the second on p. 38) piles comparisons and personifications on top of each other, but leaves unmentioned the relationship between love and art, and says nothing to the point on the spoilt artist role. In short, through discursiveness and the overuse of tropes it deprives us of any sure sense of Cranston's function in the plot.

(An intermediate passage—Ledger, pp. 111-112—expands and embroiders the treatment on Ledger, p. 10, without sacrificing the contrast between creative unselfishness and destructive selfishness.)

[70] Thus Book II, Chapter IV, straggles through pp. 200-206 of the Ledger, but is much more compact in the printed version.

[71] The most obvious omission is that of the two-page interchapter which opens Fragment B and which has Lanier and Percymmon discussing whether an author should speak of himself in the third person and whether "the cause of the enmity between Cranston and Rübetsahl" should be divulged at once or kept back till the end. But expunged also or made less explicit are certain references to the family and especially to Lanier, and dropped are some citations of music, authors, and books.

the South was exaggerated and unfair and that discussing the two Northerners was indulgence in personalities. Nine days later Lanier indicated that his views were unchanged, but that he would defer to decorum. The net result of his revision, in which he may have been cautious not to appear partisan, was that he still censured folly in his own section but not malice across the Potomac. In shunning personal comment, however, he insisted that the whole Southern populace, and not Jefferson Davis alone, was responsible for the course the South had taken.[72]

With regard to style there is no marked cleavage between the text set up by the printer and the earlier manuscript. To be sure, the volume shows countless revisions, most of them so minor that they are confined within individual sentences, some so extensive that whole passages are recast. But the quality remains at much the same level.

In mechanical matters the published text and the manuscript alike are far from being impeccable. The former is not free from typographical errors. Both follow certain now outmoded practices, such as placing a period after a chapter number or quotation marks around a set-off excerpt. Both show inconsistencies of usage—for example, regarding capitals, italics, apostrophes in contractions, and dialect terms ("hadn't" is matched with "couldn'," "again" with "agin," "your" with "yer," "as if" with "as ef," "afore" with "buffore," etc.). Even the printed version gives quotations inaccurately, as on the title page, at the head of the initial chapter, and in the three ways in which Book I, Chapters XI and XII, print five words from *Antony and Cleopatra*:

Egypt, thou knewest too well
Egypt, thou knew'st too well
Egypt, thou knowest too well[73]

The basis of the text in the Centennial Edition is the print of 1867. Obvious mechanical faults are corrected; but quotations stand as Lanier gave them, and in the reproduction of his original material care has

[72] In deleting reference to other Southern leaders he shut off this interesting sidelight on Stephens:

"Let no man believe that Mr. Yancey, or Mr. Davis, or Mr. Toombs, led us into these things. . . . Led into the war? The man, who was perhaps the only man, in all the country who could have led us into anything, the man about whom clustered more love, more respect, more gratitude, more confidence than perhaps were ever given to any one among us, up to that time:—this man, Mr. Alexander Stephens, was opposed to the war, and spoke against it with such eloquence as we had never heard before nor since. If he could not lead us, no one could.

"We were not led—, by any one save the Spirit. . . ."

[73] But at least one apparently botched quotation is sound: the motto to Book I, Chapter IV, is from Pope's Shakespearean text.

been taken that the formal changes, of which all are slight, shall in no instance disturb the meaning or the emphasis.

Except for *Tiger-Lilies* the selections in this volume are printed chronologically. This Introduction, however, considers them in groups according to species or topics.

The group to be examined first is that of the imaginative prose of the period ending with Lanier's removal to Baltimore in 1873.

He pondered more imaginative prose than he wrote. In his College Notebook and his Ledger he jotted down ideas and a few actual fragments of composition of fictitious or semi-fictitious nature.[74]

The young Lanier leans also toward the informal essay. The early pieces in this kind are gaily irresponsible; those coming a trifle later have an undertone of purpose; both the earlier and the later are unfinished and tend to lack focus.[75]

Of the present selections four may be termed imaginative prose.

[74] The college scribblings (mainly in the Notebook, Clifford A. Lanier Collection, Johns Hopkins University)—a specimen may be glimpsed on p. xxxi, above —suggest future essays as much as future stories. In so far as they are narrative they look less to plot than to situations of a rather fantastic kind. When they provide characterization at all, it is not of individuals but of types, such as the jury lawyer and the theorizing clergyman. In diction, turn of sentence, esthetic approach, predilection for farce, amiable satire, gleams of realism, and fascinated observation of mountaineers these early efforts anticipate the later style and material.

Items in the Ledger show the narrative bent persisting. On pp. 70, 265, and 681 are hints and first sketches of characters. On p. 250 " Subjects for Comedies & Farces &c " are set down. On p. 675 the climax of a highly romantic tale is blocked out. On pp. 678-680 is a potpourri of ideas for characters, topics, scenes, and motifs under the heading " Mem. for Novel "—possibly a novel to follow *Tiger-Lilies.* Most of the human beings and strands of plot in the Ledger seem fabricated and remote. One person—labeled " a consumptive: temporarily estranged from his family "—brings autobiography and artifice together. There are foreshadowings of realism, as on p. 679 in the notation for a theme: " The Jury system in the South. Lawyers practise Judge & Jury; they do not practice law."

[75] A farcical, posturizing skit on flirtations is drafted in the Notebook; one called " Breeches " is written upside down on a lower half-page of the poem " Sermon Hymn " (Clifford A. Lanier Collection, Johns Hopkins University); a " Chapter on profane swearing " (Ledger, pp. 14-15), conceivably intended for use in *Tiger-Lilies* (which opens with a polyglot fanfare), drowns its chance for excellent foolery in a morass of puns. Further topics and beginnings appear in the Ledger, pp. 250, 264, and 576.

Of his knack for skimming pleasantly over a subject Lanier subsequently made collateral use in swift turns of thought or phrase, in the sportive tenor of longer passages, in conversion of matter for serious discussion into a *jeu d'esprit.* As he wrote Mary Day Lanier, Sept. 13, 1874, he also meditated articles in Addisonian manner " on certain phases of modern life." To our regret he never mined his ore directly, never devoted mature skill to light essay.

The first—" Timeo Danaos! A Voice of the Night "—was dashed off within a few months after the overthrow of the Confederacy. The holograph, laid aside, was soon forgotten, even by the family. The sub-title is an echo of Longfellow. The Greek-borne gifts against which the title warns may be emancipation for the enslaved or Negro charity for Southern whites. Though the tone is tolerant and amused, the piece is a social document of some worth because it catches the first reaction of both races to the new order.

It has greater importance as a venture into Negro dialect. Though from early times clumsy efforts had been made to convey Negro utterance through print, scholars feel that authentic rendition waited for the Laniers, Irwin Russell, Harris, and Thomas Nelson Page. Precedence among these has not been altogether settled: opinion has inclined in Russell's favor, the Laniers being only a little behindhand and Clifford on some counts ahead of his brother. But the now-discovered " Timeo Danaos! " antedates by some years the first page by any of the other four writers and must be recognized as the pioneer, literary and linguistic. It has minor discrepancies in form, partly because it was not revised, perhaps partly because Lanier held, as he explained in a letter of November 23, 1879, " that the commonest mistake in reproducing the negro's dialect is to make it *too* consistent." Nevertheless its author's acquaintance with Negro speech, the Negro sermon, the Negro parable, the Negro audience, the Negro character, and the Negro psychology makes " Timeo Danaos! " in a surprising number of respects the forerunner of what the following decades did with the talk and folkways of Negroes.

" The Sherman Bill " is almost certainly the " letter " which Lanier on March 15, 1867, submitted to his Syracuse friend Northrup. When published, it was read with pleasure by several ladies in Macon and reprinted in the *Daily Telegraph*, which called attention to it editorially.[76] Otherwise it attracted little attention, and a projected series died from lack of encouragement.

Though on April 11 Lanier spoke of the article as " a little light communication," the letters of March 14 and 19 show that he wrote it when he was " infinitely lonely." Public affairs as well as physical conditions were depressing; for the First Reconstruction Act, introduced in the House by Thaddeus Stevens and amended in the Senate by John Sherman, had become law on March 2. This measure divided the South into five military districts, threatened to supersede all existing government there, and stipulated the framing of new state constitutions, a work in which Negroes were to have a voice but the natural leaders of the whites were not.

[76] See note 38, Letters of 1867.

"The Sherman Bill" might well have been an embittered polemic. But Lanier had power of detachment even where his feelings were engaged. He was moreover a true son of the man who on March 7 wrote to Clifford, "We may accept with quiet dignity what we cannot prevent. The best manhood is seen in adversity." Perhaps too he wished to entice Northern readers; for, as he informed Northrup on April 11, he planned that his series "should grow more sober as it progressed." [77]

In any case "The Sherman Bill," the earliest published example of his imaginative prose, is perhaps the sprightliest. Its aim is high-spirited description of a doleful atmosphere. This atmosphere it establishes at the outset, confirms through appropriate illustrations, and maintains to the exaggerated climax. As art the method is sound. For effect the levity may be overdone. Readers may get more entertainment than sense of the heinousness of the legislation.

Except in some references to hotel life and courtroom procedure, and in an occasional colloquialism, "The Three Waterfalls" is disjoined from the world of reality. On September 5, 1867, Lanier tagged it "my little *jeu d'esprit.*" To us it is rather farce in the manner of the masque-ball chapter of *Tiger-Lilies*, with a father's rather than a mother's mentality and behavior as the butt, and with the narrative shouted down in an orgy of punning. Pivotal in the plot is the heroine's *chignon*, an object likewise prominent in Harte's "Muck-a-Muck," published in book form (*Condensed Novels*) the same year.

"The Three Waterfalls" may have been offered, perhaps in more concise form, to the Mobile *Times*.[78] It was among the manuscripts which Lanier, one early spring day in 1867, took from his trunk on the third floor of the Exchange Hotel and showed to a guest, the editor of an Atlanta magazine. The Rev. W. J. Scott carried it away, esteeming it "a masterpiece of wit and humor" and "one of the finest specimens of classical punning within the wide range of American literature." [79] Letters of September 16 (?), September (?) 29, and October 10, 1867, show that in the printing Scott took liberties Lanier thought unwarranted and that he was a trifle laggard in forwarding the $33 payment he had promised.

More ambitious than the three imaginative prose pieces already examined is the fragmentary novel *John Lockwood's Mill*. From each

[77] That expediency was not a main consideration is suggested by his letter of Mar. 14, 1867, to his aunt. This describes the prevalent gloom in terms similar to those of the article.

[78] See note 23, Letters of 1867.

[79] "Life and Genius of Sidney Lanier," *Quarterly Review of the Methodist Episcopal Church, South*, V, 157-171 (Oct., 1888).

it differs in tone. The year that had elapsed since the writing of "The Sherman Bill" had been portentous and calamitous for Lanier and the South.

He had personal ground for forebodings. Married and with parenthood in prospect, he stood in need of more money than he was likely to earn. Music and authorship were bringing him only a pittance; at this stage indeed his writing had run him into debt. Teaching, which took heavy toll of time and energy, offered but a precarious income. Spiritually and esthetically he was cramped for leisure and outlet. On top of all this, the first fateful hemorrhage had depleted his stamina and made continuance of his very life uncertain.

For public affairs the outlook was as dismal. On June 29, 1866, Lanier reported that "mortal stagnation" was paralyzing business. On September 29, 1867, he was apprehensive because of "the terrible decline in the price of cotton." On December 16, 1867—just three days before his marriage—he spoke of "our wretched poverties and distresses here,— . . . the slow terrors with which this winter has invested our life in the South." On January 12 and January 21, 1868, he feared radicals or hotheads would fan racial antagonisms into riots and butchery. As late as August 7, 1875, he was to declare "that with us of the younger generation in the South since the War, pretty much the whole of life has been merely not-dying."

This degradation of his people he thought gratuitous. It astonished and pained him. Unable to cherish hard feelings himself or to stay angry with anybody,[80] he had expected of the North "the vast generosities which whirl a small revenge out of the way as the winds whirl a leaf." [81] But proof of spite and oppression grew. In the "Furlow College Address" he was to deprecate the vindictive littleness of Reconstruction.[82] In "Retrospects and Prospects" he was to deplore "those hundreds of laws recently promulgated . . . which have resulted in such a mass of crime and hatred and bitterness." In "Civil Rights" he was to reveal the desperation to which Southerners had been goaded. And when the war-after-war had spent its fury, he was to summarize ruefully, "We had to grip religious fanaticism & frantic patriotism for four years & rascality for ten."

From these ordeals, private and public, his spirits were unprecedentedly low. Apparently his dejection reached its nadir in the earlier

[80] Letter to Bayard Taylor, Feb. 7, 1877.

[81] This quotation and the one in the last sentence of the paragraph are from the letter to Logan E. Bleckley, Nov. 15, 1874.

[82] P. 248, below. The references in the next two sentences are to p. 303, below, and to vol. I of the present edition.

half of 1868. It was the time of his most despondent and even resentful poems. It was the time of *John Lockwood's Mill.*

In "The Sherman Bill" he had skilfully woven his exposition into his incidents. Now his procedure was more blunt. In an opening chapter which was virtually a preface he declared that in the spring of 1866 the South had been animated by "happy resoluteness" and "cheerful energy." In the spring of 1868, he went on, the South knew only "the intolerable gloom of [enforced] idleness." [83] This direful, two-year change, so far from being anything in which "we" had a part, was shaped by "vile party" politics. Lanier will devote his novel to the picturing of this change; the story will be "sternly realistic"; every participant and every transaction will come from actual life.

Had Lanier fulfilled this promise, his novel, though it might have lacked esthetic distinction, would have been socially illuminating beyond anything else the era produced. But regarding it he faltered from the start and throughout.

He faltered in settling to the task of composition. On January 21, 1868, Clifford—who, to be sure, may have been trying to divert his thoughts from his hemorrhage—exhorted him, "Work, work at the new novel," and a week later appended, "*The Novel! The Novel! Carthago etc.*" On March 3 he himself reported that because of interruptions, though he had "gotten off several little poems lately," he had "found it almost impossible to do anything in the novel line." For some time before May 20 and 28 he had been applying himself—to essays. Here plainly is procrastination because the task is uncongenial.

He faltered in hitting upon mood, approach, and theme. On February 17, 1867, R. S. Lanier—always deeming the state of American civilization meet for literary treatment—suggested a political novel which should be a new *Hudibras* and should "tear the mask from . . . the modern Yankee Puritans . . . [and their] canting 'loyalty.'" [84] The suggestion may have been what prompted the young author to compile a list of "Subjects for Comedies & Farces &c" (Ledger, p. 250) and to head it with the topic "The Radical Outradicalled." But when he came to write his novel he did not poke fun and he did not focus on Reconstructionists. Though the first chapter announces a sober exposé of Reconstruction, the three remaining chapters and the Ledger's partial summary do not talk about the South in economic revolution under political duress. Trade rather than an act of Congress, business

[83] Letters of about the dates specified do not fully bear out these contentions. On June 29, 1866, Lanier saw "a vast and sultry spell of laziness" encompassing the region. On Dec. 16, 1867, he saw his family and presumably other folk performing unaccustomed manual labor.

[84] See note 23, Letters of 1868.

trickery rather than the behavior of the North, is the villain of the piece. Even the consequences of individual wrongdoing become a theme.

He faltered in deciding upon his narrative framework. On January 21, 1868—four days after his first hemorrhage—he was casting about for a plot. Clifford, he observed, was "at work on a very good thing," that is, on a novel (*Carpet-Baggery*) conceived and perhaps in a fashion begun by July 1, 1866. At length he himself found a plot—by appropriating the fundamentals of Clifford's.

He faltered in showing "the very age and body of the time" its "form and pressure." The topographical setting, we may assume, is authentic enough.[85] But the social atmosphere seems contrived, and often a reader may suspect the happenings and the cast. If these persons and transactions are taken from life,[86] they wear their reality with a difference. Readers feel that these do not represent truth; they question whether these always represent fact. Their conclusion is that, had Lanier gone on with his novel, he might have given it realistic elements, but would not have given it over to them. His romanticism was too ingrained for him to be "sternly realistic."

The four chapters he wrote have poetry of concept and diction. They toy with symbolism. They cast lingering glances at nature and art. They show an infusion of philosophy, of autobiography, even of German romance. In all these respects they resemble *Tiger-Lilies*.

[85] The unnamed state corresponds to Alabama. Lockwood's home and mill are presumably not far from Point Clear, where Lanier had once gone for his health.

[86] Blockade running, the fall of Wilmington, the return to the Confederacy by way of Galveston strongly savor of Lanier's past experiences or Clifford's. An actual kinsman "did a . . . thing in sugar, during the war," another had business dealings with the British in Bermuda, and some acquaintance (if no kinsman) must have "owed heavy debts North." That Lanier (as here) and Clifford (as in *Carpet-Baggery*) knew someone who in wartime shipped cotton to England and got cheated is likely. R. S. Lanier resembles the elder Royston in being impoverished by the war. Lanier himself, like Royston the younger, was thrown upon his own resources after the conflict and sought the principalship of an academy. Gertrude Lanier had the same ties of loyalty and blood as Anne Royston. Mary Day, who according to Lanier's letter of Sept. 10, 1867 (?), was to be put "upon paper" in his next novel, shared Meta Lockwood's devotion to nature and poetry if not her skill in navigating sail-boats, and had obtained schooling in New York. Mary's father, like Lockwood, was a widower with business acumen, though without Lockwood's tendency to plunge. If (as circumstances indicate) he objected at first to his prospective son-in-law because doubtful that artistic dispositions provide bread and butter, he far surpassed Lockwood in general sympathy for his daughter's tastes. (And there was no estrangement: in Sept., 1868, Mary's first-born was christened Charles Day Lanier.) All in all, it is probable that there were prototypes for virtually all situations, incidents, and characters, but that in transplanting them to fiction Lanier modified them greatly.

In others as basic they reveal dissimilarity. Instead of being tolerant toward governmental acts and political trends, they definitely brand these. Instead of withdrawing into the past (however recent), they stand in the forefront of the contemporary (though with glances backward). Instead of investing their hero with Philip Sterling cheer, they enshroud him in Brontëan moroseness. In short, they promise a further and changed *Tiger-Lilies*, but not a much better one.

Before the three remaining groups of selections are considered, the fact that much prose exists from the period before 1873 may be noted. This material has been preserved in various ways—among the papers written at college, in the College Notebook, in the after-the-war Ledger, in individual post-collegiate documents, and through print. It survives in all stages of evolution—as mere jottings of germinal ideas, as tentative and often fragmentary drafts, as finished work. It is too heterogeneous to be divided into mutually exclusive categories: some of it (as has been shown) is imaginative, more may be called non-imaginative, not a little displays an overlapping of the two. It relates itself, over and over, to Lanier's later writing. Most of it is of scant intrinsic worth and seems destined to remain in manuscript. A fair number of the better and more representative pieces are reproduced in this volume.[87]

The second group of articles here printed have to do with immediate problems and memorial occasions.

Believing that the scholar should relate himself to whatever men do and think, Lanier early studied the contemporary scene. The college essays, debates, etc., ponder such subjects as the woman suffrage movement and the exemption of naturalized citizens from military service to their native land. The "Essay on Democracy" (January 11, 1860) analyzes dangerous conditions in the country and the forces which produced them. Several papers, including that just cited, probe the dispute between free and slave states; for example, the inaugural as president of the Thalian Society[88] (December 10, 1859) affirms that John Brown's raid, abolition incitement, and the Northern legislative program are imperiling the peace, freedom, and social structure of the South. After the war Lanier was watchful of incidents and tendencies at home and abroad, sometimes alluding to matters—as those of the China, Candia, and London *Times* references toward the close of "Retrospects and Prospects"—which are now hard to identify.

Some opinions—however common at the time—sound strange as

[87] Three selections—"Peace," "Letters from Texas," and "San Antonio de Bexar"—appear in vol. VI.

[88] Clifford A. Lanier Collection, Johns Hopkins University.

coming from him, even in his collegiate stage. He upholds slavery as Scriptural and as free from political or moral harm. He denounces large classes in the North as not merely fanatical, but malign and murderous. In an alternate, though rejected, draft of the "Essay on Democracy" he favors the "commercial independence" of the South because this "will terminate in a dissolution of the union."

On the other hand, he was evolving an ideal of omniscient, passionless detachment and a largeness of outlook which war was not to impair, nor in any permanent way was Reconstruction.

"Flag Presentation at Oglethorpe University," first of the pieces reproduced in this volume, seems also to be the first of any kind Lanier got into print. Somewhat pompous and allusive, it shows heed for public events but not the pungency with which Lanier described a similar ceremony in his letter of March 1, 1861.

"Bombs from Below: Wanted, Engineers!" illustrates Lanier's allegorical propensity. As early as April 23, 1858, he attempted an "Allegory" in his College Notebook. Throughout the period prior to 1873—and in several selections here printed—he employed at least snatches of this kind of writing. How consciously he could make it govern a poem his description of the process on January 4, 1864, reveals.

Now allegory was a convenient device. He wished to warn against the iniquities of Reconstruction and of the tolerated moods which engendered them, but he was solicitous not to affront the North. Readers knew of the bomb-proofs or shelters used in 1861-65 against explosive projectiles. He would call on the engineers of the army of civilized society for shelters against the devil's bombs of discord and hatred.

"Bombs from Below," differing from "The Sherman Bill" in that it does not let allegory carry the message unaided, is cut from the same cloth as the beginning of *Tiger-Lilies*, Book II. Like the first chapter in that book, it uses a comparison basically unconvincing and overlong sustained. Like the second, it so vividly concedes Southern ante-bellum faults that its counsel against Northern post-bellum faults becomes pallid. Like both chapters, it makes dismay at unleashed partisanship its mood and conciliatory admonition its purpose. It is near the two chapters in date of composition; indeed a phrase inserted in the novel in midsummer, 1865—"Passion springing mines under the calm entrenchment of Reason" [89]—may be the embryo of its symbolism.

At six-month intervals in 1870-71 Lanier delivered three memorial addresses. All three have cumbersome apparatus of introduction and usage, as well as passages of sincere emotion. All are alike, and all

[89] P. 37, below.

akin to the poem "The Dying Words of Stonewall Jackson," in the absence of any word of repining and vengeance. Lanier hardly seems disquieted. Reconciled to loss, he speaks in a mood of unquestioning acceptance, solemn consolation, high consecration. The virtuous dead have done their work well. To think of them is not to mourn. It is to touch eternal forces. Inspired by those forces, we will grapple with error and wrong, associate ourselves with God's unfolding plan, exalt ourselves to nobler living.

The "Confederate Memorial Address," unlike the two later pieces, was not evoked by a single demise. In an undated note Lanier's friend Mrs. S. M. Boykin notified him, in behalf of the Ladies' Memorial Association, that he had been "unanimously elected the Orator, on the occasion of the decoration of the soldiers' graves on the afternoon of the 26th of April," 1870. She asked that the address be "impromptu" and almost put a plea into her statement of confidence that it would be "appropriate and impressive." "The winds & the waters," her final sentence ran, "chant a lonely Requiem there, but excuse me if I say, let us have the music of your eloquent tongue for the human listeners who desecrate, too often, the place & occasion, by unbecoming hilarity."

Lanier spoke, deliberately and feelingly, from a stand in the hillside cemetery at Macon.[90] Surrounding him were the flower-heaped graves of old friends and comrades, and near by was the headstone of his mother. The effect of his words was instantaneous and profound. And it lasted. For days the townsmen were commenting. The Macon *Telegraph and Messenger* printed the speech; other journals copied it; readers swelled the chorus of approval. Salem Dutcher, who had feared that his friend was "given overmuch" to Baconian Modernity, hailed the reverence for "the glory of the Old." Hayne declared that the address was "a noble poem throughout" and that "an original *key-note*" struck in the beginning was "beautifully *maintained*, or suggestively carried off into many exquisite and pathetic *minors*."

Though Lanier hoped the art of the address would be liked, the key-note had been struck, however unintentionally, by other fingers than his. The note of invitation stressed the need for human utterance; the winds and the waters—the voices of nature, of benignance, of everlasting truth—would not suffice. Lanier thought otherwise. Forces and influences that were timeless should speak; he would be only the mouthpiece. The address is characteristic of him in that he himself is lost in its "large tranquillity."

Mrs. Boykin, knowing Lanier was "indisposed," had hoped he would

[90] Details in this paragraph are taken mainly from three letters—R. S. Lanier to Clifford, Apr. 28, 1870, Lanier to Virginia Hankins, May 20, and Aug. 26, 1870—and note 30, Letters of 1870.

recover before the day arrived. Recover or not, he spoke. But the physical and emotional stress of preparation may have been what caused him to suffer shortly afterward " a severe hemorrhage from the lungs " and to be " completely disabled . . . for some time."

Recovering from illness and returning to Macon from New York, he made an address at services commemorative of Robert E. Lee. His own words were a prelude to closing resolutions of sympathy, which included a call for a monument to which the humblest citizen might contribute. The call was to lead, fifty-nine years later, to the establishment of the Robert E. Lee Memorial Foundation, which acquired and restored Stratford Hall.

The address itself was a tribute to the dead leader which reached its climax in the account of Lanier's last sight of Lee, an account to be compared with the more informal one in the letter of August 3, 1864.

That he revered his old commander is certain. In particular he esteemed his patience, his poise, his loftiness and knightliness of character. On April 17, 1872, he wrote that " Trade . . . broke the saintly heart of Robert Lee," and he may have amplified the thought six days later in an address which has been lost.[91] All his other references envision a soul completely steadfast, on however evil times fallen. " The calm grandeur of Lee " is one of the three qualities he on October 18, 1874, declared a great artist must possess.

" Memorial Remarks on Judge E. A. Nisbet " belongs in a symposium of tributes to the jurist. Nisbet had counseled Lanier's boyhood with kindliness and wisdom. He had signed his petition for admission to the bar and had conducted part of his examination.[92] Genial and generous in personal relations, he also had Lanier's professional respect. The address, sincere and measurably adequate, yet does not satisfy a reader today. The first half of it has the chill of formal remoteness, and the one human incident warms only a part of the remainder.

The third body of selections are a product of Lanier's longing for the good life. They reflect his thought on scientific and speculative knowledge, on the essentials of sound culture, and on the nature and function of art. Behind them are unpublished writings which show how

[91] An unidentified newspaper clipping owned by Mrs. Walter D. Lamar of Macon shows that, as the first of fifteen speakers at an anniversary meeting of the Macon Volunteers, Lanier responded to the toast " The Christian Patriot Hero: The peerless Lee." The response was especially commended. The Macon *Telegraph and Messenger* of Apr. 24, 1872, without naming the speakers, establishes Apr. 23 as the date of the meeting.

[92] See note 40, Letters of 1869.

early the interest in these things began, how strongly it persisted, what forms it took, and through what stages it grew.[93]

[93] Of MSS, other than letters, levied upon in this Introduction the following (here listed by topic) are in the Clifford A. Lanier Collection, Johns Hopkins University: variety as the spice of life, the legitimacy of happiness as an object of pursuit (one section of the argument), the justifiability of the assassination of tyrants, a collegiate " sermon hymn " in verse (one draft), the College Notebook, the Thalian Society inaugural address, the valedictory address (one draft), and Louis Napoleon's Mexican empire. The Ledger (see note 18) belongs to Mr. Henry W. Lanier. Other MSS (see note 1) are in the Charles D. Lanier Collection, Johns Hopkins University.

The development of Lanier's intellectual and cultural interests calls for brief summary.

In his senior year at Oglethorpe he studied science under a teacher trained under Agassiz and at Heidelberg. Penciled at the back of his College Notebook are the words: " Sidney C. Lanier—Took notes in this book on Prof. James Woodrow's Lectures on Chemistry, commencing October 10th 1859—Future Ages read and ponder!!! " In addition three college papers labeled as recitations " from amplified notes " have been preserved. The notes do not indicate that experiments or demonstrations, at least on any large scale, accompanied the lectures. The principal subjects covered are heat and motion, which were to fascinate Lanier through life. Woodrow also, it is known, was willing to discuss the implications and relations of science. From this teacher Lanier received what he afterward described as " the strongest and most valuable stimulus of his youth."

Much of the scientific lore Lanier crowded, from this time forward, into letters, prose screeds, and poems carries a figurative alloy or has an ornamental purpose. But the point may be easily overstated. It was Woodrow's pupil who held that a fact must be respected and an assumption, even if theological, scanned. In an age when ideas about the physical world underwent vast and rapid changes Lanier differed from nearly all other American men of letters in neither shunning the subject nor lightly toying with it. He related science notably to esthetics, as regards both theory and creative use.

Meanwhile he yearned to grasp the large truths and abiding principles of philosophy. At Oglethorpe (witness the letters of Nov. 14, 1859, and May 7, 1860) he lectured and debated in class on philosophic themes, drawing further upon them in extra-curricular forensics. In the early post-bellum years he filled pages of the Ledger with ingenuities about them. At his death he was still pressing his inquiries.

Despite his zest for exploring subtleties, he was disturbed that so many of the sages reckon exclusively with thought. His philosophy, like his art, has a strongly moral cast. It lays primary stress on the emotional faculties. For example, Lanier devoted many pages, at college and afterward, to determining how responsible we are for our states of mind. The conclusion he reached is that we are responsible, not directly, but through the emotions: we must feel rightly in order that we may think rightly in order that we may act rightly.

The paramount emotion, he was convinced, is love. In the loosely metrical " Sermon " written at college he exalts it above the intellect and laments that, in his unwithholding use of the term, " few men love at all." In the Ledger article " Desire and Thought " (later restyled " The Error of Cousin & Hamilton ") he weighs love against cognition. On p. 241 of the Ledger he replaces the apothegm *Cogito, ergo sum* with *Amo, ergo sum.* In *Tiger-Lilies* love redeems war. In

The selections themselves were all three published during Lanier's lifetime. The one finally known as "Retrospects and Prospects" may have had its inception in the speech which on July 1, 1866, he stated he had made the preceding night before the Literary Society in Montgomery. The first clear reference to it was on the following March 22, by which date it had assuredly been read before the society and was captioned "The New Time." There can be little doubt that Lanier took it with him to New York in April or that he expanded it into approximately its present form in May.[94] It seems to have experienced

"Nature-Metaphors" it draws alien elements together. After Lanier's removal to Baltimore (1873) it still pervades his work: "From Bacon to Beethoven" (II, 274), "The Symphony," and "How Love Looked for Hell" (vol. I of the present edition) are among the pieces which show it as an uplifting and redeeming force, and *The English Novel* (IV, 145) makes it "the organic idea of moral order."

Regarding education he had two central ideas.

The first—expressed in the discussion whether tyrants should be assassinated, the argument upon our responsibility for our states of mind, "Desire and Thought" (in the Ledger), p. 266 of the Ledger, a detached note (less than a page) on "a single proposition," the letter of Dec. 6, 1860, and elsewhere—is that the emotional nature as well as the mind must be trained. Human beings are taught what and how to think. They are not taught what and how to feel. They should have such instruction, and above all should have guidance in the right things to love, not only for the enrichment of their individual lives, but as the only possible way to give stability to the republic.

The other—expressed in the "Essay on Democracy," "The Philosophy of History," the "Valedictory Address," an isolated college notation (in pencil) on the Greeks, and the letter of Dec. 6, 1860—is that man's training should be comprehensive and balanced. The Greeks alone, Lanier declares, have attempted "the harmonious education of a *man*: . . . of his parts, his physical faculties, & his mental, his emotional, & his volitive or optative faculties." They utterly failed, however, to recognize "the place in the educational economy which the moral susceptibilities of man should occupy." We must regain Greek completeness and crown it with religion.

While at college Lanier stated (W. H. Ward, *Poems*, New York, 1884, p. xiv) that to become a great composer seemed a "small business in comparison with other things" he might do. Yet he believed profoundly that an artist must be a lofty, catholic soul, that life and song must merge into each other, and that the social order cannot be wholesome unless the benefits of art extend to every class and every individual.

The only arts with which he approached a connoisseur's acquaintance before 1873 were literature and music. "Infinite Solecisms" (Ledger, pp. 384-409) shows that he regarded the latter as "that most wonderful phenomenon of modern days": "Music," he concluded, "is our best and highest and vaguest formulation of the Infinite." In his early years he manifested less interest in the technique of music than in the technique of verse or fiction; also, though using mechanics in creating art, he hesitated to use them in critically "dissecting" art.

[94] On Mar. 15, 1899, Mary Day Lanier wrote that she had found in Lanier's

various vicissitudes and rebuffs before it was issued in two instalments (March and April, 1871) in the Baltimore *Southern Magazine*, edited by W. H. Browne.[95]

For the article Lanier was not to be compensated except through

desk the last MS page with signature and date " May—1867 " (letter in possession of Charles Scribner's Sons).

[95] The early draft (" The New Time," 28 small pages) survives, as does most of an amplified version which must have approximated 100 5 x 8 pages, of which the last extant is numbered 91.

The amplified version, entitled " Retrospects and Prospects," must be the MS of the same work—" about one hundred pages " in length—which Lanier turned over to Parker's literary bureau and which Parker (see his letter of June 24, 1867) put into the hands of his reader. " If we find it promises availability," he explained, " $8, will be fair for pushing its chances, & critically examining it." On July 12, the reader having made a complimentarily adverse report, Parker transmitted the criticisms: " . . . excellent thoughts. . . . Lanier evidently has *genius*; only he is too Old English in expression, and critics would call him finical. Possibly after his novel gets published this may have a chance; though it is doubtful. . . . If . . . shorter it would do for a magazine, only his somewhat affected style of speech must be weeded out."

On Aug. 6 Lanier contemplated issuing in pamphlet form " a metaphysical essay "—one product of two years' toil on a system—and submitting it, perhaps with " some popularized metaphysical discussions " from the forthcoming *Tiger-Lilies*, in evidence of his fitness for a professorship at the University of Alabama. Though " Retrospects and Prospects " may well have been the essay, no pamphlet was published nor was Lanier appointed. Invited in September to write for the Baltimore magazine *Southern Society*, he speculated that " ' Prospect & Retrospect,' retouched a little," might serve; but the piece, if offered, was rejected (note 86, Letters of 1867, and letter of Sept. 16? 1867).

Letters of Nov. 4, 1868, and Apr. 13, 1869, show Lanier fruitlessly submitting " a small volume of [recondite] Essays " to Hurd & Houghton and afterward to the literary bureau. This volume, as a volume, has not survived, even in longhand. But two extant MSS—" The Error of Cousin & Hamilton " and " Formulations of the Infinite "—arrest notice. Though a later hand has marked these documents " School boy essays," they patently are revisions of matter in the Ledger—the first of " Desire and Thought " (pp. 74-93), the second of rough notes headed " Time, Space, & Motion " (pp. 58-63, 267-274) and the more finished treatment of " Infinite Solecisms " (pp. 384-409)—and the Ledger is post-bellum. The two revisions may be assigned to 1868 because Lanier was engrossed in metaphysical writing in that year and because " Formulations of the Infinite " mentions Albert Taylor Bledsoe's *Philosophy of Mathematics* (a work not published till 1868) as " recently issued."

That the two MSS belonged to the " small volume " is likely because the pages of the first are numbered 68-100 and those of the second 101-129. A credible surmise would then be that " Retrospects and Prospects " occupied 1-67. True, no MS of it containing 67 pages, 7½ x 10 inches, has been found. But, as indicated above, nearly all of a MS about equal in content—91 of approximately 100 smaller pages—is still extant. Thus the theory is tenable, though not proved, that " Retrospects and Prospects," " The Error of Cousin and Hamilton," and " Formulations of the Infinite " comprised the small volume. If they did, " Retrospects and Prospects " was probably detached for periodical publication.

retaining the payment on any subscriptions he might secure.[96] Publication caused no great stir among readers, though in Virginia Hankins it awoke longing and pain for the life she once had hoped for, "a life ever developing & hourly renewed through art, a life devoted to beautiful things." [97]

The style of the essay, though leavened by poetic fancy, is clogged and often confusing. The thought also sometimes becomes cloudy. But the large purport is clear. Lanier does two things in relation to each other: he considers whether the world of his day is advancing or retrograding, and he propounds what he calls "that great central idea of the ages," the theory that "as time flows on, man and nature steadily etherealize." This theory is to be detected in *Tiger-Lilies*, where we may assume it partly derives from Novalis. It is recorded moreover at the beginning (page 2) of the Ledger: "The days of chivalry are not gone, they are only spiritualized . . . [in] a later and more blessed age." But here it receives its most elaborate statement.

In examining his time in the light of the theory Lanier ventures boldly and broadly. For absolute success he would have to know every department of life. Though he does not command this omniscience, he is well if not evenly informed, is widely curious, and has freshness of vision. Hence his analysis is stimulating. He applies his theory first to nature, then to sundry branches of art, and finally and more briefly to politics and religion. It is regarding music that he waxes rhapsodic, though he shows aversions too and singles out the Italian opera—which Whitman loved and lauded—for peculiarly rabid dislike. In tracing the progress of the centuries with respect to the mood, subject matter, and technique of poetry he adumbrates his later liberalism in the use of his medium.

When Lanier wrote "Nature-Metaphors" is uncertain. Jottings in the Ledger [98] indicate that from within a year or two after the war he was meditating the subject, and on pages 546-572 he drafted his essay in pencil. The excursion into Hindu thought and literature points to 1868 or 1869 as the year of composition, for in 1869 Lanier wrote "Nirvana." Though the metaphysical content suggests that "Nature-Metaphors" might have been included in the "small volume of Essays" (see note 95, above) which in 1868-69 publishers shied from, the letter of November 4, 1868, shows Lanier "pushing some researches into the theory of Greek accents," as if at least one passage were still to be written.

[96] See note 2, Letters of 1871. [97] See note 17, Letters of 1871.

[98] Notably the following: "Metaphors &c," p. 38; entries for a "treatise," p. 47; definition ("A Metaphor is an expression of the *intersection of two lines of thought*"), p. 275; quoted newspaper simile, p. 465.

On December 18, 1871, Browne welcomed "so charming a paper" for the *Southern Magazine*.[99] He published it in February, 1872, and on the 26th of that month forwarded Lanier's stipend—$2 a page, or $22 in all.

Cross currents of thought connect "Nature-Metaphors" with sundry other works, especially "Retrospects and Prospects." The intricacy of the ideas, not all of them fully developed, tends to make the piece nebulous reading. The basic concepts indeed—those of the metaphor as coming of love and as "always a union of two objects," and of the nature-metaphor as a bridal of spirit and matter, spirit giving matter immortality and matter giving spirit form—are not too difficult to grasp. The inquiry into their present status leads to a comparison of modern with Greek language, thought, and love; and the hypothesis that changed modes and spirit of expression reflect changes in civilization leads to an analysis of metaphors from the *Æneid, The Tempest*, and the *Gita-Govinda.* When abstruse considerations of other sorts are interwoven, the reader must be vigilant or the reasoning will elude him.

The essay, however, has definite merits. By carrying the concept of etherealization into new provinces of esthetics and metaphysics it illustrates the continuity and the progress of Lanier's thinking. With all its exuberance it maintains a hold on realities: "For idealism, as a sole theory of life, is no better than materialism." In balancing Greek qualities against English it marks advance in a power Lanier had displayed while at college and was to consummate in *The English Novel* —the power to make sweeping comparisons and to find in things sundered in time and space unsuspected and living relationships.

"Paul H. Hayne's Poetry" is an outgrowth of friendship and literary compatibility. Hayne, a dozen years older than Lanier, had suffered harm scarcely less grievous from the war and was a fellow victim of tuberculosis. Prior to the conflict he had published three volumes of poetry; after it he published his fourth (*Legends and Lyrics*) in 1872—like the others, at his own expense; but he eked out a precarious livelihood through writing for the periodicals. To this market he sent much miscellaneous prose, and poetry which establishes him as the best and most representative poet of the South between Timrod's death (1867) and Lanier's definite emergence.

The connection between Hayne and Lanier, kept up by post, was mutually unselfish and stimulating. Hayne first addressed the younger

[99] Regarding certain linguistic matters, however, he dissented; "I fear," he said, "you were inducted into Greek poetry by a disciple of the old scansionists, in which case, no wonder you find Greek measures unmusical." To his request that the point be a little modified the printed passage (p. 310, below) shows that Lanier acceded.

poet, apparently in 1868, in appreciation of an unidentified lyric.[100] Thereafter each of the correspondents sent the other many pieces in manuscript and bestowed upon the other frank and valued criticism. By odd chances Hayne's most adverse verdict on anything of Lanier's was written just before "Paul H. Hayne's Poetry" was accepted for publication, and Hayne's letter of thanks for the review commended "Corn," by which Lanier supplanted his friend as foremost Southern poet. Success in no wise undermined Lanier's grateful loyalty: "I do not, and will not, forget." Hayne, after requesting Lanier to edit his literary remains, himself lived to publish in the *Critic* in 1886 a selection of his dead friend's letters.

Lanier decided by early 1872 to review *Legends and Lyrics*, but because other duties, ill health, and accidents intervened he did not write his article until the summer of 1873. There were vexatious hitches before publication in the *Southern Magazine* in January, 1875. There may have been enforced abridgment as well, for an January 25, 1875, Mary Day Lanier wrote her husband, "The review is improved also—more finished, yet more pointed;—still, I mourn many things which have been expunged to shorten it."

The review is more than a notice of *Legends and Lyrics*; it is a general appraisal of Hayne's poetry in the light of large principles. In devoting a whole article to the work of a contemporary it is unique among Lanier's writings. His friendship for Hayne neither warped his judgment nor imposed restraints. He did as he had promised Virginia Hankins on March 9, 1869, "I love you too well to be insincere with you, and I love mine Art too well to be false to it."

He had, in the correspondence, praised the music of Hayne's verse and the felicitous rendering of the objects and moods of nature. On April 17, 1872, he had said that the review was "particularly near" his heart because he was "keenly desirous" of dwelling on "the entire

[100] See note 47, Letters of 1868. Through the index of the present edition the relationships and interests of the two men may be traced in much detail. Four matters call for references here. (1) Changing attitudes to William Morris: Hayne's letters of Sept. 7, 1868, Oct. 30, 1869, and Jan. 19, 1875; Lanier's of Mar. 5, 1870, and May 26, 1873; and Lanier's to Virginia Hankins of July 7, 1869(?), and Aug. 15, 1875. (See also Hayne's to E. C. Stedman of Oct. 11, 1881, in Daniel M. McKeithan, *A Collection of Hayne Letters*, Univ. of Texas Press, 1944, pp. 277-278.) (2) Lanier's epistolary scrutiny of four Hayne poems afterward noticed in his review: letters of Mar. 20, 1871, Mar. 2, 1872, Apr. 17, 1872, and May 26, 1873. (3) Lanier's further comments on qualities in Hayne's poems: letters of Mar. 5, 1870, May 26, 1873, and June 10, 1873. (4) Circumstances of the composition and publication of "Paul H. Hayne's Poetry": Hayne's letter of Feb. 15, 1872; Lanier's of Mar. 2, 1872, Apr. 17, 1872, May 26, 1873, June 10, 1873, and May 23, 1874; and Lanier's to Mary Day Lanier of Nov. 11, 1874, Jan. 12, 1875, and Jan. 22, 1875.

absence, in every thing" Hayne wrote, "of *Trade* in any of its forms." Yet the review as printed offers no diatribe against Trade. It objects that too much of Hayne's work is in the manner of the dreamy and melancholy Morris rather than of the vital and sunshiny Chaucer. The Hayne who escapes from the Morris-bred "dream-of-the-past" is the Hayne it approves. It welcomes him as a genuinely tuneful bard "in a time when popular poetry is either smug and pretty, or philosophically obscure and rhythmically rugged." It applauds his freedom from the -isms of the day, his adherence to basic themes and emotions, his apt seizure of local phenomenon and mood. It regards him as a true poet, destined to fame.

On January 19, 1875, Judge Bleckley had a notice of the review in the Atlanta *Constitution.* The same day Hayne wrote his thanks for the "wonderful critique." Hayne denied being dominated by Morris and defended the use of "the old world legends" when the "inner, vivifying *Spirit*" and not merely "the *externals* & *environments* of a theme" is caught. "Every *other point* of censure urged against my poems," he said handsomely, "I unconditionally acknowledge as right." And he expressed happiness that a work of his had "been made the text for an article so profound in insight, so suggestive, and altogether able."

The final body of selections have to do with the South as a region, its peculiar problems, and its place in the economy, the governmental fabric, the culture, and the life of the nation and the planet.

Regarding slavery Lanier's views shifted. At college he accepted it as a fixed order and as Scripturally sanctioned. Within a few years after Appomattox he wrote the words (page 301, below) which hailed its extinction as proof that politics were being etherealized. Toward the Negro as an individual he felt kindliness throughout. From the Negro he had devotion. On pages 344-346, below—in one of his very last works—he envisioned whites and blacks as leading the same kind of lives in the same areas in utmost friendliness.

Regarding sectional matters his utterances contradict each other. Many times he was sharply critical of the North, many times of the South. A single vehement pronouncement must not be incautiously accepted as expressive of his whole view.[101]

[101] Thus on Nov. 29, 1873, Lanier wrote two phrases which may easily be misleading. The branding of Oglethorpe as "a farcical college" is significant; even so, however, Lanier was making out a case and his words should be coupled with his later tribute to Woodrow (*Poems*, New York, 1884, p. xiii). The reference to "being born on the wrong side of Mason-and-Dickson's line" should be read in its pragmatic context and tempered by other utterances—that, for

Before John Brown's raid (October 16, 1859) Lanier betrayed no sectional feeling. But promptly thereafter—in the Thalian inaugural (December 10), the "Essay on Democracy" (January 11, 1860),[102] and the "Essay on the Philosophy of History" (March 29, 1860)—he condemned Northern hatred and fanaticism. In a suppressed close to the second paper, indeed, he went so far as to favor "a dissolution of the union." Any doubts he felt that this was the right course seem to have been swept away by the election of Lincoln. On December 6, 1860, Lanier announced himself "a full-blooded secessionist."

During the conflict, as has been shown, he neither argued nor denounced. At its close he accepted defeat unresentfully. Looking back afterward upon the struggle, he not only saw its material and moral havoc;[103] he had a good deal to say about the issues. In a debate regarding Louis Napoleon's Mexican empire (August, 1866), in the "Furlow College Address" (June, 1869), in an unpublished address at Marietta, Georgia (August, 1871), and elsewhere he maintained that centralization of authority was destroying the republic; in the "Confederate Memorial Address" (April, 1870) he said of the Southern dead, "These men died for liberty"; and in "The New South" (October, 1880) he still spoke of the need for "constitutional safeguards."[104] On the other hand, he declared (June 8, 1879) that "the belief in the sacredness and greatness of the American Union" was the conquering Northern principle, and from the day he laid aside his Confederate uniform he ardently wished North and South alike to give their fealty to the country as a whole.

The status and prospects of the post-bellum South were never far from his thoughts. Much that he saw was disturbing. As late as June 8, 1879, he asserted, "By the best information I can get the country is substantially poorer now than when the war closed." And not all the responsibility lay with Reconstruction. There were deep-rooted faults of

instance, about his regret that outsiders saw the pleasant old Southern civilization "in the unfavorable glare of accidentally-associated emotions" (VI, 158), and that about his readiness on Dec. 29, 1878, to go back to Georgia cheerfully.

[102] This may have been begun as "Government" by Nov. 14, 1859.

[103] Occasional wartime letters show him observing that plenty of Southerners were engaged in anything but a selfless struggle for country. Afterward, in "Bombs from Below" and *Tiger-Lilies*, he began to stress the evils of war, wherever and by whomever waged. In the South, besides its destructiveness of life and property, it had enabled the grasping to exploit human needs and bereavements, had blighted the futures of thousands of youths, and had brutalized countless folk spiritually. Often if briefly in his later works Lanier pointed out these terrible effects.

[104] The passage in the "Furlow College Address" is on pp. 257-258, below; that in the "Confederate Memorial Address" is on p. 266; that in "The New South" is on p. 335.

temperament and outlook. The South lived too far from the currents of modern thinking, too much in memories of the past, too content with unrealities, too aflame to political provocation, too heedless of humble means of building a sounder civilization. Lanier was eager for her to advance, not only for her own sake, but in contribution to richer national life.

But advancement did not necessarily mean falling in with forces and trends from beyond the Potomac. Lanier strongly protested against two. The first was the woman's rights movement. In a page and a half of notes penciled at college, probably for debate, he had contended that " Woman is physically, morally, and intellectually weaker than man " and " is eminently unfitted for . . . suffrage." Later he continued to oppose her presence at the polls, but for a different reason, that she can best uplift indirectly, through her influence on man. The " Furlow College Address," the address at Marietta, and the " Confederate Memorial Address " all pay tribute to her inspiring and ministering qualities.

The other force was Trade. Regarding this his ideas were doubtless largely shaped by Carlyle, and perhaps by other English writers. The fact remains that above any other American man of letters, and throughout the period, he decried corrupt and ruthless commercialism. We may interpret that commercialism, with all its grossness, as an inevitable development whereby valuable functions were performed. Lanier too came to acknowledge these functions and to see that the great corporation is indispensable to the social economy.[105] None the less he declared, with repeated iteration, that workers must not be deprived of the things that make life sweet and full: right domestic circumstances; access to nature, to the library, to the gallery, to schools for adults; participation in the community theatre or the community band. What he most desired for the South was not manufacturing but diversified, subsistence farming, of which " robust manhood " and a wholesome way of life would be accompaniments.

Of the two selections here reproduced, the " Furlow College Address " (June 30, 1869) was the first large-scale social interpretation of Lanier's native section, and " The New South " (October, 1880) was the last.[106]

Lanier spoke at the Furlow College commencement as a substitute for

[105] Pp. 266 and 337-338, below.

[106] Such collegiate papers as the " Essay on Democracy " and the " Valedictory Address " analyze general conditions. The post-bellum Marietta address (Aug., 1871) was of the general stamp of the Furlow College one, but hastily prepared. Intended as " a mere outline-sketch " of perilous tendencies in politics, social life, art, and religion, it skipped discussion of art because the speaker's time was limited.

his uncle, Clifford Anderson. Circumstances were not too auspicious. He had returned from a business trip of five or six weeks to New York. He was to stand examinations in early July for admission to the bar. On July 7 (soon after the address) he stated, " A thousand things, in the way of sickness, of business, of speechifying &c &c, . . . have kept me stirred up to my utmost energies." The sickness was to take him from his desk for months and was almost to end his life.

Quipping about the occasion, Dutcher mentioned (July 1) "the bucolic mind" of the hearers. Lanier himself explained (January 7, 1870), " I was speaking to an *agricultural* audience, principally." But the quality of the address was not unperceived. The Sumter *Republican* commended Lanier for his " broad and liberal mind. . . . There was nothing of the politician, but all of the man of principle and integrity, . . . in the positions assumed and thoughts spoken." The paper gave the subject as " The Future of the Land We Love."

The title is an appropriate one. In carrying out his exhortation, " Let us see where we stand and whither we go," Lanier examines large trends and sundry " weird and incongruous elements " in five departments of Southern life—social condition, agriculture, politics, art, and religion—and then examines an unannounced sixth department—education. In the first department he studies mainly what ballots for women involve, his opinions being conservative but conscientious and thoughtful. In the second and third he predicates in women an intelligent and constructure interest in activities in which they do not directly share, and he makes realistic and even statesmanlike analyses of agricultural and political forces. In the fourth he renounces merely provincial art and lucidly states his views about the functions of the artist. In the fifth he holds fast to his faith. In the sixth he urges symmetrical development, including education of the emotions. As a whole the address shows that Lanier can criticize frankly where he loves deeply. It shows that he has width of vision and excellence of temper. It shows that the sick soldier, the thwarted artist, and the impoverished family man has wisely used his scant opportunities in the four years since Appomattox.

The ideas expressed in " The New South " had been accumulating through many years. Lanier probably saw the editorial " Advice to the South " in the Syracuse *Courier and Union* of March 9, 1867, recommending (among other things) that the section turn to small farming as its surest deliverance. Certainly he had revolved this thought by the time he wrote the cracker dialect poems and " Corn." Clifford was to recall that during a visit in April, 1876, " much of his talk was about the economic condition of the farming people of the country." [107]

[107] Letter to Edwin Mims, July 18, 1904, Johns Hopkins University.

By November 14, 1877, J. G. Holland, editor of *Scribner's Monthly,* had engaged Lanier for "four papers on Southern life" and had advanced $200 on a $350 or $400 stipend. Lanier planned that, to gather materials for the articles and for a proposed travel book on Georgia, he would go South the next spring. The trip fell through. He had begun to clip pertinent items from Southern journals.[108] By September 10, 1878, it was agreed that he should write only two articles. These he had sent in by January 25, 1880, but he secured permission to condense them into one. Despite ominously deteriorating health, he "managed to finish" this "troublesome job" by July 17. The single article into which his work had resolved itself was published in the October issue, on sale by September 20.

Two fragmentary manuscripts and three loose pages [109] survive from the two-article draft. These do not reveal the precise range and sequence of matter. Broadly speaking and with variations in order, Manuscript A is an earlier version of parts of Section II of the article finally published, Manuscript B of parts of Section III. Neither stands in its original form; both show the successive strata of an evolving work, and both seem to comprise only such pages as, instead of being transferred, had to be rewritten for the new single-article version.[110]

Certain questions arise—in some respects without receiving fully satisfactory answers—with regard to data borrowed from periodicals. In the draft of an unpublished letter (presumably about September 24) to the Baltimore *American* Lanier declares that, as regards the possible increase of large farms in the Northwest, "The New South"

> simply used the conclusion of two recent writers who wrote after personally visiting the large farms in question: one in the *Atlantic Monthly* for last December [1879] or January, and one in *Harper's* Magazine of a later date.

First, the identity and nature of the articles thus drawn on. The *Atlantic* one, anonymous, is on pages 33-44 of the issue of January, 1880, and bears the title "The Bonanza Farms of the West." It examines unsympathetically and with statistical detail the great corporation-run wheat farms of Minnesota and the Dakotas—their purpose, their methods of operation, their economic and social implications.

[108] Including the Atlanta *Constitution* and the Macon *Telegraph and Messenger.* See letters of June 15 and July 9, 1878, and p. 339, below.

[109] Numbered 15, 35, and 36. The present editor tentatively assigns 15 and 35 to MS A.

[110] Both are fuller and more detailed than the print; both insert longer quotations; A pastes in many clippings which the print disregards or merely summarizes; B employs even less modern spelling than the print in transcribing from old tracts. Pages from A have been transported to B, with necessary deletions and transitions. A contains among its inventories the Middle Georgia scene with which the print closes.

The *Harper's* article is presumably "Dakota Wheat Fields," by C. C. Coffin, on pages 529-535 of the issue of March, 1880.[111] This is less adverse than the *Atlantic* article.

Second, the chance that Lanier consulted these articles before writing his own two-article draft. He may just possibly have borrowed from the *Atlantic* writer, though the time factor makes the odds against this all but prohibitive.[112] He could not have gleaned from *Harper's* writer.

Third, the use of these sources for Lanier's final draft. In Section I of the print Lanier makes copious use of facts and ideas from the *Atlantic* article. He apparently makes some use of *Harper's* account.

By September 28 Lanier could report that publication of "The New South" had "awakened great interest." A small outburst of periodical notices was prompt and, on the whole, favorable.[113] On March 21, 1881, A. Pope, sponsor of *Florida*, offered $1,500 for another travel book, an offer which was to cause Lanier only care and worry during his last months. Individuals wrote for information about Southern land values and other inducements to immigrants. On November 5, Mary Day Lanier stated to Tabb that "about two letters weekly" were

[111] As a conceivable though not probable alternative it may be "The Red River of the North," by Henry Van Dyke, Jr., on pp. 801-817 of the issue of May, 1880.

[112] Lanier's draft was complete by Jan. 25, 1880, a few weeks at most after the appearance of the *Atlantic* article. The editor finds unmistakable indebtedness on MS p. 15 only—and this does not certainly belong to the two-article draft.

[113] The following clippings or reprints have been preserved in the Lanier Room, Johns Hopkins University: the Baltimore *American*, Sept. 22; the Philadelphia *Evening Bulletin*, Sept. 22; *The Nation*, Sept. 23; and an unidentified paper, perhaps Oct. 9.

The Baltimore *American*—described by Lanier, on Sept. 24, as "a Republican paper, which four years ago was fond of abusing me"—hailed publication as "a notable occurrence," praised Lanier's originality, versatility, and style, and commended his interpretation of Southern trends. It assumed, however, that he looked to the South alone "for the assertion of the principle of individual independence as against the principle of corporate control"; it thought his "speculations" about "factory farming in the Northwest . . . quite in the air"; and it contended that legal circumstances in sixteenth century England spoiled the analogy with the Northwest. In the draft of his probably unsent reply Lanier denied that he had restricted the small farmer to the South, that he had made unsupported statements about Northwestern large farming, and that sixteenth century English landlords could control legal regulation.

The Philadelphia *Evening Bulletin* appraised the article as "solid and striking." *The Nation* commended Lanier for investing "an economic topic with a palatable husk of philosophy and history," for emphasizing "the multiplication . . . of small farms with diversified products," and for being "the first, as far as we know, to compare the censuses of 1860 and 1870 for evidence of the great change in holdings since the war." The unidentified paper (conjecturally Georgian) quoted figures to demonstrate that "the hope of the country" lay in the replacement of the plantation system by the small farm.

arriving.[114] To all inquiries Lanier seems to have replied cordially and conscientiously, and when he needed further data, he called upon real estate dealers in Macon and Montgomery and upon the Georgia Department of Agriculture.

As a composition "The New South" employs a pattern so gigantic as to strain unity and almost to yield three articles instead of one in three parts and an introduction. In the introduction and Part I Lanier examines the broad character and import of two contemporary forces. Of these he knows Southern small farming more directly and intimately than Northwestern large farming. He feels more strongly about it too; for he has dreamed of the individual as self-sustaining and has denounced Trade as soulless and exploitive. His perspective, however, is mature; he sees that the two forces are complementary and that we need both. In keeping with the bigness in thought the style is sweeping and compendious. In Part II he looks searchingly into the benefits small farming is bringing the South. Because of his closeness to his material his style, though somewhat journalistic, is warm and forthright. In Part III he explores conditions in rural England three centuries and more earlier. Here he utilizes discoveries made by scholarly societies and adduces the evidence of old tracts, sermons, statutes, ballads, etc., in proving that the bygone is like the contemporary and has lessons for it. His style, partly on account of the excerpts, has an archaic flavor which, however, does not make it less earnest.

"The New South" is many years later in date than the other selections here printed. It more surely exemplifies the quality they all possess of relating an immediate topic in a vital way to realms of knowledge whose pertinence is not usually perceived. Indeed it focuses and expresses most of its author's powers and interests. Geographically, it ranges over the Northwest, the South, and sixteenth-century England. It probes economics and historic scholarship, and is mindful of art and morality. It is scientific in approach and method. It is philosophic in proceeding from surface fact to ultimate principle. It is poetic in phrase and tone. It has the lift of Lanier's optimism and his friendly

[114] Five letters of inquiry have survived, the writers, areas, and dates being as follows: S. Beaumont, England, Oct. 20, 1880; A. Lodeman, Mich., Nov. 13, 1880; Dr. Henry Boynton, Vt., Nov. 22, 1880; A. F. Willmarth, Ill., Nov. 30, 1880; F. W. Seger, Minn., Mar. 9, 1881. (Perhaps the most interesting is that by Beaumont, who asked whether it would be advisable to settle Italian families, skilled in small farming, on land he owned in Alabama.)

There are also communications regarding data to be supplied to inquirers, these being from A. G. Butts, Macon, Nov. 13, 1880, and J. S. Newman, Atlanta (the Georgia Dept. of Agriculture), Nov. 20, 1880. Regarding "The New South" Newman says, "The only criticism I make is that it was somewhat overdrawn & may cause disappointment."

wishes for the good of all men. With this inclusiveness, it yet is distinctively of the South, Southern. It exults that the Southern small farmer is fashioning for himself a self-sufficient and satisfying life in an indigenous and civilized community. It halts, with childhood memories of the Negro, to savor the literary skill and the human validities of the Uncle Remus stories. At the end it turns with deep affection to look once again across "this gracious land" of Middle Georgia. The act is symbolical. As the worn-out body of the poet was to seek the familiar mountains for the closing struggle, so now his spirit half-sighs its longing "Here to return and die at home at last."

G. G.[115]

[115] The editor takes pleasure in making acknowledgments supplementary to a few individual notes in this book and to the general Preface in vol. I.

He has had unrestricted access to the unpublished studies in *Tiger-Lilies* begun by Mr. Cecil E. Abernethy at Vanderbilt University in 1936 and has made extensive use of them, especially in considering the significance of the title, *Tiger-Lilies* as German romance, and *Tiger-Lilies* as a war novel. Despite this great indebtedness, however, he accepts full responsibility for the Introduction and the notes.

He has had access to many source materials through Mr. and Mrs. Charles D. Lanier, Mr. Henry W. Lanier, Mr. and Mrs. John S. Tilley, and Mrs. Samuel L. Creath. He has received aid in special matters from Mr. James De Witt Hankins, Mr. Richard P. Hankins, Mr. Aubrey H. Starke, Mrs. Mary Callaway Jones, the late Mr. Oliver Orr, the late Mr. John S. Short, the Macon *Telegraph* (especially Mrs. W. N. Northrop), the Doheny Library at the University of Southern California, the Joint University Libraries at Nashville (especially Mrs. Brainard Cheney, the reference librarian), the Western Reserve Historical Society (especially Misses Margaret Dempster and Virginia Himebaugh of the Library staff), and other individuals and institutions. Finally, he has had invaluable help from the General Editor, Professor Charles R. Anderson.

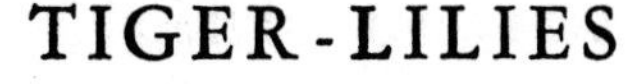

TIGER-LILIES

TIGER-LILIES.

A NOVEL.

BY

SIDNEY LANIER.

For mine is but an humble muse,
And owning but a little art
To lull with song an aching heart,
And give to earthly Love his dues.
Tennyson.

NEW YORK:
PUBLISHED BY HURD AND HOUGHTON,
459 BROOME STREET.
1867.

PREFACE

PITIABLE CASE, when one's book, in the hour of birth, must wear steel on dimpled shoulders and grasp swordhilt with chubby fingers; must be laid into a battle as into a cradle, like Hercules among the serpents; must be its own *accoucheur*, nurse, and defender!

If each child, immediately after finding itself sprawling on this earth, were required to stand up in swaddling-clothes and pronounce some *raison d'être* satisfactory to the world at large, —what a bore were life to the living, what a dread to the unborn, what a regret to most of the dead! A man has seventy years in which to explain his life: but a book must accomplish its birth and its excuse for birth in the same instant; it must renounce all fair prerogatives of babyhood; it must scorn the power of weakness; it must enter life as a certain emperor enters his carriage,—at once smiling to the smiling people, and sternly frowning into the set eyes of assassins in the crowd.

And so, protesting against an exaction in which humanity has outrageously discriminated in favor of itself—this book declares itself an unpretending one, whose interest, if it have any, is not a thrill of many murders nor a titillation of dainty crimes. That it has dared to waive this interest, must be attributed neither to youthful temerity nor to the seduction that lies singing in the grass of all rarely-trodden paths, but wholly to a love, strong as it is humble, for what is beautiful in God's Nature and in Man's Art.

This love, with love's vehemence, swears that it is not well to multiply those horrible piquancies of quaint crimes and of white-handed criminals, with which so many books have recently stimulated the pruriency of men; and begs that the following pages may be judged only as registering a faint cry, sent from a region where there are few artists to happier lands that own many; calling on these last for more sunshine and less night in their art, more virtuous women and fewer Lydia Gwilts,* more household sweetness and less Bohemian despair, clearer chords

* [The unscrupulous heroine of Wilkie Collins, *Armadale.*—Ed.]

and fewer suspensions, broader quiet skies and shorter grotesque storms; since there are those, even here in the South, who still love beautiful things with sincere passion, and who fear that if the artists give us more fascinating female-devils, we too will fall in love with them as school-girls do with Milton's Satan and Bailey's Festus; whereupon the old sweet order of things will be reversed, and, instead of fair marriages between the sons of Heaven and the daughters of Earth, we shall have free-love alliances between the sons of Earth and the daughters of Hell, —the hybrid consequences of which sad event one has neither heart nor breath to pursue.

This book's chief difficulty has been to avoid enriching reality at the expense of truth: a difficulty well known by those who have been astonished to find how the descriptions of eye-witnesses may contain nothing but facts and yet express nothing but falsehood.

S. L.

MACON, GEORGIA, September, 1867

BOOK I

CHAPTER I *

"I'll tell it your Honor," quoth the Corporal, directly.
"Provided," said my uncle Toby, "it is not a merry one."
"It is not a merry one," replied the Corporal.
"Nor would I have it altogether a grave one," added my uncle Toby.
"It is neither the one nor the other," replied the Corporal.
"Then I will thank thee for it with all my heart," cried my uncle Toby: "so prithee begin it, Trim."

Sterne [,*Tristram Shandy*]

"HIMMEL! *COSPETTO! Cielo!* May our nests be built on the strongest and leafiest bough of the great tree Ygdrasil! May they be lined with love, soft and warm, and may the storms be kind to them: Amen, and Amen!" said Paul Rübetsahl.

Now, a murrain on all villainous lodging-houses, say I! Here one's soul has but now taken a body to shelter in, a year or two, from the rains of time; and, *diable!* the poor tenant must straightway fall to and arrange for repairing his house three times a day, or else the whole building will give way, break down and rot in a week, and the unhappy soul must crawl out from the ruins, full of bruises and bad odors, a regret to old neighbors and a laughing-butt to angels!

Old Adam, thou shouldst be tried for a swindling landlord, in that thou hast erected this long rotten row of tumble-down houses for thy tenants, who were also, more shame on thee, thy children!

Now, gentle reader, strange to say, the ability of an author to rise above the mere drudgery of these tri-daily repairs and plunge into his beloved music,—into his beloved music which must now forego fine melody by reason of the din and vile clatter of work about the house of the body,—this ability, I say, depends upon nothing but thy name.

* [Fragment A of the MS begins here.—ED.]

Thy name, most sweet reader, should be Legion: and it is done.

Poets' logic, forever! and so, O twenty-five thousand gentle readers, there is probably among you but one individual who is totally unaffected by some ghost of a shadow of an inkling of a curiosity to know the causes precedent of those ejaculations which commence this chapter.

That one individual?

You all know him.

He is a grocer.

His sign extends across the sidewalk, obtrusively and triumphantly: as who should say, "Pass *sub jugum*, conquered customers!"

His sign beareth device

G. PERCYMMON,*

and there is a certain complacent truculency in the whole of it. For the G is a round sound G; and the P is as if a man should stick thumb in his vest armhole after a good dinner, and the E extends his arms to see the mad R lifting his right foot and kicking poor C over against Y with his hands thrown up protesting, while the two M M's scramble away on all fours, to the round amazement of O, who would fain see the N of it all!

Mr. Percymmon is a match-maker. He says to himself, "Love and Liquor, Friendship and Fools, Fiddles and Fol-de-rol!"—that is the way he pairs them off.

Mr. Percymmon is a philosopher. He accounts for the aggregation of men into societies, in this way:—"Once upon a time," says he, "there arose in the breasts of men a simultaneous desire for the formation of stock-companies, and for the protection of their charters and vested rights: hence villages, towns, cities, municipal governments, state governments, United States!"

Mr. Percymmon is a satirical iconoclast. Once he was decoyed into a theatre. In the critical and supremely pathetic moment when Romeo was declaring the pain of his passion,

* [The MS states that "G. stands for Greene . . . in honor of the hero of Eutaw Springs," but admits that the sound of the name suggests "a certain vegetable with . . . ridiculous and even disagreeable associations."—Ed.]

Mr. P. said, in a voice audible to the whole assembly, " Try J. Bovee Dod's Stomach Bitters! "

Mr. Percymmon is a punster. He believes that marital bonds are flat i' the market, and that the ties of humanity are railroad ties.

Well, one saved makes more rejoicing than twenty-four thousand nine hundred and ninety-nine that were not lost. And I *will* have a word with thee, O Percymmon!

When thou higglest over mackerel prices, occurreth ever to thee that, as mackerel swim in the sea, so swim men in the diaphanous waves of time? And when thou hearest the noise of thy busy trucks, dreamest thou ever it is the never-ending melancholy monotone of the time-sea beating upon the desolate sands of death? And that this monotone is the devil's dainty hush-song and lullaby wherewith he lulleth himself to rest? And when thy new customer drinketh his whiskey with thee, anticipatest thou that some day soon the vast thirsty Cyclops-shadow of eternity shall stoop and drink down the sea of time at a swallow? Hast thou studied the intimate inter-balance of the prices of cheese and of salvation? And thinkest thou there is any wide difference betwixt cutting down the salary of John Simpson, thy pale book-keeper, and cutting up the coat of him for whose garments they cast lots?

And knowest thou the tie betwixt mess-pork and poetry?

Gentle Twenty-four-thousand-nine-hundred-and-ninety-nine, who have waited so long, it were but just you should forthwith see Paul Rübetsahl, who has as yet been nothing more than the voice of the fisherman's Genie, and who has lain like a cloud confined in the sealed brazen vessel of

Chapter II

Theseus.—And since we have the vaward of the day,
My love shall hear the music of my hounds.
Uncouple in the western valley; let them go!
We will, fair queen, up to the mountain's top.
Midsummer Night's Dream

NOT FAR above the junction of the Little Tennessee and Holston rivers, immediately upon the banks of the former stream, occurs a level plat, or "cove," as it is there called, of most romantic beauty. Here the river suddenly ceases its wild leaping down the mountains, and, like a maiden about to be married, pauses to dream upon the alliance it is speedily to form with a mightier stream. On each side the wide expanse of this still river-lake, broad level meadows stretch away some miles down the stream, until the hoydenish river wakes from its dream and again dashes down its narrow channel between the mountains.

The meadows are inclosed by precipitous ridges, behind which succeed higher ridges, and still higher, until the lofty mountains wall in and overshadow them all.

The hills sit here like old dethroned kings, met for consultation: they would be very garrulous, surely, but the exquisite peace of the pastoral scene below them has stilled their life; they have forgotten the ancient anarchy which brought them forth; they dream and dream away, without discussion or endeavor.

On the last day of September, 1860, huntsman Dawn leapt out of the east, quickly ran to earth that old fox, Night, and sat down on the top of Smoky Mountain to draw breath a minute. The shine of his silver hunting-gear lit the whole mountain, faintly. Enough, at any rate, to disclose two men who with active steps were pursuing a road which ascends the mountain half way, and which at a distance of two miles from the cove just described diverges from a direct course to the summit, passing on to the Carolina line. The younger of the two, equipped with a light sporting-rifle and accoutrements, walked ahead of his companion, a tall, raw-boned, muscular mountaineer, who with his right hand carried a long slim-barrelled gun, while with his left he endeavored to control the frantic gambols of a brace of deer-hounds whose leash was wrapped round his bony fingers.

"Waal I reckin!" exclaimed the mountaineer, whom the 24,999 may hereafter recognize as Cain Smallin; "and how many bullets, mought ye think, was fired afore he fotch the big un to the yeth?"

"O! Gordon Cumming * was a hunter, you know, and all hunters exaggerate a little, perhaps unconsciously. He *says* he fired two hundred balls into the elephant before he fell."

"A maaster heap o' lead, now, certin, to kill one varmint! But I suppose he got a mortial sight of ven'zon, an' hide an' truck o' one sort an' another off'n him. I recommember Jim Razor flung fifteen bullet into a ole b'ar over on Smoky Moun-t'n, two year ago come Chris'mas; but hit ain't nothin' to your tale. Would'n' I like to see one o' them—what was't you called 'em? I'm forgitful."

"Elephants."

"One o' them elephants a-waddlin' up yan mount'n of a hot summer's day!"

As this idea gained upon the soul of Cain Smallin, he opened his mouth, which was like a pass in the mountains, and a torrent of laughter brawled uproariously through it.

"I hardly think he would make as good time as that deer yonder, that you've frightened half to death with your monstrous cackle. Look, Cain! In with the dogs, man! I'm for the top of the mountain to see the sun rise; but I'll come down directly and follow along, as you drive, to catch any stragglers that may double on you."

With a ringing yell the mountaineer loosed his dogs, and followed after with rapid strides.

"Take my hat," muttered he, "*an*' boots! The boy said he had'n' seen a deer sence he left here four year ago fur college, an' I raally thought he'd be master keen for a drive. An' he a-runnin' away f'om the deer, an' hit in full sight, an' the dogs a'ter it! But them blasted colleges'll ruin any man's son, *I* don't care *who* he is!"

* [Roualeyn George Gordon-Cumming, author of *Five Years of a Hunter's Life in the Far Interior of South Africa.*—Ed.]

Meanwhile, Philip Sterling, the unconscious object of the mountaineer's commiseration, by dint of much climbing and leaping over and across obstacles which he seemed to despise in the wantonness of youthful activity, at length reached the mountain-top, and stood still upon the highest point of an immense rock, which lay like an altar upon the very summit. A morning mist met him, and hung itself in loose blank folds before him, like the vast stage-curtain of some immeasurable theatre. But the sun shot a straight ray through the top of the curtain and, as if hung to this horizontal beam with rings of mist, it drew itself aside and disclosed the wonderful-scened stage of the world—a stage (thought Philip Sterling) whose tricksy harlequins are Death and Chance, and whose trap-doors are graves—a stage before which sits an orchestra half composed of angels, whose music would be ravishing did not the other half, who are devils, continually bray all manner of discords by playing galops for our tragedies, and dirges for our farces—a stage whose most thrilling performances are sad pantomimes, in which a single individual's soul silently plays all the parts—a queer " Varieties " of the Universe, where rows nightly occur, in which the combatants are Heaven and Hell.

Airy 24,999 who hover with me round this mountain-top, ye might almost see these thoughts passing in review in Philip Sterling's eyes, as he stands dreamily regarding the far scene below him. Ye do not notice, I am certain, the slender figure, nor the forehead, nor the mouth, nose, and chin; but the eyes—Men and Women!—the large, gray, poet's eyes, with a dream in each and a sparkle behind it—the eager, hungry eyes, widening their circles to take in more of the morning-beauties and the morning-purities that sail invisibly about—these ye will notice!

> From the eyes a path doth lie
> To the heart, and is not long;
> And thereon travel of thoughts a throng!

—quoth Hugo von Trimberg.* And these eyes of Philip Ster-

* [Lanier's source for translation and quotation is almost certainly Carlyle, " Early German Literature " (in *Critical and Miscellaneous Essays*), where the lines are attributed to a " chapter " called " The Maiden " in Trimberg's long poem *Der Renner*.—Ed.]

ling's go on to say, as plainly as eyes can say: " Thou incomprehensible World, since it is not possible to know thee perfectly, our only refuge is to love thee earnestly, that, so, the blind heart, by numberless caresses, may learn the truth of thy vast features by the touch, and may recognize thy true voice in the many-toned sounds that perplex a soul, and may run to meet thee at hearing thy step only."

" Yet I know not, O World, whether thou art a wrestler whom I must throw heavily, or a maiden whom I must woo lightly. I will see, I will see! " cried Philip Sterling to himself.

(Bless my life, 24,999! How long our arms are when we are young! Nothing but the whole world will satisfy their clasp; later in life we learn to give many thanks for one single, faithful, slender waist!)

"And so," continued our young eager-soul, " I choose to woo thee; thou shalt be my maiden-love. I swear that thy voice shall be my Fame, thy red lips my Pleasure, thine eyes my Diamonds; and I will be true knight to thee, and I will love thee and serve thee with faithful heart and stainless sword till death do us part! "

" But what a fool I am," said Philip Sterling aloud, " to be vowing marriage vows before I'm even accepted, nay, before I've fairly declared my passion! Hasty, mi-boy! But I wish I were down in the cities; I'm ready for work, and it's all a dream and a play up here in the mountains."

One may doubt if Pygmalion, being so utterly in love, was at all surprised when his statue warmed into life and embraced him. Philip Sterling, at any rate, making love to this sweet statue of the world, did not start when he heard a step behind him. He turned, and beheld a tall figure, in whose face, albeit mossed like a swamp-oak with beard, beamed a cheerful earnestness that was as like Philip's enthusiasm as a star is like a comet.

" ' Life is too short,' " quoted the stranger, advancing with open hand extended, " ' to be long about the forms of it.' My name's Paul Rübetsahl! "

"And mine is Philip Sterling! "

The two hands met and clasped. Philip had always a *penchant* for the love-at-sight theory, and I know not if Paul Rübetsahl was any more sensible. The two young transcendentalists looked in each other's faces. The frank eyes searched each other a moment, and then turned away, gazing over the valley, along the river dividing the mountains, on, to the far horizon. In this gaze was a sort of triumphal expression; as who should say, " Two friends that have met on a mountain may always claim that as their level, and their souls may always sail out over hills that are hard to climb, over valleys that are tilled with sweat and reaped with Trouble's sickle, over cities whose commerce perplexes religion, over societies whose laws and forms oppress a free spirit; from such a height we may look down and understand, at least not despise, these things."

And with that high egotism of youth whereby we view the world in its relations to us, and not also in our relations to it, and stretch out our eager hands to grasp it, as if it were made for us and not we also for it; in this happy exaltation, each of these two youths cried out in his heart, " Behold! O world, and sun, and stars—behold, at last, two Friends! "

CHAPTER III

> *First Keeper.*—Under this thick-grown brake we'll
> shroud ourselves:
> For through this laund anon the deer will come.
> ——And, for the time shall not seem tedious,
> I'll tell thee what befell me on a day
> In this self-place where now we mean to stand.
>
> *King Henry VI* [*Part III*]

CAIN SMALLIN'S deer-drive was now in the full tide of success. The ridge, or bench, along whose "backbone" ran the road which has been referred to, was admirably adapted for the style of hunting now in progress. On one side of it yawned the deep ravine down whose fern-bedded declivity the mountaineer was conducting the drive; whilst, on the other side, at the foot of a continuous steep precipice, the river foamed and brawled and dashed madly down the rocky descent, as if it fled from some horror in the mountains. As the bench gradually descended the mountain-side, however, approaching the valley, its perpendicular escarpments became less savage, and began to slope more gently, until near the foot of the mountain, they changed into cool beautiful glades running by almost imperceptible descent into the water. It was along that part of the road which passed through these glades, just commencing the ascent of the mountain, that the standers had been posted; in the expectation that the deer, naturally seeking the lower parts of the ridge by which to cross over to the water, would come in gun-range of some of the party.

Nor was this anticipation disappointed. It was not long before the mountaineer, who seeing his dogs well on trail had now begun to pick his way with more deliberation amongst the huge fallen logs and boulders which strewed the side of the ravine, was gratified by the sharp crack of a rifle, quickly followed up with the shout which announces the success of the lucky stander.

"Jim Razor's rifle," muttered he, "Jim Razor's holler; thar's ven'zon, certin. And yan crazy Phil Sterlin' away off up yan mount'n, a-watchin' the sun rise an' not a-carin' whether the dogs is come in or not! Ef he'd 'a' seen the sun rise as many times as I have, I scarselie think he'd be leavin' a fresh trail an' climbin' the steepest bench this side o' old Smoky, for nothin' but that! But them blasted colleges'll ru— what *is* old Ring a-doin' *now?* " said he, stopping short and listening.

Ring was the swifter of the two hounds: if both dogs had been on trail of the same deer, Ring should have arrived at the stand first;—he was still in full cry far down the ravine.

" Lem me look for sign," muttered the curious driver, and bent himself close to the ground, attentively scanning the clear spots in various directions.

His suspicions were soon verified. " Each dog's got his deer, an' I'll be dad-blasted ef old Ring ain't a'ter the biggest buck in Smoky range! Whoop! "

With his customary yell the mountaineer turned and began rapidly ascending the side of the ravine in order to regain the road and make better time. Down this unobstructed path he struck out with huge strides. He hoped that, as sometimes happened when hard pressed, the stag had turned aside from the water with its deadly line of standers, and had run in among the farms of the cove, where the chase would be prolonged and would become intensely exciting. As he arrived at the foot of the ridge where the road turns off among the open meadows, away from the water, an animated scene met his eye. The standers, attracted by the continued and excited trailing of old Ring, had all gathered here and were loading, firing, and talking as rapidly and as ineffectually as possible. Not a hundred and fifty yards distant, the stag, a noble, eight-pronged fellow, was swimming rapidly towards the opposite bank of the river, and was now more than half way to freedom.

The mountaineer joined his forces to the main army immediately and commenced to fire " at will."

" Whar'd he cross the line? " inquired he, as he rammed down his bullet.

"At Mr. Sterlin's stand! " replied some fiend in human shape.

" Why didn't you kill him, Mr. Sterlin'? " shouted Smallin in the ear of a well-dressed gentleman of forty-five or fifty, whose countenance wore that half-foolish, half-defiant expression that distinguishes the derelict stander; and who was loading and firing his double-barrel energetically, although the deer was far out of his range, in the apparent sweet hope of drowning in noise and good intentions the memory of his unpardonable sin.

" Well, Smallin, the—the fact is," wiping the powder-grime and perspiration from his eyes, " I,—I was reading, and upon my word "—hastily pouring down a handful of buck-shot—" I had no idea he was so near. Did *you* never lose a deer, Mr. Smallin? " concluded John Sterling, defiantly carrying the war over the border, and at the same time discharging both barrels, with a roar like a salvo of artillery among the thin-cracking rifles. The victorious goddess reclined in the smoke of John Sterling's double-barrel. Cain Smallin was too indignant to reply.

" Whar's the canoe? " asked he, turning to the crowd that had gathered from the field at the unwonted firing.

" Jeems is gone up the creek a-fishin' in it! " replied one of those disagreeable-information-furnishers, of which every crowd boasts at least one.

" By Jove, what a pity to lose him! " said John Cranston, a tall, black-mustached, wicked-eyed man, guest of the Sterlings, and honored with this deer-drive.

" Hit's a maaster buck! " observed a native.

" The biggest I've seed sence I was in the Smoky! " echoed a second.

" How come he to git thru'? " inquired a late arrival, drawing upon his devoted head a bodeful look of undying revenge from John Sterling.

Amid all this confusion of questions and exclamations, which were uttered far more quickly than they have been read, the stag was gallantly breasting his way through the water unheeding the shots, which fell far wide of him. But who could have foretold Blücher? Suddenly the fortunes of the day changed. The dripping deer had emerged from the water and was in the act of taking his first leap toward his hills and liberty, when a puff of smoke floated from behind a bush a few yards from him, the crack of a rifle smote upon the ears of the disappointed hunters on the other side, and the poor buck, with a mighty bound, fell back upon his antlers and lay still.

"Good!" shouted he of the wicked eyes: "Blücher with his thirty thousand! And the day is ours!"

"Told you so, Smallin! Told you so, gentlemen!" said John Sterling. "If I hadn't let the buck pass, we wouldn't have had half as much sport!" and the guilty stander held up his head and waved his hand triumphantly, like one conscious of being a great public benefactor.

"Them blasted Injuns!" said Smallin, whose indignation, not yet subsided, seized upon the first vent-worthy object: "always a-sneakin' about an' a-eatin' of some other person's meat! Well, a fool for luck, they say!" with which comforting reflection the mountaineer wheeled away, and winded his horn with vigorous too-toos to fetch in the dogs.

Meanwhile the fortunate hunter on the other side, whose dress—of an old slouch hat, homespun shirt and trousers, and yellow moccasins—betokened his Indian blood, had glided from his place of concealment, and having "bled" the game stood quietly watching the red stream flow, when Philip Sterling and Rübetsahl joined the unsuccessful party. These two young gentlemen, having descended to the untranscendental common-level of humanity, suddenly became aware of the usual "forms" of life.

"My father,—Mr. Rübetsahl!"

Hand-shaking, and so on.

"My friend, Mr. Cranston,—Mr. Rübetsahl!"

Philip noticed that at the first mention of Rübetsahl's name John Cranston's face turned white, and his hand trembled a moment; but he quickly recovered himself, and expressed his high sense, as in duty bound, of the happiness which had fallen upon him in knowing Mr. Rübetsahl.

"And now, gentlemen," cried John Sterling to his son and his two guests, "it's high breakfast-time; wherefore I move that we adjourn to my house and discuss a rib of the buck there, broiled as only old Ned can broil it."

The hearty old gentleman led the way towards Thalberg; whither you, O 24,999, and I, albeit none of us are invited, may follow, for even if I failed to make you invisible, and John Sterling saw the whole crowd, he would welcome you every one,—so big, so big was his heart!

Now, I promise to quit apostrophizing when I get fairly into my tale; but while we're walking up this slope behind old John, indulge me, I pray ye, in a little of it done on mine own account. For how can I forget that jocund party of friends with whom, in the early fall of '60, I penetrated these mountains, on a camp-hunt?

Can I forget the mighty hunter of the black eye and beard whom in solemn convention we did dub (it was the time of the Japanese invasion! *) the Grand Tycoon; or the six-footer uncle whom, being unfamiliar with the Japanese gradations, we assigned him as Deputy Tycoon; or old Ned, the French cook, whom the Deputy touched off; or Cricket, the dog, who climbed on old Ring's shoulders and stole the meat one night, as Ned averred? Can I forget how, one divine morning, when we had just returned to camp from the killing of a buck, and were taking our several ease (as Lorrie said), *recubans sub tegmine* of certainly the most *patulæ fagi* ** any of us ever saw, the Grand Tycoon, in his lordly way, suddenly exclaimed, "Get out of the way, old Ned, with your French fripperies; hand me the side of that buck, there!" and how the Grand Tycoon did then purvey him a long beechen wand with a fork on the end thereof, did insert the same in the ribbèd side of the deer, and did rest the whole upon a twig deftly driven in juxtaposition with a bed of glowing coals of the wood of hickory; and how the Grand Tycoon did stand thereover with his muscular right arm outstretched, like Hercules over the Lernean Hydra, save that our Hercules held in his right hand a bottle of diabolical hue wherefrom he ever and anon did drip upon the crisping ribs a curious and potent admixture of butter, hot water, lemon-juice, mustard, pepper, salt, and wine; and how, presently, the Grand Tycoon came to me and said, "Try that rib,——!" and how I took hold of the rib with both hands, it being long as my arm, and near as large, and did forthwith, after the hyena fashion, bite into the same; and how as the meat, with its

* [*I. e.,* the first Japanese mission to America. From Panama, in the spring of 1860, its ninety-three members sailed up our eastern coast to New York and Washington, to ratify a commercial treaty and study occidental ways. The visit aroused public interest and evoked comment in our newspapers and magazines.—ED.]

** [Virgil, *Eclogues*, I.—ED.]

anointments and juices, did fare slowly down the passage appointed for such, the titillation thereof upon the uvula or palate was so exquisite that the world grew brighter upon a sudden, and methought even the brook that ran hard by did murmur a stave or two from the Drinking Song of Lucrezia?

Alas, and alas! O jocund hunters of the fall of '60, how hath the "rude imperious surge" of the big wars tossed us apart, hither and thither! The Grand Tycoon is sunken; he hath gone into a wood contract with railroads, and old Ned languisheth. The Deputy beareth scar of Gettysburg, and yet deeper scars beareth he; I scribble; and poor Lorrie, the ever-genial, went, I hear, at Shiloh, to the happy hunting-grounds! *Abiit ad plures*; * whither, I forget not, we also, O Tycoon and jocund hunters, go soon to join him!

* [Petronius, *Satyricon*.—Ed.]

CHAPTER IV

King Henry.—Let me embrace these sour adversities,
For wise men say it is the wisest course.

King Henry VI [*Part III*] *

IT IS a full mile, and up hill too! to John Sterling's house, from where we started; and I have yet time, before we enter the doors of our host-in-spite-of-himself, to button-hole these 24,999 people and tell them how it came about that John Sterling found this soft valley far off there among the hills and, as it had been a violet, plucked it for his own long delight.

John Sterling's essays, at college, were broad and open and genial, like a breeze that blows with equal beneficence upon the hot foreheads of the virtuous and the sinful; and his speeches, hung with sparkling fancies and mellow with calm sunlight, made his hearers feel as if they were a-field early, in one of those charming old sedge-fields that one finds in quiet corners of the plantations, where the silver dew-drops and the golden broom-sedge strive together to see whether the early sunlight shall be mellow or sparkling. Now, because all healthy men love sunlight and fresh breezes and dew, all the college loved John Sterling, and he them. Of course, John Sterling studied law—what young man in our part of the country did not?—and one day came to John Sterling, senior, with news that he had been admitted to the bar, with credit. The old gentleman, in his bluff way, drew a check and pushed it to John's side of the table, remarking, "Well, my boy, I have foreseen it and prepared for it. Here's a thousand or two that'll open your office for you, and so forth. Go to work and make your fortune. When I tell you that your success depends entirely upon yourself, I do not say anything that ought to frighten a Sterling!"

John Sterling junior went forth and committed what may be most properly called a chronological error. He took a wife before he took any fees; surely a grand mistake in point of

* [The MS shows that Lanier at first planned the use of two mottoes from E. B. Browning, *Aurora Leigh*.—ED.]

time, where the fees are essentially necessary to get bread for the wife! Nor was it long before this mistake made itself apparent. Two extra mouths, of little Philip and Felix Sterling, with that horrid propensity to be filled which mouths will exhibit spite of education and the spiritual in man, appeared in his household; outgo began to exceed income; clouds came to obscure the financial sky.

Even to those of us who are born to labor and know it, it is yet a pathetic sight to see a man like John Sterling going to his office every morning to sit there all day face to face with the "horny-eyed phantom" of unceasing drudgery, that has no visible end; to know that every hour this man will have some fine yearning beat back in his face by the Heenan-fists * in this big prize-ring we call the world, wherein it would seem that toughness of nose-muscle, and active dodging do most frequently come out with the purse and the glory.

And how shall I speak of that first bill that John Sterling could not pay? The poor men in this crowd will believe that when, a few minutes afterward, John met his creditor on the street and did not look him in the eye as they passed, he stopped suddenly short, gazed for one hesitating moment at the pistols in the gunsmith's shop-window there, then thought of wife, and little Phil, and Felie at home yonder, and so walked on to his business, with a final glance of piteous appeal up towards the blue skies which smiled and smiled away in infinite unconcern and did *not* send down the sun to see about it!

Happy is he who, like John Sterling, has courage under such circumstances to say broadly and without subterfuge, "I cannot pay you, sir!" and so saves his manhood's truth, wherewith to draw to himself a little solace in the bitter hours.

But, one summer, the weather in the city grew diabolically warm. Wife looked pale and the children languished. John Sterling sware his great oath.

"Wife," said he, "let the world end in the fall! but we'll go and spend this summer in the mountains!"

The world did not end in the fall; and John Sterling brought back with him a new idea that helped to stave off many a bit-

* [The prize fighter John C. Heenan (see also p. 218, below).—ED.]

terness. In his explorations among the mountains, of whose scenery he was passionately fond, he had discovered the little valley, or cove, which has been described. Many a night he would sit round the fire in midst of wife and children and amuse himself by building ideal houses on sites he had selected there, by planning grounds and gardens and fountains, and the like; into all of which wife entered, heart and soul, and when the interest in the topic waned, would draw him back to it in her sweet artful way, by all manner of cunning devices, because she saw that it served to chase away the wintry look that in these days was beginning to dwell in his face. "If we only had about three hundred thousand, wife!" he would say, and a genial smile as of old would overspread his face.

24,999, you will be glad to hear, in a general way, that troubles and stories have their end; and, in a special way, that one day when John Sterling came home to dinner, his wife met him at the door, and with that extremely reasonable procedure which women adopt when they have important information to communicate, fell a-sobbing, with her arms round his neck, insomuch that she could not speak for a little while.

But it came out presently that one uncle Ralph of hers had been sick years ago, and that she had tended him and laid cool girlish hands upon his hot forehead and so on, and that whereas he was rich, now he was dead, and she was legatee!

Therefore, John Sterling built his house in Valley Beautiful.

And there it stands!

The Arabs say, the best description is that by which the ear is converted into an eye: for saying which I am infinitely obliged to the Arabs, because it gives me color of title to beg these 24,999 that they shut their eyes and listen; since I am bent on having a word or so on John Sterling's house.

To-wit: Nature surely intended that a house should be built here! For the mountain, half-way up whose side the house lies, sends out a bench, or level shelf, which then begins to slope and so gradually falls away down to the river's edge. Yonder, to the eastward, the hills and ridges lean kindly to right and left, opening so a vista through which one can see old Smoky and the Bald and the other kingly peaks, each with his group of smaller peaks and mountainlets around him, like chieftains standing in midst of their clansmen when Montrose caused the pibroch sound war through Scotland. And here, below, lies the valley with its lake-like river: shut in, far away yonder to the westward, by ridges upon whose heads, every sunset, the sun lays his last wavering beams of light, that are like the tremulous thin fingers of an old man, dying and blessing his children.

This house acknowledges the majesty of the mountains, and, feeling itself in the presence, scorns to display any architectural flippancies or fripperies. Standing severe in simple dignity, it somehow makes me think of old Samuel Johnson, who took a chair and sat when the king bade him, although the king stood up, and who, when afterwards questioned about it, replied, "Yes, sir, it was not my place to bandy civilities with my king!" This house does not bandy civilities with the mountains, but presents to them a simple reverential front, while on the other side it turns to the valley a broad façade, smiling with many windows and long Doric-pillared colonnade. Small unadorned balconies present themselves everywhere: whether one wish to admire the chieftains over yonder marshalling their clans, or to pity the foolish frightened river fleeing through the upper end of the valley, or to amen the sun's blessing upon the hills at the lower end, or to get a plenteous smile from the rich meadows just beneath there, one will always find some balustraded niche or stand-point, from which to look and be filled. One battlemented tower rises up, as if the architect just wished to record that he remembered the feudal castles among the mountains. Parks are here in which are no tame deer, but many a wild one; and over the hill, on the south slope, the vineyards cling. Somehow the stables and outer offices, though well-built, are cunningly hid; and rightly, for here in the high presence of the primary intrinsically-beautiful, no mere secondary economically-beautiful should obtrude itself. In the rear rises up the mountain, a benignant, overshadowing *genius loci.*

Inside?

I am done with description; but I wish ye were all in the music-room, for in this house Music is a household-god. I think ye would say with me that even the dumb walls were eloquent with the harmonies of fair colors; and with John Keats,—

Heard notes are sweet, but those unheard
Are sweeter: therefore ye soft pipes, play on,
Not to the sensual ear, but more endeared,
Pipe to the spirit ditties of no tone! *

As John Sterling, his son and his two guests, walked up the steps of his house, they turned and stood still a moment, and saw the river below lying in the arms of the brawny mountains and smiling up like a blue-eyed child to those from whose loins it sprung. It was a sight John Sterling could never brook without saying some pretty thing.

"Look, gentlemen!" cried he. "It is like a Raphael's Madonna in a gallery of dark Salvator Rosas!"

"It is like sweet Joan of Arc smiling in midst of the grim knights of France!" said Cranston.

"It is as if Liszt, in the rush of that storm-galop on the piano, should suddenly glide away into a peaceful *Lied* of Mendelssohn!" said Rübetsahl.

"Or like a sudden lull in a battle, during which one hears a Sister of Mercy praying over a man just killed!" said Philip.

"Aye, it is like a sunshiny Sabbath coming between twelve stormy week-days. It is my Valley Beautiful. Come, enter, Mr. Cranston. Mr. Rübetsahl, I had a fancy to call my house Thalberg, because it belongs equally to the mountain and the valley; and I bid you welcome to it very heartily," said princely John Sterling.

* [" Ode on a Grecian Urn."—Ed.]

Chapter V

Hotspur.—And 'tis no marvel he is so humorous.
By 'r Lady, he is a good musician.
Lady P.—Then should you be nothing but musical,
For you are altogether governed by humors.

King Henry [*IV, Part I*] *

IN YOUTH, when each moment brings before us some new soul with whom ours is to clasp hands or cross swords, perhaps both, there is an inexpressible charm in meetings that occur first under beautiful and uncommon circumstances. To him who has not loved some man with the ardor of a friendship-at-first-sight, one can only say, Nature has dealt hardly with you, sir!

For I am quite confident that Love is the only rope thrown out by Heaven to us who have fallen overboard into life.

Love for man, love for woman, love for God,—these three chime like bells in a steeple and call us to worship, which is, to work. Three notes to a full chord, say the musicians; and this is the three-toned harmony our world should make, in this immense musical festival of the stars.

Inasmuch as we love, in so much do we conquer death and flesh; by as much as we love, by so much are we gods. For God is love; and could we love as He does, we could be as He is. So thought Philip Sterling, and loved his friend Paul Rübetsahl.

And somehow it did not seem strange to anybody at Thalberg that Philip should have found this man wandering among the mountains at sunrise, in that lonely country. For Rübetsahl talked of mountains as he would talk of absent friends; he seemed to have peered into their ravines and nooks as if he were studying a friend's character, and to have slept upon them as on a friend's bosom.

An hour after supper on the night of that first day at Thalberg, John Sterling laid down his pipe, and, as he had been

* [The text of 1867 wrongly assigns the excerpt to *King Henry VI.*—Ed.]

lost in that cloud of smoke he had puffed forth, sung out at the top of his voice,

" 'And where be ye, my merry, merry men?' "

" Here," chorused voices in the music-room.

As he entered, Philip was turning over some music on a stand; Cranston was stretching a new E upon his violin, frowning savagely and breathing hard the while, as if he were strangling the poor instrument by the neck; and Rübetsahl and Felix Sterling were conversing composedly at the piano.

It was about this moment when Rübetsahl began to discover that he had mistaken the tall, gray-eyed girl with whom he was talking; that her coldness was rather a transparent purity like that of star-beams which seem cold to the hand but warm to the soul, and that her apparent unimpressibility was rather the veiled impressibility of an enthusiasm which was so strong that it feared itself. He had yet to find that music was the Moses-wand that could smite this crystalline rock into a soft refresher of the thirsty. For indeed the soul of Felix Sterling was like a sea, concealing in its immense translucency myriads of unknown things; but, when music was toward, it was as if a spirit plenipotentiary sailed down the wind and stood over the centre of this sea, and uttered some tremendous word at which all the sea-shapes, terrible and beautiful together, rose in strange shoals to the surface.

That day, at dinner, Rübetsahl had remarked that Frankfort-on-the-Main was his birthplace; and Felix added that Mr. Cranston had passed some time at that place when he was in Germany; whereupon quick flashing glances were exchanged between Cranston and Rübetsahl; all of which Philip had detected, and he was puzzling over it, as he idly turned the leaves of his music.

" Come, Phil; your flute, man! I always begin my musicale with the flute, Mr. Rübetsahl: it is like walking in the woods, amongst wild flowers, just before you go into some vast cathedral. For the flute seems to me to be peculiarly the woods-instrument; it speaks the gloss of green leaves or the pathos of bare branches; it calls up the strange mosses that are under dead leaves; it breathes of wild plants that hide and oak-fragrances that vanish; it expresses to me the natural magic in music. Have you ever walked on long afternoons in warm sunny spots of the woods, and felt a sudden thrill strike you with the half-fear that a ghost would rise up out of the sedge or dart from behind the next tree and confront you, there in the broad daylight? That is the sensation Phil's solos—he won't have an accompaniment—always produce upon me." Old John stopped: he was out of breath.

"Father, give me half a chance!" said Philip, already toot-tooting low flourishes and runs.

"'How sharper than a serpent's tooth' * and so forth!" rejoined the father, holding up his hands in mock horror. "O filial impiety! But you will believe, Mr. Rübetsahl, that I love to hear it as much as I do to talk about it. Go on, Phil—*age!*"

A series of irregular modulations comes purl—purling along, like a rivulet shooting down smooth moss, then eddying over rough pebbles, and shooting and eddying again; straight lines and circles of notes, as it were. But he manages that through all the modulations a certain note is dimly but repeatedly presented to us. Presently he stops on this note, lingers there a moment, and then glides into a simple liquid adagio of sixteen notes. Comes suddenly a warbling movement in which the lower notes are fingered so rapidly that they make harmony instead of melody, and we quickly discover the adagio displaying itself in short upper notes struck between the lower ones, as the sky displays itself in patches, each with a faint star in it, through the crevices of an arabesque ruin. Then comes a thin clear romance, as if stealing from afar, in which the notes rise and fall, and complain and rejoice, and echo and answer, till one voice pours out a stream of tender appealings, which seem to prevail, and the piece ends with a long sigh of satisfied relief.

"Well, and what do you mean by it?" impatiently broke in Felix, "for your 'descriptive music' is all humbug unless you give us the idea!"

"Well, I'll tell you. One day, at college, I had just read this magnificent line:

—Or Lady of the Lake
Lone sitting by the shores of old Romance! **

---

* [Shakespeare, *King Lear.*—Ed.]

** [Wordsworth, *Poems on the Naming of Places*, IV. Perhaps Lanier first met when a messmate broke into the room, and swore our ham was out and the mess fund was dry, and begged my assistance in an expedition then organizing in my mess to steal the President's turkeys, that night! I didn't go with 'em, but played that piece, in defense of my poor, lonely Lady of the Lake!"

Even the ridiculous could not cloud the sparkle that was now shining in the eyes of Felix Sterling.

"O," cried she, "I see, I see. Romance,—

Fresh as a spouting spring amongst the hills,

seeks to clear itself of the vile commonplace 'cares that have rilled into it,' and asserts itself and exhibits its beauty, and pleads and prevails and becomes pure again! It was too beautiful, brother Phil, and I'll kiss you this night, and there's my hand on it!"

"Good!" cried old John, and laughed, and bravoed uproariously at the girl's sally.

"*Himmel!*" said Rübetsahl. "Friend Philip, you are a poet: Miss Sterling, you are a poem!"

Whereat "Bravissimo!" from old John again, while Cranston sat still, with wicked eye, and lip just curling into the semblance of a sneer.

"Well," said John Sterling when he had subsided, "my time now, eh, Phil? And I do protest, Mr. Rübetsahl" ("Bless my life, what a listener that German Rübetsahl was!" old John used to say after Paul had gone to the wars), "I wonder how it is that many good American people even now consider music a romantic amusement, rather than a common necessity, of life! When surely, of all the commonplaces, none is more broadly common or more inseparable from daily life. Music! It is as common as—as—as—Phil, I'll thank you for a simile!—as—"

"Bricks, father!"

"So—common as bricks, common as anvils (I only wanted a start, d'ye see!), common as water, common as fire-places! For every brick-mason sings to his trowel-strokes, and blacksmiths strike true rhythmical time, even to triplets—I've heard

the lines in *Noctes Ambrosianae,* No. XXII, October, 1825 (a work he had treasured), where North quotes them correctly.—ED.]

'em—and sailors whistle in calm or windy weather, and households jangle and thrum and strain on all manner of stringed and wind instruments. Music is in common life what heat is in chemistry, an all-pervading, ever-present, mysterious genius. The carpenter whistles to cheer his work, the loafer whistles to cheer his idleness. The church for life, and the bar-room for death; the theatre for tears, and the circus for smiles; the parlor for wealth, and the street for poverty—each of these, now-a-days, has its inevitable peculiar orchestra. And so every emotion continually calls, like the clown i' the play, 'Music without there!' Victory chants; defeat wails; joy has galops; sorrow has dirges; patriotism shouts its Marseillaise; and love lives on music, for food, says old Will!

"Moreover, the Chinese beats his gong and the African his jaw-bone; the Greek blew Dorian flutes; the Oriental charms serpents with his flageolet; German Mendelssohn sends up saintly thanks, Polish Chopin pleads for a man's broken heart, and American Gottschalk fills the room full of great sad-eyed ghosts—all with the piano! Aye,—

> There's not a star that thou beholdest there
> But in his motion like an angel *sings,*
> Still choiring to the young-eyed cherubim! *

"And so from 'street-mud' up to 'star-fire,' through all grades, runs the multitudinous song of time. From a christening to a funeral is seventy years; one choir sings at the christening, another choir sings at the funeral; all the life between, the dead man sang, in some sort, what tunes his heart could make.

"Late explorers say they have found some nations that had no God; but I have not read of any that had no music! Wherefore, since in all holy worship; in all unholy sarcasm; in all conditions of life; in all domestic, social, religious, political, and lonely individual doings; in all passions; in all countries, earthly or heavenly; in all stages of civilization, of time, or of eternity; since, I say, in all these music is always present to utter the shallowest or the deepest thought of man or spirit—

* [Shakespeare, *The Merchant of Venice.* North quotes these lines also, and in correct form, in *Noctes Ambrosianae,* No. XXXIX, November, 1828. The conversation, throughout this chapter, is filled with verbal echoes of *Twelfth Night* and *Macbeth* as well as *The Merchant of Venice.*—Ed.]

let us cease to call music a fine art; to class it with delicate pastry-cookery and confectionery; and to fear to take too much of it lest it should make us sick! Fine Art, indeed! It is no more a fine art than—than—than—help me, Philip, or I sink!—than —"

"What do you think of bacon and greens, for instance, now, Pa?"

"Good: no more than bacon and greens to a Southerner; or beans (I'm off, children!) to a Northerner; or rats to a Chinaman; or lager-beer to Mr. Rübetsahl there!"

"And that's a good place to say," cried Philip, "that it's a burning shame that here in the South so many of those Germans who teach their divine music are continually found haunting the lager-beer saloon when they are not giving a lesson. I wish that in all the colleges the Professor of Music were considered, as he should be, one of the Professors of Metaphysics, and that he ranked of equal dignity with them; and that he stood as much chance of being elected President of the college as the Professor of Chemistry or the Languages! It will be so, it must be so; and I hope, not long hence!"

"Ah," exclaimed Felix, "we spin out the subject. Why not sum all up, and say: Music means harmony, harmony means love, and love means—God!"

"'A judgment, a judgment,'" said Cranston. "Proven by irrefragable poet's logic. It reminds me of the old schoolboy's brocard: An eel-pie is a pie of fish, a fish-pie is a Jack-pie, a Jack-pie is a John-pie, a John-pie is a pie-John, a pie-John is a pigeon; ergo, an eel-pie is a pigeon-pie; and damned be he who doubts logic!"

"Cranston, an' you will scoff," said John Sterling, "I'd rather hear you scoff on your violin, than a-talking. Rübetsahl, he's the most musical of skeptics; listen to him; he fiddles Pyrrhonisms and wickedness! Scrape away, man!"

Cranston seized his violin and played; and although his black eyes gave no sign of feeling, and a half-smile, sometimes shading to a half-scowl, dwelt upon his lips, yet it somehow seemed as if the violin had fastened its serpent-fangs in the throat of the man, and he had grasped it, as Laocoon grasped the serpent, to thrust off the horrible snaky hold; you could almost see the violin writhe and shudder through its length.

And the music? It was an improvisation; Cranston never played anything else. The only way to give any idea of it is to say that it made one think of some soul that had put out its own eyes in a fury, and gone blindly dashing about the world in spring, wounding itself against fair trees, falling upon sweet flowers and crushing odors out of them, rising and cursing and falling again, too busy in imprecating to perceive the fragrance it created even by its fall. I always knew that in the glittering brocade of music there ran (as is the case in all earthly weaving) a dark thread, but, until I heard Cranston, I never saw this dark thread grow so large and overshadowing, nor assume such fantastic and diabolical patterns. Presently, while the man and his violin still struggled,—

"Quit, Cranston; quit, man!" shouted John Sterling. "The devil's in the fiddle, and the lights are burning blue, and we'll all be dancing a diabolical saraband in five minutes more, as if a tarantula from the lower regions had crawled up and bitten us! Phe-ew! I smell brimstone!" concluded he, sniffing the air and awrying his nose.

All were glad to laugh, like children when they've just heard a ghost-story before bed-time. Cranston ha-haed louder than any; but it was too uproarious to be natural. Evidently, the man was getting excited by his own *diablerie.*

"Mr. Cranston," commenced Felix curiously, as if she were inquiring the habits of some strange wild beast of his keeper, and were half afraid he'd jump out of his cage, "you do not show any sign of that strange pain which good music always produces—at least, produces in me, and in every other musician I ever saw. Why? Don't you feel it?"

"I may confess to a twinge or two sometimes, very much like the gout, I imagine; but I always crush it as a mere sentimental weakness."

"Humph! a lucky man, you!" said Rübetsahl; "now I never could crush it, nor wanted to, even!"

"Jean Paul," said Philip, "once exclaimed to music, 'Away, away! For thou remindest me of what in all my endless life I have not seen, and shall not see!' And Emerson speaks of the strong painful yearning created by the beautiful either in sound or sight. Even old rugged Tom Carlyle cries out, 'Who shall say what music means in his soul? It leads us to the verge of eternity and lets us gaze on that.' " *

"Yes," said Felix, "if, by 'the verge of eternity,' he means a sort of boundary-line between pleasure and pain; a wavering boundary, too! There must be a wild debatable-land between joy and sorrow; borderers are predatory, you know, and this border-land is one while devastated by forayers from the dark side, another while cultivated by peaceful villagers from the bright side; and it's fine that music should carry us to such a place! I do not think it is exactly the fascination of a flame for the moth; for we walk deliberately into our flame, and our wings don't scorch!"

"Too much flame, Felie, and 'fuliginous glare,' about that! But you are young, yet; and I remember I used to like to go to a big fire in town, and see the huge smoke-billows foaming with flame, and didn't think much of the poor weeping families in the street! But we've talked enough. Felix, exorcise Cranston's devil, there! Sing us a prayer with Rübetsahl's accompaniment!"

Felix chose one of the *Lieder ohne Wörter*, merely articulating the tones; and Rübetsahl's accompaniment did not follow, but went with the voice, waving and floating and wreathing round the voice like an airy robe around a sweet flying form above us. The homage which the Thalberg household paid to this holy music of Felix Sterling's and Rübetsahl's and Mendelssohn's, was perfect stillness, which reigned for some minutes, until Philip repeated in a low voice,

> The notes kept falling silverly,
> Till it was almost like a pain
> Until the next should come again.**

Was John Cranston drunk? He had only taken a glass or two of the sherry. Was he intoxicated with the music, or with Felix Sterling's eyes and queen-limbs, or with his mysterious hate of Rübetsahl? Who knows? As the party met in the centre of the

* [Carlyle, "The Hero as Poet." Also quoted by Lanier many years later, again inaccurately, in *The English Novel* (see IV, 128, of the present edition). —ED.]

** [In the MS he quotes the last stanza of Longfellow, "The Day is Done." —ED.]

room, all saying good-night and wishing pleasant dreams, suddenly Cranston looked fiercely into Rübetsahl's face, held his head aloft, and said, in German, in a harsh husky voice,—

"I am the man!"

"Then," answered Rübetsahl, quick as lightning, speaking also in German, "for her sake, not for mine, receive that!"

Whereupon, with open palm, he struck Cranston a mighty blow upon the cheek, that felled him to the floor.

"Sir," said John Sterling, "you came here unknown, but supposed to be a gentleman. Must you be brawling in my parlor the very first time you enter it? Leave my house instantly."

"O, Rübetsahl—!" exclaimed Felix, and checked herself and blushed, as Rübetsahl, who had stood with folded arms listening to John Sterling, silently turned towards the door.

This sweet interest made Paul Rübetsahl turn again.

"Sir," said he, "you are just; but I was just too. I am loth to leave your kind house unjustified; but if to ask for time before I justify myself be to ask too much, then I must go; I cannot do it now."

The calm dignity of the man appealed to all manhood.

"Father," said Philip, "I believe him. I know—!" and he pointed to Cranston, still prostrate. "Make Rübetsahl stay."

An appealing glance from Felix supported Philip's attack. John Sterling's genial face was full of pain. That a night so full of music should have so pitiful end as this! Yet he could not resist Rübetsahl's noble look of honest self-assertion, and honest regret that self-assertion was necessary.

"Have your own way, my children!" said he, and walked hastily to his den, and fell to smoking vigorously.

Meantime, servants had come, and Cranston, still stupefied with the reaction of his unnatural excitement and the stunning surprise of the blow, was conveyed to his apartment.

Presently, he opened his eyes, and sternly commanded his attendants to leave him.

In the morning, his room was empty. No one knew whither he had gone.

CHAPTER VI *

But Reynard, having heard his voice, said, "Well, to be sure! and I should have been frightened, too, if I had not heard you bray!"

The Ass in the Lion's Skin [*Æsop's Fables*]

Bottom.—Masters, you ought to consider with yourselves; to bring in—God shield us!—a lion among ladies, is a most dreadful thing; for there is not a more fearful wild-fowl than your lion living; and we ought to look to it.

Snout.—Therefore, another prologue must tell he is not a lion.

Bottom.—Nay, you must name his name, and half his face must be seen through the lion's neck; and he himself must speak through, saying thus, or to the same defect,—"Ladies,"—or "Fair ladies,—I would wish you"—or "I would request you,"—or "I would entreat you—not to fear, not to tremble; my life for yours. If you think I am come hither as a lion, it were pity of my life: no, I am no such thing; I am a man as other men are;" and then, indeed, let him name his name, and tell them plainly he is Snug, the joiner.

Midsummer Night's Dream

SOCIETY (bless her heart!) loves a lion.

Any prudent gentleman, however, who decides upon earning his "sixpence a day in Pyramus," by performing the lion *rôle*, will surely heed the admonitions of sweet bully Bottom. He must be none of your horrid man-eaters out of the wild desert; but a decent, well-curried and well-behaved lion, who will roar an' 'twere any nightingale, at the command of his keeper, and who can be uncaged without fear of personal detriment. Nay, however much she may laugh with Theseus, Society would yet, rather than not, see half a human face through the neck, or hear the familiar ass-voice. These conditions being answered, with what a pretty boldness does Mrs. Society trip near to the pseudo-royal animal, the quasi-kingly beast, the Snug-alias-lion, the lion's-hide-over-joiner's-heart, and stroke the mane of the gentle-terrible one with her plump, white, be-diamonded fingers!

But, alas! this *penchant* of Madame Society for quasi-royal wild beasts is become known to the real lions, and is sometimes

* [Fragment A of the MS ends with Chapter V. Fragment B begins with an interchapter (see Introduction, p. xxxv, n. 71) and then proceeds to Chapter VI.—ED.]

taken advantage of for horrible ends. It occasionally happens that a genuine fierce man- (or woman-) eater does simulate the simulation of honest Snug, the joiner, so that when Society, in her charming bravery, has drawn near to stroke his mane (ostensibly; but white fingers look well through a maze of hair), horrors! upon a sudden, in a twinkling, some member of Society (a finger, perhaps, or even so important a member as the head of Society) is snapped off, and gobbled up!

John Cranston was a veritable woman-eater, with neither asinine nor clownish qualities beneath his leonine exterior.

It has for a long time been the peculiar privilege of this glorious country to produce John Cranstons; for the exercise of which prerogative the country at large is responsible to almost as great a degree as the immediate progenitors, or producers, of such articles. For when John C., senior, went about to beget John C., junior, that worthy and prudent man probably embarked in the only enterprise of his life in which he could not see his way clear from beginning to end. Under these circumstances, it being impossible that John C., senior, could have foreseen the precise result of his action in the premises, he is surely not to be blamed for departing in this one instance from the hitherto unbroken rule by which he guided his conduct; for, as the Prince Rasselas very sensibly remarked, "The world must be peopled by marriage, or peopled without it." Nor can I at all agree with the somewhat sarcastic sentiments contained in the reply of the Princess Nekayah,—

"How the world is to be peopled" (said that pert young lady), "is not my care and need not be yours. I see no danger that the present generation will omit to leave successors behind them!" *

A cold-blooded shirking of manifest responsibility, thou Abyssinian maid! In which suppose thine own royal father and mother had concurred, where then had commenced thy search after happiness, thou tawny and o'er-froward minx!

But—John C., senior, having presented his boy to the country, that amiable foster-mother ought to have done much for him, because John C., senior, had done much for the country, with

* [Samuel Johnson, *Rasselas.* That Lanier pondered this moralizing narrative is shown by his making four excerpts from it in his Ledger, p. 4.—Ed.]

his charities, his dry-goods, and his prosperity on Broadway. Now it was an ill turn of the country to John Cranston, junior, that, at the age of twenty-one, he entered life as if he had been invited chief-guest to a complimentary dinner; and, forgetful even of customary forms of politeness, reached out both his hands for the *crême de la crême* and the *patês* and all the other world-dainties on the table, unheeding that shorter-armed neighbors were starving about him; and that the " Low vulgarities, the children of Rahag, Tahag, and Bohobtayil" were living, or rather dying, upon the smell of the roast beef.

When Cranston thought of virtue and such things, he formed to himself a vague idea that the earth was a mysterious wild-cat bank, doing a very inflated business by brazenly issuing, every day, multitudes of irredeemable bills in the shape of hypocritical men; and in his heart Cranston was certain that the teller of this bank had long ago robbed its vaults of all the virtue, or bullion, and absconded to very unknown parts. A brave, nervous-souled boy, strong of limb, strong of passion, unboundedly energetic, unconquerably persevering, with an acute intellect to guide these qualities; but thoroughly selfish, and without even the consciousness that this last was his bad trait—John Cranston was capable of building up many things; but his life was nothing more than a continuous pulling down of all things.

A terrible *mêlée* of winged opposites is forever filling the world with a battle-din which only observant souls hear: Love contending with Impurity; Passion springing mines under the calm entrenchment of Reason; scowling Ignorance thrusting in the dark at holy-eyed Reverence; Romance deathfully encountering the attack of Sentimentality on the one side and Commonplace on the other; young Sensibility clanging swords with gigantic maudlin Conventionality, whose reliance is upon main strength and awkwardness,—and a thousand more. I have seen no man who did not suffer from the shock of these wars unless he got help from that One Man whom it is not unmanly to acknowledge our superior.

Cranston was too proud, that is to say, too selfish, to get any help: he became impure, not loving; he was unreasonable, passion firing him; he did no reverence, being ignorant of its objects; he despised romance, foolishly confounding it with sentimentality; he killed and utterly destroyed conventionality, instead of merely disarming and subduing it.

Allusion has been made to an occasion in the life of the elder Cranston when he did not precisely foresee the result of certain actions. Twenty-two or three years afterwards, he involved himself in a similar uncertainty. Which is to say, he hung a golden chain about the neck of his young lion-cub, and turned him loose upon Germany.

At Frankfort-on-the-Main, people said young John was like Goethe. He had Lucifer-eyes; he spoke French and German and English; he walked like a young god; he played them mad with his violin; he accepted invitations with little return-poems that breathed sweetly a satanic despair; * he was six feet one; —what more should one want to make one a lion at Frankfort-on-the-Main?

* [The MS reads, "which breathed of Werther's fiery sorrows."—Ed.]

Chapter VII *

They were together and she fell,
Therefore revenge became me well.
O the Earl was fair to see!
Tennyson, *The Sisters*

". . . AND SO, since I am left alone for the day, if Herr Cranston will bring his violin at six, he will be considered very kind by his friend, "OTTILIE"

To receive such a note as this, from which, as it is opened, a faint violet odor floats up, as if the soul of the sweet writer exhaled from her words; to know that she is gray-eyed, oval-faced, lissome-limbed, full-souled, rising up to anything beautiful as quickly and as surely as shadows in water rise to meet their falling flowers;— this is meat, drink, and raiment to a young, untamed, venturesome lion, who is currying himself and curling his mane in the best den of the city, or ere he begins to rampage over Germany.

Young John was not a deliberate man; he had no *affaires du cœur*, and he had not resolved not to have any.

Young John was accustomed to declare to himself, in a lively way, "Who will say to-day that he will do so and so to-morrow? Does not man change with time? The past is gone, it is nothing; the future is to come, it is nothing; the present, even while I speak, is gone—it is become the past, it is nothing; time is a lie, and clocks do not measure time, they only measure life, and only waking life, for our dreams have no clocks and no time. Of all clocks, clepsydras, Geneva-watches, hour-glasses, sun-dials and Linnæan flower-clocks,** commend me" would say John Cranston "to thy clock, O

* [Here, and at the head of Chapter VI, the MS places before the published mottoes these words from Longfellow's *Hyperion,* "That Night a Star fell from Heaven!"—ED.]

** [The initial entry and other passages in the Ledger refer to the twenty-four flowers in the garden of Linnæus which indicated time by unfolding at different hours. Lanier probably learned of the garden through Carlyle's translation of Jean Paul's *Life of Quintus Fixlein.*—ED.]

Festus, which was a heart, and measured time by throbs. If old Doctor Brain wants to know the time of life, let him look down there and count the beats."

Of course Cranston knew, because everybody in Frankfort-on-the-Main knew, that Ottilie had been long engaged to one Paul Rübetsahl whom Cranston had not met, he being away in the mountains on unknown mission; and of course this knowledge of her engagement only heightened John Cranston's devotion to her, since it gave her the only additional charm she could have possessed, and crowned her allurements with that sweet necessity-to-be-stolen which sugars the forbidden fruit.

Cranston's contempt for time-pieces in general, like most such truculent disgusts of youth, did not extend to that particular hunting-case whose chain dangled from his vest button-hole; and so he did not fail to consult its oracular countenance, nor to obey its warning hands when those members pointed, like the hands of a man in a stretch, to twelve and six.

"You are punctual: I thank you," said Ottilie, as Cranston entered her music-room.

"Fraulein, you make a virtue of what was to me a necessity," replied he, and bowed.

"Ah, a compliment! What necessity is the mother of so pretty an invention as that?"

"No less a necessity than the fitness of things. Fair greeting to a fair woman; like to like!"

"But we Germans say, like *cures* like; and so your last compliment destroys your first."

"And that is well, too; otherwise the *embarras de richesses* would cause the Fraulein to suffer."

"Again! Herr Cranston reminds me of the good maiden in the fairy-tale, from whose mouth, whenever she spoke, there dropped either a pearl or a diamond." *

"If it be so, then you are the fairy that has conferred this gem-gift upon me!"

"*Du Himmel*!" cried Ottilie, and seizing a Chinese parasol from the *étagère*, spread it out between herself and Cranston.

* [The MS reads "the maiden in the Wunderhorn," presumably Arnim and Brentano's *Des Knaben Wunderhorn*. Further, an item in the Ledger mentions "Diamonds and Toads—a Fairy tale."—Ed.]

" One might as well be killed with a shower of hail-stones as of diamonds; it is but death after all."

" Thou rose! No shower would ever disturb one petal of thine, save to pelt a perfume out of it."

" Ah, well! one way remains. I will, in the woman's way, conquer you by surrendering to you. So; I announce myself tired of compliments, Herr Cranston, and I long for some music. See, there is your violin, which your servant brought an hour ago! "

Cranston unlocked the case.

" Poor violin! Take him up tenderly out of his dark case, Herr Cranston. Ah, when life has played its long tune upon me, and locked me up in my grave-case, I hope the Great Musician will take me out so, and draw a divine love-melody from me. Is not a violin wonderfully like a man? It can be heavenly, it can be earthy, it can be fiendish! It can make lark-music that draws our eye towards heaven, it can make dance-music that keeps our feet moving upon the earth, and it can make Circe-music that allures us to— "

" To hell, Fraulein? "

" Yes."

" Which of these styles does the Fraulein prefer? " said Cranston, gravely arranging his bow.

" O, Mephistopheles! play what pleases thy satanic fancy."

Who, being led to the edge of a precipice, has not felt the insidious and alluring desire to leap over it rising stronger and stronger within him, until he draws back, shuddering?

There are some unaccountable moments when one is wild with insane longing to leap from the rock of what is fixed and known as virtuous, into the terrible mist of the unknown and bad, floating below.

It was this desire that sparkled in Ottilie ———'s eyes, and drew her to the very brink.

" Sound me," said she, " some strains from thy native Hades. I do not want any brimstone and agitato and thunder, and all that traditional infernal-music; but something beautiful and wicked and very sweet."

" As if tawny Cleopatra peered wickedly at you over Godiva's white shoulder? "

" So; and play, thou Satan in chains, till I bid thee stay! "

Let it be said only, that this music which John Cranston improvised was like a rose, with the devil lying perdu in its red heart; was like a soft, gray eye, with a voluptuous sparkle in it; was like a silver star-beam, only not cold, but hot with intoxicating perfumes.

Ottilie sat at the open window. Presently the sun sank beneath to the horizon.

" Stop, Herr Cranston, look yonder! "

One modest star had stolen out in the east, and stood, with all its dainty silver-soul a-tremble, in the passionate gaze of the sun. And all the west blushed to see the sun stretch out two long beams, like arms, which drew down a cloud towards him for a kiss. A costly caress! For, as the kiss of the heaven-born Zillah consumed his earth-born beloved to ashes before his eyes, so now the cloud, as it neared the sun, caught a-fire, and flamed with unutterable brilliancy.

Ottilie turned away, with sparkling eyes—into the arms of Lucifer.

O, Ottilie, thou should'st have looked a little longer at the display in the west, yonder! For, presently, the unpitying sun went on his way down the heaven-slope, and left the poor cloud alone; and the cloud gradually darkened from glowing red to a bruise-purple, and then to ashen-gray, dull and dead.

So shalt thou fare, Ottilie, thou poor gossamer summer-cloud; so shalt thou be consumed with bliss, and then left in the ashen-gray of grief that changeth not, of regret that blotteth not out its sin, of crime that hateth itself, and stingeth itself; but never to death.

And that day sank slowly into its night, as into a grave.

CHAPTER VIII

Who cross the sea, but change their sky,
And not their thought. Horace [, *Odes*]

POSSIBLY THE reason why few heroes are so to their valets, is because full many a hero pulls off his pantaloons and his heroism together. What! That spindle a heroic leg?

Bah!

This is what the valet says to himself, and glances at his own well-developed calf.

I will not pursue this subject.

But, surely, every woman is a heroine to her maid!

Why?

Who knows?

Perhaps it is because the maids are themselves also women; and women have a Hindoo faculty of making idols out of the most commonplace wood and stone, and weaving their beautiful faiths and worship about these like strings of precious beads, and building churches for these in their hearts.

For which faculty let women give thanks; for they have need of it in this world.

"And so, Gretchen," said Ottilie to her maid that night, "thou shalt not kneel to take off my shoes, to-night. It were better I knelt to take off thine! Sit here by me. Thou hast been a faithful, good maid. How much dost thou love me?"

"I will go with thee to the end of the world!"

"It is answered as if thou wert the oracle of Heaven! Thou shalt go with me to the end of the world. I must leave my Germany. The glance of my friends will blast me. The Rhine-breeze would scorch my face. I am glad that my father and mother are in heaven, where I cannot see them, and where I hope they have forgotten me. Pack, Gretchen! Let us go where there are strange mountains, and solitude disturbed by none but thee and me—and God, whom alas, alas, I cannot banish!"

In the old poisoning days (I've heard) a delicate kind of Venetian glass was used by the suspicious, which, if poisoned wine were poured into it, would instantly shiver into a thousand pieces. It is so with that dainty world which an imaginative woman builds up in her soul, out of the things that surround her. One drop of poison, concealed in whatever wine of pleasure, does straightway jar the whole delicate fabric into destruction. And it would seem that there is no re-building of the old soul-world after this. If she still have pure aspirations, there is for her only a waiting here, to see what the most blessed Christ may do for her hereafter. And, at first, there is not even this. The cry is then, " Fall upon me, ye mountains, and crush me out of sight! "

Ottilie thanked Heaven that no brother or sister bound her to the places which had suddenly become terrible to her. As for her betrothed, she did not dare think of him, except to long that she might get away where she would never again meet his eye.

Gretchen packed, the bankers received instructions under secrecy, and the two thickly-veiled women took departure by night for America.

To the sick soul, rapid physical motion is like a sea-breeze to fevered men.

" Gretchen," said Ottilie, as the steam—good genius of our day!—bore them bounding along, " I think I know why the world and the stars move. And the sea—must it not be happy, since it is forever in motion? Poor, unhappy trees on the shore, there—they cannot move. They seem to thank the good kind breeze with swelling whispers and sighs of delight, when it but shakes their unwieldy arms! Motion forever, for me! Gretchen, what is thine idea of heaven? "

" It is to sink into the Everlasting Arms and be at rest."

" And mine is, to dash about like lightning, my soul being unclogged by dull old sins; to move through thousands of worlds, wherever I list, with unlaborious motion which is but the result of a mere volition, yes, to *think myself along* through the Paradises! Perhaps I would stop, sometimes, and dream on meditative wing, feeling myself well and buoyantly upborne by nothing grosser than the atmosphere of sunlight which I breathed. Once I could almost do this; but now—Gretchen, look at that sea-bird, yonder! he can hardly fly for the weight of the fish he is carrying in claws and beak; and it is so with us on earth: we cannot make a flight, without being dragged down by some fleshly provision-for-the-morrow."

Sorrow makes poets. Memnon's statue sang when the morning-light struck it, but I think men and women sing when the darkness draws on. Nevertheless those are the best poets who keep down these cloudy sorrow-songs and wait until some light comes to gild them with comfort.

The two women arrived at New York, and travelled on, through Virginia and Tennessee. Ottilie had glimpses of the mountains occasionally. These blue distant hills enticed her to them, as the blue distant skies entice a lark upward.

At Knoxville, even patient Gretchen must needs confess she was a little tired.

"Well," exclaimed Ottilie, with a sudden resolution, "yonder are the mountains—they look lonely. Let us stop here, and go to them. I yearn to plunge myself into that blue ocean of loneliness over yonder. What a color is blue, Gretchen! I will wear it hereafter. The sea is blue, the mountains are blue, the heavens are blue. One might think blue was good for sick souls as for weak eyes."

The road from the Knoxville depot into the city is a perilous one. As Ottilie's hack started, the horses became frightened. In vain coachee cracked whip and jerked rein. The animals became unmanageable, and reared; in another instant they would have backed the carriage over the precipitous embankment, when a tall Indian, in slouch hat and moccasins, who, with folded arms and stolid countenance had been watching the passengers emerge from the train, seized the bridles with strong arm, turned the hack into the road, and at length succeeded in quieting the horses.

Gretchen was half-dead with terror; but Ottilie, who had been looking on with a half-smile of admiration at the quivering muscles and magnificent attitudes of the rearing horses, called to the driver to stop, and beckoned their preserver, who had again resumed his position of apparent indifference, to approach. Possibly her eyes grew more eloquent, as she thought of the melancholy remnant of the fine old Cherokees that once bounded over these hills, while the Indian, a majestic, brawny man, was walking up to her carriage: at any rate, those great orbs beamed in upon the half-tamed soul of the fellow like a beautiful gray dawn. Half-shamefully, Ottilie offered him money. Believe that this Indian was in love at first sight: he refused it!

"Do you live here?" asked Ottilie.

"No. Way over yonder!"

"When do you return?"

"To-morrow mornin'. We carry books to Obadiah. Obadiah our preacher."

"Listen, Gretchen. Let us go with him!"

"I go with you, Fraulein, anywhere."

"What is your name?" asked Ottilie, addressing the Indian.

"Me? Jim Saggs!"

"O Gretchen, what a name for that magnificent creature! He says he lives beyond—what did you call the mountain?"

"Chilhowee."

"Beyond Chilhowee. Let us call him that. I like good names.

"Chilhowee, come to the hotel at twelve, to-day. I wish to make arrangements to be guided by you over to the mountains, where you live. Will you come?"

"Yes."

The arrangements were made, and after infinite trouble, the two women got themselves transported to a small "cove" in the mountains, a few miles from John Sterling's Valley Beautiful. Here they fitted up a cabin with a piano and a few books and pictures, retaining Chilhowee in their service to supply them with game and be guard for the house. The sparse population of simple mountaineers at first regarded with much wonder the two lone women who never visited, and were always riding and walking about the mountains; but the wonder soon settled into a vague feeling of suspicion and dislike, which vented itself in "them stuck-up creeturs over yan on the hill," and other the like epithets. News does not travel fast in these mountains, and Chilhowee, possessing all the proverbial taciturnity of his race, never tattled. The Thalberg family knew nothing of these singular visitors.

So, the mountains received the lost. To Ottilie, a majestic maternity dwelt in the broad bosoms of these hills. They seemed to have swelled and heaved, long ago, in a mighty love-sigh, and been petrified into eternal symbols of an eternal passion. With a delicious abandon she plunged into the deep ferny ravines, or sat upon rocky heights and sung to opposing rocks across the foaming streams far below. If the stern, pure rocks upbraided her with their seams and furrows, got in resisting so long the temptations of the wanton winds, she had only to turn to the trees, that ever lifted their arms toward Heaven, obeying the injunction of the Apostle, *praying always:* the great uncomplaining trees, whose life is surely the finest of all lives, since it is nothing but a continual growing and being beautiful; the silent, mysterious trees, most strong where most gnarled, and most touching when wholly blasted, for gnarling is but another name for conquering, and they were blasted only by wayward lightnings, for no sin.

Wretched men and women in this world, wretched with the only wretchedness that deserves that name, which is the suffering of one's own transgressions,—have ye ever been "alone with God in His mountains?"

Up along those broad ascents one's thought glances straight to Heaven. These be the kings that fling to the plains kingly largesse of water that is better than gold coins. Here come breezes right from the sea, that have not been low enough to get the reek of the cities nor the malaria of the valleys upon their wings. Here salutes the sun, in the morning like a brother with dewy-pure blessing, in the evening like a lover with warm, passionate caresses. Here grow the strong, sweet trees, like brawny men with virgins' hearts. Here is the baby-hood of the rivers. Here wave the ferns, and cling the mosses, and clamber the reckless vines. Here Falstaff-beeches stand rollicking by straight Puritan-pines and substantial Flemish burgher-oaks, while the maples * and ashes, forest dandies, pose in nonchalant attitudes.

Here old giant Convulsion, horrible ogre that wont to swallow up so many young things, is tamed and humanized into deep and benign Repose.

And here one's soul may climb as upon Pisgah, and see one's land of peace—seeing Christ, who made all these beautiful things.

* [The printed text of 1867 has "mosses," which does not fit the context. The MS reading has been restored.—Ed.]

CHAPTER IX

You are very good to put yourself to all this trouble for a young girl!

Prince Cherry *

SILENTLY, SEVEN months like seven ghosts flitted by our two women in the still mountains. At last came a day which was not ghostly, but which opened its mouth and gave news.

On the day before the deer-drive at Thalberg, Gretchen was stirring before Ottilie awoke, and must needs run out to pluck a fern-spray and a heart-leaf, and mayhap a lingering tiger-lily, that her beloved Ottilie might be greeted with something beautiful upon the breakfast-table. At about this same hour Mrs. Razor, the nearest neighbor of Ottilie, had an exposition of gooseberry-pie come upon her, and the good lady had sallied forth, basket on arm, to gather wherewithal to satisfy her longing.

"Goot morgen, Mrs. Razor." Gretchen was not on good terms with the king's English.

"Mornin', mum. A'ter gooseberries, this mornin'?"

"No. I am come to find some little grün leaf for mein frient. How ish all widh your house?"

"Waal, so's to git about, thank ye. Th' ole man's jest started over to Mountvale Springs. Gwine to have a mighty shootin'-match thar to-day; an' I *do* hear as how there's to be a treemenjious fancy-ball thar to-morrer night, *ur* the night a'ter, an' I forgit which, preecisely! Hain't a-gwine, I reckon?"

"No, no."

"Thought may be you was, like. All the folks from Talburg is a-gittin' ready to go. Mister Cranston——"

"Who?" quickly interposed Gretchen.

"Mister Cranston tole my Jake yistiddy as how they was all a-gwine from thar, an' tole him he must come over an' shoot fur the beef."

"Who ish dis Mr. Cranston?"

"Why, massy me, ain't you heerd of him afore this? He seed John Sterlin's gal at the Springs this season, an' follered her

* [Comtesse d'Aulnoy, *Le Prince Cheri.*—ED.]

over to ther house, in the cove, yan. They *do* say as how he is gwine to marry her, afore long."

"Und was für ein man ish Mr. Cranston?"

"Waal, I hain't nuvver seed him *my*self, you know; but my Jake says, he's a maaster tall un', 'ith black beard to his face, an' says he kin play the fiddle jest about as peert as the next un.' Mought know him maybe?"

"Oh no."

Forgetting fern-leaves and Mrs. Razor, and the conventionalities alike, Gretchen turned and walked rapidly back toward her cottage.

If I could only get them together, what might not happen? She dies here. Her heart grinds itself to powder, revolving upon itself with its weight of grief.

But she would never go willingly to meet him.

Then I must bring him to meet her.

But she would refuse to see him.

Then I must manage it without her knowledge.

The fancy-ball;—if she would but go! The excitement of strange faces would be charming for her pale cheeks. Ah! would Cranston be willing to meet her?

I must mystify him till it is too late for him to retreat.

These thoughts flashed through Gretchen's mind, as she hurried home. Her heart was lighter, because her brain was busier than it had been for many a day. The premonition of some catastrophe which, whatever it should be, would at least change the dreadful monotony of these dead days, animated her soul as she entered and saluted Ottilie, just sitting down at the breakfast-table.

"Well, Gretchen, since they do not print any morning paper in Cade's Cove—"

"O Fraulein, the idea!" said Gretchen, glad to speak her German again. "A morning paper here! Imagine the local column: 'We are pained to record that our esteemed friend and neighbor, Mrs. Razor, met last night with a serious domestic calamity, in the loss of two fine chickens and a goose, supposed to have been kidnapped by a wild-cat:' or, 'It is our unpleasant duty to record an unfortunate personal rencontre, which took place late on yesterday afternoon, in the streets of Cade's Cove, between a black bear and four hounds belonging to Mr. Razor, in which, though the bear was worsted, two of the dogs were badly wooled;' and then, Fraulein, the commercial column: 'The market in Cade's Cove has been exceedingly quiet the past week, and commercial transactions extremely limited. Indeed, except in the single article of whiskey, we have to report absolutely nothing doing. We have account of sales of whiskey, yesterday, amounting in all to twenty-six (26) drinks, twenty-five (25) of which being bought on time or by barter, we make no cash quotations, especially as the twenty-sixth sale might prove a false criterion and mislead dealers, it being a drink paid for, cash, by a stranger going through to North Carolina, who, not knowing the prices of whiskey in Cade's Cove, was charged double rates by our enterprising friend who runs the distillery.' And so forth, and so forth, Fraulein!"

"Why, Gretchen, thy tongue trips it garrulously this morning!"

"Indeed, I am the morning paper to-day! I am just come from ''Change:' that is to say, I have been talking with a neighbor. Do me the favor, Fraulein, to glance down my column headed 'Great news! Grand things toward, not far from us! Our readers will be thrown into a state of frantic excitement, when we tell them that there is soon to be a masque ball at Montvale Springs, in which, besides the present guests, the whole country-side is expected to take part. The enterprising managers have determined to close the season with an affair worthy of the brilliant company now sojourning at that popular watering-place, and to make this ball one unsurpassed in variety and splendor of costume. Madame So-and-So is to come over, to superintend the costumes;' and so forth, and so forth—you need not read the whole column, Fraulein!"

And then came silence. Gretchen plotted and plotted, the hypocrite! and Ottilie became grave and thoughtful, as if a curious idea had presented itself.

Toward the close of the meal Ottilie looked up, and with a nonchalance which did not half conceal from Gretchen the earnestness which underlay it, inquired:—

"How far to these Springs, Gretchen?"

"It is but four or five miles." Aha, thought Gretchen, my

little trout nibbles! Entice thou, O bait, as never bait enticed before!

Ottilie went out for her walk; whereupon ensued a diplomatic interview between Gretchen and the Indian, Chilhowee, which resulted in the departure of that taciturn individual toward Thalberg, where he had arrived, as was related, just in time to kill John Sterling's escaping buck.

He met with no opportunity to speak with Cranston that day, and had lounged idly about the grounds until night came on, when he threw himself upon the grass and slept; that is to say, dreamed of Ottilie.

Chapter X

I would that each might scrutinize the passion within him, for each passion exacts and builds its own world. Anger wishes that all the world had but one neck: Love, that it had only one heart: Grief, two tear-glands: and Pride, two knees.

J. P. F. Richter [, *Flower, Fruit, and Thorn Pieces*]

WHEN JOHN Cranston awoke from the short stupor into which he had fallen, his first feeling was a vague sensation of disgrace, followed by a more defined wish to be alone.

Sending away the servant who had been ordered to remain in his apartment, he sat up in bed, clinched his fists and pressed them tightly against his head, to stop, of course, the giddy whirlpool which was amusing itself in a very noisy way in that member.

Performing that strange operation which seems almost to indicate that each man has two selves—namely, concentrating his mind,—Cranston gradually began to see and hear over again the occurrences of the night. But the sprites that worked the panorama in his brain were tricksy elves, and it was long before they would show him the particular scene upon which he wished to fix his attention. A strain of music floated from behind some mysterious curtain in his brain. The music was from Mendelssohn, and, while it sounded, the curtain rose and displayed the face of Felix Sterling, with that shoal of deep-sea shapes floating in her eyes, as she sang.

Cranston shook his head, as who should say, "Tempting, but I'm looking for something else." And so, amid a confused intermingling of sounds and faces, he at length managed to fix his attention upon the face of Rübetsahl, until a full recollection of the whole last scene in the music-room shone before him.

Perhaps anger is the most complex deceit of them all, shifting its wrath from one's self, richly deserving, to some other self, undeserving, upon the most pitiful excuses. Indignation may be just; but anger forever cheats for a victim. And so, John Cranston, instead of cursing his own crime, or gnashing his teeth over the insane folly which had prompted him to betray himself, cursed Rübetsahl instead, and snarled at him.

"Good God! Good God!" he said, setting his teeth and stretching out his hands as he sank back on the bed. "He struck me—in her presence—in presence of them all! The miserable scoundrel—to take advantage of me when the sherry had unsteadied my nerves! And now, I suppose, he'll blab every thing to make capital for himself; and add from his own invention, until he gets capital enough to buy the whole family!"—with a bitter laugh. "And he struck me; he *struck* me; he struck *me!*" An idea hard to grasp!

"I can see the whole tale he'll tell. 'He heard of my — adventure with this Frankfort friend of his; she had no father or brother; he determines to avenge her'—the dear, chivalrous knight of damsels in distress—; 'he will devote his life to this sacred cause; he thinks he will likely find me in America; he comes over, nay, 'gad, he rushes over, flies over, inquires for me, tracks me here, and if he can find me again,'—for the fool will know that I'm going to leave to-night—'he'll—play the devil,' and so forth, and so on. He's probably gone through the whole tale by this time.

"But, by God," said he, jumping from the bed, a maniac in eyes and face and hair, "and by the devil and all, I'll kill him,—I swear it,—I'll kill him this day!"

Cranston walked to his window, and examined the ground outside. It was an easy leap. He turned, and glanced round the room, which was one that Philip Sterling had occupied. Opposite the bed hung two swords, which had been wont to serve his young friend in the peaceful capacity of dream-provocatives, or reverie-superinducers, the said swords being respectively a long, two-handed, naked blade like Richard Cœur de Lion's, and a delicate rapier such as a gallant might wear at court. This huge brand, that looked grim as a battle, and this dainty rapier, that could make one think of nothing but waving plumes and arras and lovely women, seemed strangely opposed, as if war and love had married: a lion lying down with a lamb. Many a long, delicious hour had Philip spent over these two relics of chivalric days; as the Lily Maid of Astolat watched the shield of absent Lancelot:—

And made a pretty history to herself
Of every dint a sword had beaten in it,
And every scratch a lance had made upon it,
Conjecturing when and where: this cut is fresh:
That, ten years back: this dealt him at Caerlyle:
That, at Caerleon: this, at Camelot:
And ah!—God's mercy!—what a stroke was there!
And here a thrust that might have killed, but God
Broke the strong lance, and rolled his enemy down,
And saved him: so she lived in fantasy.*

And so had Philip wound his fine dreams, like silken scarfs, about his swords.

But John Cranston, bent on destroying the greatest of all dreams—life—cared little for idler reveries of romantic boys; and, taking down the rapier, whose use was nearly all he had learned at college, he leaped from the window and strode up the abruptly swelling knoll, as if, upon some height, he could better see what course to pursue.

Like a tear upon an eyelid, wept in a dream, glittering, tremulous, ready to drop, hung the morning-star upon the fringed horizon. A white mist, which had sought shelter in the water-valley for the night, was beginning to wake and ruffle wing for another day's journey.

Cranston had stopped and smiled a bitter smile,** that such peaceful things should dare to go on in the world when he was angry. As he turned to mount the knoll, the morning-star was suddenly obscured by a tall form which uprose as if by magic out of the earth, and which loomed gigantically in the dim light before him. All the blood in his frame rushed backward toward his heart, as the reflection flashed across his mind that it was Rübetsahl, waiting for him. For one moment, the consciousness of being in the wrong subdued his natural bravery, and he fairly staggered with the weakness of relaxation.

But his vengeful anger restored his courage and heated his soul. Unsheathing the beautiful taper blade which he carried, and throwing the scabbard as far as he could hurl it, in emphatic token of war to the death, he advanced rapidly toward

* [Tennyson, "Lancelot and Elaine," one of Lanier's favorite poems at this time. He had set to music its lyric, "The Song of Love and Death."—Ed.]

** [The MS quotes from E. B. Browning, *Aurora Leigh*: "Some people always sigh in thanking God!"—Ed.]

his opponent, speaking, as he went, in passionate jerks and crowding eddies of words.

"Aha, you—you waylay me in the darkness, do you?" O Cranston! was it waylaying a man to rise up in front of him and stand still with folded arms as this tall figure did? "Not content with taking advantage of a moment when I was—was—" (he has objections to the word *drunk*), "when my nerves were unsteadied, you—you wait all night to ambush me, do you?" The said ambuscade being on the top of a bare knoll, which would reveal a cricket against the sky, to one ascending!

"I suppose you've told 'em all how it was by this time, and got your maw full of praise for your—your heroism and your devotion, you dear good man, you sweet constant man, you—you damned contemptible scoundrel!" thundered he in an irrepressible flood of fury, and leapt forward to thrust, forgetting to put himself *en garde* even.

"Why you kill me?" said the Indian; for it was Chilhowee. He had slept until his light slumbers had been broken by the sound of approaching footsteps. He quickly recognized the man with whom he had in vain sought an interview the day before.

Cranston dropped his sword with an oath, as he saw the mistake into which his blind rage had led him, and took from the Indian's hand a piece of paper which he was silently holding out.

"For me?"

"Yes."

"From whom?"

"No tell."

"'Gad!" muttered Cranston, opening his cigar-case and striking a match, "but the German is prompt with his challenge! He *might* have waited for it to come from *me*. Maybe he was afraid it wouldn't come,"—with a murderous laugh. "Let's see what the poor injured man says."

The note was short. It was written in German.*

Translated, it said:—

"Would'st thou an adventure? Follow the bearer.

(Signed) "FRANKFORT"

* [The MS gives it in German.—ED.]

CHAPTER XI

> A jest's prosperity lies in the ear
> Of him that hears it, never in the tongue
> Of him that utters.
>
> [*Love's Labor's Lost*]

EDGAR POE declares, with much gravity, that he has often thought he could distinctly hear the sound of the darkness coming over the horizon; and some one else, perhaps the same poet, has listened to the growing of the grass.*

Late in the afternoon of this day when Cranston had plunged into the forest behind the Indian, as the sun was declining behind the ridge which bounds Montvale Springs to the westward, a noise similar to the sound of flying darkness and growing grass might have been borne to the ears of three or four invalids, who had crept out of their cabins to take the cool air and a draught of the Chalybeate.

But this noise came neither from the gathering of dark powers, nor from the struggle of grass-growth.

It was the rustle of silken dresses, and so forth, and the crinkling of sundry coats, and so forth, in which the male and female sojourners at beautiful Montvale were at this moment arraying themselves for the masque-ball of that night.

The impudent and invisible 24,999 may go with me up into room 93, west wing, gentlemen's quarters, of the seven-gabled hotel at Montvale.

B. Chauncey Flemington, a gay representative of a big plantation in Mississippi, is drawing on the left individual of a pair of boots, whose yellow " insides " he has caused to be cut and pulled over, after the manner of the boots that Pizarro wears in the theatre.**

John Briggs, whom nor I nor anybody know, except that he was the best fellow in the English language, is tying a blue ribbon round his knee to fasten a flesh-colored long stocking, such as the genteel shepherd wears in the theatre. Alf Aubrey

* [Both ideas are expressed in " Al Aaraaf."—ED.]

** [Presumably in Sheridan's adaptation (*Pizarro*) of Kotzebue's *Spaniards in Peru*.—ED.]

is tying the thong of a Roman sandal upon his foot, occasionally pausing to glance at an open Shakespeare lying on the table, after each glance throwing back his head and shutting his eyes, while his lips move slowly, as if he were repeating in silent enjoyment the words of the master.

Boots, towels, trunks, trunk-trays, cologne-bottles, and a thousand miscellanea of the masculine toilet, lie scattered in inextricable confusion about the floor of No. 93.

"John," said Flemington, giving a last hitch to his boots, "I wish to direct your serious attention to Aubrey, there. I,"—regarding the right boot with intense gaze,—"I wish to remind you that I have known Aubrey from—I may say, from his youth up, or, I *should* say, in view of his present course of life, from his youth down. Now, during all this amazing stretch of time that I have known Aubrey there, it has never been my lot to see him read any book whatever; but adhering with great consistency to his belief that books were theoretical things, he has continued to study human nature in the light of the sternly-practical, without the assistance of written help. I wish to direct your serious attention (after this short preamble) to the fact that from a period nearly contemporaneous with the first hints that were given of this fancy-ball to-night, my friend Aubrey there, discarding that rigorous practicality which has hitherto distinguished him, has become nothing more nor less than a—bookworm! The singularity of this change is heightened by the fact that this worm crawls only in one book,—that book, Shakespeare: only on one page of that book,—that page, the page where occurs the ninth scene * of the third act of *Antony and Cleopatra*, about the middle of the left-hand column, beginning with the words—with the words,"—and with an adroit movement, Flemington snatched the book off the table before Aubrey could interpose, and assuming a tragic attitude, continued:—"with the words, I naturally imagine, which my friend Aubrey there has marked in brackets with a pencil, to wit:—

> *Antony* . . . Egypt, thou knewest too well
> My heart was to thy rudder tied by the strings,
> And thou should'st tow me after: o'er my spirit
> Thy full supremacy thou knewest, and that
> Thy Beck—

* [Actually scene xi.—Ed.]

I entreat you to believe, Briggs, that the capital B which commences this word ' beck ' is Aubrey's and not Shakespeare's,—

> . . . and that
> Thy Beck might from the bidding of the Gods
> Command me.

" John Briggs, have I your serious attention? "

" At your request, I have concentrated my serious attention, like the nozzle of a fire-engine, upon our friend Aubrey there. It is now spirting against him, full steam. If you don't relieve it shortly, I have no doubt it'll knock him out of the window! "

" It is well. I wish you to retain this quotation, marked in brackets by my friend Aubrey there, in your mind, while I relate a little circumstance that befell, a matter of ten days ago. While I was one day reading Shakespeare at the big oak out yonder, the sun crawled round and shone too warmly for me, insomuch that I was fain get behind the tree and lie down on the grass, leaving my book open on the bench. In this situation I fell asleep. Being presently awakened by the sound of voices, I perceived a gentleman and lady approaching, down the walk, and my attire being somewhat disordered, I lay still, hoping not to be discovered. It is hardly necessary for me to state that the gentleman was my friend Aubrey there,"—Aubrey leaned his face upon his hands—" and it is almost equally unnecessary for me to state that the lady was the mother of Rebecca Parven, whom Aubrey has been adoring in sight of everybody for a month or more. They sat down on the bench.

" ' And so, my dear Mr. Aubrey,' Mrs. Parven said, ' Beck and I (I call my daughter Rebecca, Beck,— you know ' call me pet names, dearest '—ah!), Beck and I concluded that we would bring you into our little plot for having something *recherché* in the way of costumes for the ball; because we want your advice about the dresses, and we wish that you'd get up a little speech to make the characters go off natural like, you know, and so on. Now, Beck wants to come as Cleopatra, because Beck, you know, is a brunette, and Cleopatra was a brunette, wasn't she, Mr. Aubrey? '

" ' Ah—ah—so far as my recollection of history serves me, Mrs. Parven,—she was! ' says Aubrey.

" ' Very good. Oh, I knew we would get on famously, for

our tastes run *so* together,' says Mrs. Parven, with a heavenly smile at Aubrey. 'Well, now, Beck, as I said, will be Cleopatra, and I thought that I, being her mother, would go as—as Egypt, you know, Mr. Aubrey, represented in an allegorical costume. Now, mind, Mr. Aubrey, this is confidential; what costume shall I wear to—to represent Egypt allegorically?'

"Aubrey did not reply, Mr. Briggs, for some minutes. I think I can see the exact process which went on in his mind. 'Let's see,' says he to himself, 'Egypt,—Egypt:—Alligators, no, Crocodiles: and Mummies: and—Sphynx;—yes, and Pyramids: —good!'

"'Well, Mrs. Parven,' says Aubrey at last,—'Crocodiles: have you any crocodiles' skins among your very extensive collection of—of furs?'

"'Oh, Mr. Aubrey,' cries she, 'I thought they were scaly!'

"'Ah, no, Madame. In my trip to Europe, having of course to pass through Egypt, I often saw them disporting in the cool waters, and would have taken them for beavers. However, it is immaterial. But,' says he, 'Mummies:—ah—have you any mummy-cloth amongst your very extensive collection of—*barèges*, Mrs. Parven?'

"Mrs. P., you may remember, does not hear very distinctly, Mr. Briggs.

"'Gummy-cloth?' says she, meditatively. 'Well, there's Mr. Parven's gum-coat he goes duck-hunting in; and I could rip it up, you know. Would it do, Mr. Aubrey?'

"'Oh, excellently well, ma'am,' says Aubrey. 'Splendidly; and, by the way, your naturally fair complexion must be darkened a little, Mrs. Parven; it has passed into a proverb, you know: "black as Egypt," we say. Your face must be dark—and hands,' added the atrocious scoundrel.

"'Dear me, Mr. Aubrey, how in the world shall I do it? Ink, you know, wouldn't wash off, after it was over; and I *wouldn't* like to lie abed a month to wear it off,' says amiable Mrs. P.

"'Cork, ma'am: cork's the thing. Get one out of a champagne-bottle, you know, and hold it in a candle, and then rub it on. Washes off, too, easy.'

"'Very well, then. The dress of gum-cloth. I suppose I may relieve the sombre effect of the gum-cloth by trimmings to suit my own fancy?'

" 'Oh yes, certainly. And don't forget your head-dress, which must be a pyramid. You can make it— like a pin-cushion, you understand, of bran, or something like that.'

" 'Well,' says Mrs. P., with a long breath, 'and that's all. Oh, I'm *so* much obliged to you, Mr. Aubrey. I know I shall make a good Egypt. And *so* kind in you to tell me! I should have asked Mr. Flemington, but— '

" 'Madame,' says my friend Aubrey there," (Aubrey slid from his chair and sat cross-legged with his face to the wall); " 'Madame, I advise you, as a friend, not to apply to Mr. Flemington, for the reason that his lamentable ignorance of history and of historical personages would be certain to betray you into some ridiculous mistake. And he'd never admit that he knew nothing about it. No, madame, leave out Flemington, by all means!'

" 'Indeed, I certainly shall do so; especially since you've been so kind. And we want it to be a secret, you know, so as to seem unpremeditated. And now, since all that is arranged, couldn't you, please, Mr. Aubrey, compose a little address to deliver to us, in character, as we entered the ball-room door, to make it all go off smooth and natural like?' Mr. Briggs, my friend Aubrey there was staggered for a moment; his eyes fell, —and that fall saved him! For they fell upon my Shakespeare, which was lying open at *Antony and Cleopatra.* Taking up the book, he commenced to read the identical passage which I have described as marked in brackets, and which I have just spoken. 'O Egypt,' and so forth, read he, until he came to the line—

Thy Beck might from the bidding,

when Mrs. P. cried out, 'Oh, Mr. Aubrey, that's not in the book, and you're just composing, you dear genius, you! My Beck, indeed! How could Shakespeare know any thing of my Beck?'

" 'Madame,' says Aubrey, laying his hand on his heart with that dignity for which his family is distinguished: 'Madame, the Latin word *vates* means at once poet and prophet—a philological observation which most satisfactorily accounts for the striking phenomenon you have just mentioned. For doubtless the prophetic eye of Shakespeare foresaw— '

" 'Dear me, Mr. Aubrey, I thought I heard a rustling behind this tree. Maybe, it was a snake, and I *do* fear snakes, so, and

I saw one yesterday on the hill yonder,' says Mrs. P., who felt that Aubrey was drawing her into dangerous grounds, philological and otherwise. 'There's the gong, now, for tea; let's go. Indeed, I and Beck are *very* much obliged to you, and the little speech will make it all go off *so* smooth and nat—' and then they turned out of hearing. Mr. Briggs, have I your serious attention?"

"I am an ear, Flemington," said Briggs, sententiously; but looked more like a nose, as he bent, with red face, over his second ribbon-knot.

"I wish you to support me in the demand which I feel I have a right to make upon Mr. Aubrey, after what has passed. That demand is that Mr. Aubrey shall immediately recite his little speech to us, so that our hearts may not forebode his disgrace on the great night; and that, failing in his rehearsal, he shall stand on his head and drink a cobbler. Mr. Aubrey; recite!"

Aubrey, still sitting tailor-wise, had leaned his nose against the wall, and was flattening the end of it thereagainst, as if his soul's happiness depended thereupon. At the summons he rose, and putting his best foot foremost, which was the foot with the sandal on it, the other being nude of sock or shoe, began in deep-tragic voice:

> Egypt, thou knew'st too well
> My heart was to thy rudder tied with—

"No; not 'with': '*by*'*!*"

> . . . was to thy rudder tied by the strings
> And thou should'st oh—should'st oh—oh—

The prompter pointed in pantomime of deep significance at the nude foot of the speaker; but this latter looked utter ignorance.

"Toe, Aubrey: think of your toe!"

"Ah, yes:

> And thou should'st tow me after: o'er my spirit
> Thy full supremacy thou knew'st, and that—
> And that—and th—"

"Oh, monstrous! to break down right at the joke. Briggs, he's been cramming it ten days."

"Nine, Flem; just nine!"

"Nine days, and can't say it over. I do forthwith adjudge that you, Alfred Aubrey, B. A. of Oxford, Mississippi, do immediately reverse the ordinary position of manhood, and during said reversal imbibe a sherry cobbler. Bute,"—to the waiter at the door,—"cobblers for three. John, give me your assistance in drawing out this table to the centre of the room, for my friend Aubrey there to stand on his head on, and have free play of his legs. I were loth, Mr. Briggs, that Mr. Aubrey should receive detriment in the matter of legs. Cobblers here. So;—time, Aubrey. Briggs, we must have music!"

Steadily, and without a shadow of smile, Mr. Aubrey reversed himself, head on table and feet in air, while the entire band, through hollowed fist, trumpeted, "Dying, Egypt, dying," with most brilliant intonation; but as Bute approached with the cobblers, a drop of the lemon and sherry splashed into Aubrey's eye, and that gentleman, with the most natural gesture in the world, attempting to rub his spasmodically-closed optic with his forefinger, suddenly lost balance. As he came down with a mighty crash, he involved in one wide ruin all, bringing down Flemington and cobbler with his legs, and by a wild lunge of arms upsetting John Briggs and cobbler after the most approved style of the clutch-desperate.

Now broke the icy barriers of their gravity, and each lay as he fell, with sides shaking and uproarious torrents of laughter issuing from healthy lungs. When the first paroxysm was over, "John," commenced Aubrey; but broke down, and the rest joined him in a fresh burst. At length with many a fresh jet and eddy of laughter,

"John," said Aubrey, "you ought to have seen Flem and me weigh—oh, I'll die—weighing the old lady, the other day. Flem got—ah—got it up. We invited her to take a walk with us down to the stables to loo—to look at the horses. You know the hay-scales down there. I gently, very gently, guided her course across 'em, Flem being behind; and just as we got on the plat—platform, I stopped, engaging her in a very animated discussion on Duplex Elliptics, while Flem quietly arranged the beam behind and weighed the pair. Presently he coughed, and at the signal we walked on. On the way back to the hotel, 'by the way, Aubrey,' says he, 'I must show you the result of those astronomical calculations I was making last night,' and he handed me this piece of a letter. Look on the back of it.

	lbs.	oz.
" Weight of both - - - - - -	407	6
" Mr. Aubrey (as ascertained by previous experiment), - -	139	2
Remainder. Weight of Mrs. P. - -	268	4
Deduct for Dup. Ell. and other hardware outside, say - - - - -	10	0
And exact net weight Mrs. P. - -	258	4 "

At this moment Bute announced the ball in half an hour; whereat No. 93 proceeded to dress itself.

Chapter XII

Gloucester.—Weapons! arms! What's the matter here?

King Lear

NO, 24,999! You shall not witness the enduing of Mrs. Parven with the somewhat remarkable costume which, at some expense and much labor, she had caused to be prepared for herself. The momentous undertaking was accomplished by her daughter Rebecca and her sable handmaiden. It was but once interrupted by a mild remark from Mrs. P.

"Don't put any more of it into my eye than you can help, Beck dear!" said she, while the burnt cork was being applied.

"De good father's sakes alive, Mistis! You iz black az I iz!" observed the handmaiden.

"And you," exclaimed Rebecca, "are as black as Egypt!"

Meantime, the three jovial habitants of No. 93 had hurried their toilets and moved down to the ball-room, where they had taken a position commanding all the approaches, from which they delivered a steady fire of comments upon each couple as the masquers slowly began to enter and promenade in stately circle round the hall. Aubrey personated Mark Antony; Flemington, Pizarro; and John Briggs, in slippers and tights, bearing a crook with ribbons, was a very genteel Shepherd indeed.

"By the nine gods,* Señor Pizarro! what have we here?" said Mark Antony, pointing to a couple just entering.

"General, it is as if a Russian bear or Hyrcan tiger had stolen a hawk's beak, and wore it at the end of his snout!"

"Nay, friends," interposed the Shepherd, "it is master Shylock, the Jew of Venice. How gracefully locketh he arm, and how amiably converseth he—with no less a Gentile than poor crazy Ophelia, who hath, look! just tied a flower to the end of Shylock's beard, and is laughing silverly that such grizzled and curling stems should terminate in the bloom and fruitage of a rose!"

"What manner of giant should be he that comes now?" inquired Antony.

* [The conversations throughout this chapter are filled with verbal echoes of Macaulay, Scott, Byron, Milton, Shakespeare, *et al.*—Ed.]

" Please your heathen majesty, it is Goliath of Gath, with a spear and a bass voice, denouncing death to a whole army— " replied Pizarro.

" And bearing on his arm, O acme of contrasts! sweet Jeanie Deans, with the gowden hair! " added the Shepherd.

Suddenly Mark Antony unsheathed his sword, and stood *en garde.* " Come on," cried he, " an thou be Fate, or Cleopatra's spirit, or other shape from hell, I fear thee not! "

" It is a sheep-murrain embodied in shape of a man! " said the Shepherd, and ran behind Mark Antony.

" It is the Devil! " said Pizarro, and hastily muttered a Paternoster as he ran behind the Shepherd.

" How daintily he switcheth to and fro his arrow-pointed tail! " observed the Shepherd from between the Roman legs of Mark Antony.

" *Tales sunt inferni!* " quoth the general.

" If all be well," observed Pizarro, " that ends well, then is this tail of yon Devil a most excellent good tail; for, it being already of exceeding sharp terminus, the harlequin there is tying, unbeknown to Señor Devil, a copy of Brownlow's *Whig* * to the end of it! "

" By way of envenoming ye arrow-point, and God pity ye man who reads this infernal tale, now! " added the Shepherd.

" And I could wish," said Mark Antony, sheathing his sword, " that the black cambric were not so tight about his satanic legs; for I do not love your ungraceful Devil! "

" It is in character, General, that the cambric tights should be so tight; for your immortals, being ever young, must show no wrinkles! " quoth Briggs, the Shepherd.

" But who is this fair star that steals in, shining, by the side of Lucifer? A dainty girl, by my beard! to be so arm-locked with the Devil! " inquired Pizarro.

" It is Helen of Greece, by her cymar with a battle worked on it, and her silver sandals that seem of a piece with her silver feet! " answered Antony.

" Methinks," muttered the Shepherd, " she of Greece should be i' the melting mood, so near this fiery-hot Satan! "

* [Vehement Union newspaper (Knoxville, Tenn.). The MS reads, " a copy of the Tribune."—ED.]

"Aye," groaned Pizarro, "I fear me she hath caught a Tartarus shape!"

"Friends, follow me!" suddenly shouted Mark Antony, and stormed, with stage-stride and clang of sandal, across the room.

For, at the door, appeared the face of Egypt.

It was only with a wild groan that Aubrey concealed the uproarious merriment which Mrs. Parven's appearance excited within him.

The warm weather, and Mrs. P.'s abounding flesh, had conspired to make that lady perspire copiously; and as each drop coursed from her benighted forehead across the broad and level plain of her face, it washed away a sort of cork alluvium, and left in its track a sinuous pathway of white, insomuch that the good lady's face showed like the front of a Hottentot tattooed in white.

A crowd of masquers, on the *qui vive* for fun, had followed Mark Antony's rush across the floor, and were now greeting with vociferous applause the extraordinary figure of Mrs. P., as she slowly and deliberately moved a step or two inside the door and there stopped, recognizing Mark Antony, to receive his address; which M. A. was in no sort of condition to deliver, his whole soul being occupied in endeavoring to suppress a fresh insurrection of laughter which broke forth within him, as he saw one of Mrs. P.'s blackened hands stretched back behind her to feel for that of Cleopatra-Rebecca,—who, not unmindful of her white gloves, was with great manual dexterity eluding these motherly overtures of Egypt wishing to lead her daughter in.

Flemington had glided to the side of Mrs. Parven, and stood there like Satan squat at the ear of Eve, ready to make diabolical suggestions; which he felt confident Mrs. P., in her excited state of mind, would immediately execute, however ridiculous.

Aubrey's voice trembled ominously as he began; but with a mighty effort, he dashed on:—

> Egypt, thou knowest too well
> My heart was to thy rudder tied by the strings
> And thou should'st tow me—

"Like a ship, you know, Mrs. Parven," whispered Flemington rapidly; "tow him—by the nose, for instance: that's it, take hold of his nose, so! Forward: tow him! splendid!" he continued, as Mrs. P., deliberately taking the somewhat extensive proboscis of Aubrey between finger and thumb, commenced a stately forward movement.

Aubrey followed, as in duty bound; and with a sublime gulp, like an earthquake taking down a city, continued:—

O'er my spirit
Thy full supremacy thou knew'st, and that
Thy Beck—

Here Aubrey wrenched loose his nose, and made a profound bow to Rebecca-Cleopatra walking behind—

might from the bidding of the gods
Command me!

A storm and salvo of cheers from the masquers testified their appreciation of this sally, and Mrs. P., taking Mark Antony's arm, slowly promenaded on, in the proud consciousness of having attracted more attention than anybody in the room, dispensing liberal smiles. Dispensing not only, alas! smiles; for some fiendish harlequin in the crowd had ripped a small aperture in the pyramid which adorned Egypt's head, and the bran was issuing therefrom in a miniature Nilus along her dress to the floor; whereby already the pyramid was visibly collapsing and had that foolish appearance of befuddlement which a hat has with a brick in it.

So the mirth grew furious and the crowd increased. Turk and Paynim laughed and joked with Greek and Crusader; Cavaliers and Roundheads swore friendship, York and Lancaster embraced; Moses gave his staff to a harlequin who balanced it on his chin, while the Prophet waltzed away with a masqueress in duplex elliptic and heeled shoes; the Devil was dancing with her highness the Abbess of ——, and a grizzly bear stood up on his hind paws to pirouette with a delicate Greek Naiad. All nations, all natures, mingled in a mazy whirl; costumes and customs were incongruously scattered together in a parti-colored patchwork; the ball-room wore motley like a clown; the last centuries shook hands with the first, over the heads of the middle ages; it was as if Father Time doubled together the two ends of his course, and shook all the racers against each other in the centre. White bosoms heaved, dark eyes sparkled, blue eyes glowed; soul struck against soul as body against body; spirits grew fierce in the powerful proximity of each other; the arch-genius of all intoxication waved his enchanting wings, and fanned higher the rosy flame of life.

Tall Pizarro, with black, sharp-pointed beard, was everywhere in the thickest of the press; anon leaning down to whisper nothings in the ear of some fair neighbor; anon flashing sallies of wit across the heads of the crowd to some equally tall opponent, as Jura darts back the lightning to a sister peak over the hills. Presently, he met Mark Antony, who had just left the side of Cleopatra, in search of some Octavia.

"Life! Life! Down with Death!" cried Pizarro, as he saw the glowing eyes of Aubrey.

"Aye," quoth Mark Antony, "John Death hath no part here. Let him go sulk i' the corner of space. But whither away, so quick?"

"Now, by our Lady of Madrid, thou wert better ask that question of this crowd that is rolling me along like a round stone in a river! *Himmel! Potz Tausend!*" exclaimed he as the crowd gave one of those savage lurches that crowds will give inexplicably, and forgetting that Pizarro did not usually employ German expletives.

At the moment that he uttered a German word, however, a short, plumply-made female, closely masked, looked up quickly and asked, in German, if he spoke that language.

"Yes."

"Then I may speak without fear of being understood by others; and Heaven be praised! for I fear I do not know English enough to tell you that which I want."

"Speak freely," answered Flemington, suspecting some jest. "Pizarro's life lies shining in his sword; and that, lady, is at your service!"

"No, no, I do not jest; you misunderstand me," quickly answered his companion, in tone of such evident feeling, that Flemington's attention was aroused. "Lean down your head. Give me your arm, and open a way through the crowd to the door. A life may be lost while I talk to you. Come!"

Flemington put forth all his strength and slowly clove a way through the press, his fair client holding to his arm, and following in his wake. As they walked, she rapidly related her story.

" Herr, I must be very brief. I and the Fraulein— I will not tell you her name—came to the ball with Herr Cranston, and— "

" With John Cranston? "

" Yes. Ah, I am infinitely glad that you know him! We rode with him five miles, from our house in the mountains. He told us he had had a quarrel with one Herr Rübetsahl, and swears he will kill him to-night. Herr Rübetsahl is to come with a party from Thalberg—at least I hope he is not already arrived,"—with a shudder. " We would have left Herr Cranston, he was so violent; but we were alone on the road when he told us these things, and we could not come without an escort. He brought us here, saw us in the door, and then left us. But I followed him, to see! Herr, I saw him take his place behind that large oak yonder, which grows near the main gate of the inclosure. I do not doubt he intends to waylay Herr Rübetsahl as he comes in, and kill him. He carries a long, naked rapier. O, Herr, if you would save a life, for God's sake, interpose. Aye," she added, as Flemington bent a somewhat undecided countenance to her; " you will be the murderer, and not Herr Cranston, if, after what I have told you, you do not exert yourself to prevent this deed! "

Near the door they encountered the gentle Shepherd, engaged in animated conversation with a tall, lithe girl, masqued. She was conversing rapidly, but seemed continually harassed by some recurring idea, which often caused her to turn her head and glance down the winding white-gravelled walk which led, under fine oaks and between grass-plats, to the gate of the inclosure. It was Ottilie, who was already excited by the unaccustomed pleasure of conversation with strangers to such a degree, that she would occasionally even forget the terrible anticipation, under the influence of which she had sent Gretchen, the stronger of the two, into the crowd, with the faint hope of finding some male friend who might avert the impending disaster.

For, on the ride from her cottage, Cranston, half-crazed with revengeful feelings, had given her an account of his quarrel with Rübetsahl. Ottilie knew not what to think or say, passive with that feeling which I suppose all of us know—a feeling as if the Day of Judgment, with its astounding crash, its shameful disclosures, and its dreadful dooms, was about to burst upon the world.

"Come, Shepherd," said Pizarro, "bring your Phœbe there. Let us get into the moonlight. You three shall be the army, and I will lead you to victory. Now pace we down the gravel, here,—how white it gleams!—in column of two and two, conversing upon indifferent topics."

Laughing and chatting gaily, they strolled on through the moonlight, towards the gate. Presently they came full upon Cranston, who, wild with revengeful brooding and waiting, had abandoned his position near the tree, and was pacing violently to and fro in the walk, twirling his rapier in rapid circles that flashed and glittered with deadly sparkle in the light.

"Ha!" exclaimed Flemington, as, Cranston turning suddenly, they came face to face. "By the great horn spoon! It's John Cranston that I haven't seen since we did Germany in the same year. How d'ye do, old fellow,—and over again! I'm running the Pizarro rôle to-night, you see, John; but, by Jove! the sight of you converts me into solid Chauncey Flemington in a trice. Come, turn with us, and let's get back to the festivities. We've just left 'em for a little air. You too, eh? 'Gad, a man might almost suppose you an injured lover, waiting to assassinate his rival! Come on, Cran. By the way, this is my particular bosom-friend, John Briggs, doing the Shepherd very sheepishly. Be acquainted! As for these fair ladies, I would introduce you to them with great pleasure if I had only the happiness to know them, or even to call their names."

It was scarcely possible that Cranston was moved even by the magnificent hilarity, which overflowed from generous, brotherly-souled Flemington; but he was taken aback. Stifling his anger, he muttered to himself, "One more chance, yet!" and then, forcing a smile which was bitter as death, said, with hoarse voice: "I'm glad to see you, Flemington. I was taking the air. Let us go to the ball-room."

A quick glance of gratitude shot up into Flemington's eyes from those of the two women; and, more merry than ever, the party returned, quickly separating as soon as they met the charge of the crowd inside.

It was now eleven o'clock. Lines of grotesque dancers advanced and receded and advanced again, like restless waves full of the wrecks of times and nations. Old gray Reason, the tutor of Fancy's tumultuous children, had given them holiday to-night, and they bounded forth with frantic gambols to enjoy an unaccustomed liberty. It was as if some gigantic tarantula had in an instant bitten the whole world, dead men and all.

At this moment the whole company paused to hear a loud clear voice proclaiming, "Make way for good King Arthur and his Queen!" All eyes were turned towards the door, through which, the crowd deferentially falling back on each side, entered Rübetsahl habited as King Arthur, in royal vestments, without armor. Upon his arm leaned Felix Sterling, as Queen Guinevere, and behind them, Philip, a most gentle Squire, bore the great two-handed brand, Excalibar.

"Now our Lady keep my heart stout," exclaimed Pizarro, "and stiffen my knee, or I must perforce kneel to this loveliness. Kind Heaven! Look, Antony, at yon Queen with the lissome undulating shape, undulating like a slow and tender no-wind wave of the blue main and— "

"Aye, undulating like the gentle swells the Zephyrs made in Cleo's silk sails, when we voyaged the Cydnus!" interposed Mark Antony.

"Aye, undulating like the distant velvety swell of upland beyond meadow!" added the Shepherd.

"Hush!" exclaimed Pizarro, not more than half in jest, "I speak, to keep from dying of a pent admiration. Look, Mark Antony and Shepherd, at yon Queen-feet; mark you how they show one moment beneath the heavy-trailing robe, then in successive instantaneousness withdraw again; one glitters, then is dark,—then the other, and is dark; like two white mice playing in and out the arras of a silent room! And friends! note ye her neck, how it curves, a stem bending with a rare flower-face that the botanizing angels have not gathered, I know not why: how it curves,—like a vine-tendril now it seems, so that I am fain offer my stout bosom to support it; but I look again and it is become regal proud as 'twere scorning the protection of any power save the eyes there above it! O Saxon eyes! Like two unsounded oval seas at dawn, with silver mists upon them, and sylvan mysteries within them! And I swear to ye, if the convex side of our concave firmament be alabaster-white, then is it like yon broad Queen's-forehead, in which white heaven I warrant ye a fairer world than this revolves, she creating. Nay, men," said he, hurriedly advancing, "if loyalty be manhood then am I wholly a man, for here do I homage!" Sinking on one knee, in the path of the slow-advancing Arthur, and doffing his plumed hat,—

"Most puissant Sovereign, most lovely Queen, I know not if in puissance these queenly eyes exceed those kingly arms, nor if in loveliness your kingly deeds exceed these queenly eyes: nor would I solve mine amiable doubt! I owe no subject's fealty to your throne, but I do render all true homage to your worth."

Quickly Mark Antony and the Shepherd were on knee beside him; while King Arthur raised up Pizarro, and the Queen reached him her white hand to kiss, he kneeling again to receive this royal grace.

At this moment, two long, strong arms, with gauntleted hands of mail, reached out in front of King Arthur and divided the crowd to right and left, assisting the design by circling a rapier over the heads of the crowd, and gradually lowering its sweep till room was gained for free play of sword. It was Cranston, attired in a light hauberk and helmet. These relics of the days of chivalry were the only memorials that Ottilie had brought with her from Germany; and, that morning, she and Gretchen had grown almost sportive in midst of their melancholy when, having determined to visit the Springs, they brought out the old coat of mail and casque, and arrayed Cranston in them. He had carried in his hand all day the naked rapier, whose sheath he had thrown away in the morning.

"My glove is there!" said he, throwing down a gauntlet. "I challenge to immediate combat King Arthur and all his Table Round! I am Lancelot of the Lake!"

"By Hercules!" exclaimed Mark Antony, "an I were to judge from the scowl of yon knight-challenger's brow, and the hot sparkle in 's eye, I could swear some dainty slippers in this room would be puddled with blood ere this joust be over!"

"With you there, General," sententiously observed the Shepherd.

Flemington kept his counsel. It was too late to interfere.

"King Arthur condescends to accept any challenge, but stoops not to raise any glove!" said Rübetsahl, spurning the gauntlet with his foot. "Give me the brand!"

On one knee Philip presented the mighty Excalibar.

"Sir Lancelot of the Lake, guard thyself!"

Up rose the long, wide blade and crossed with the thin one. Ottilie, with that oppressive doom's-day feeling again overhanging her sluggish soul, like sultry clouds on hot mornings, instinctively glided close to the inner edge of the living circle, and stood by Rübetsahl: who, indeed, was little aware of those glazed, distended eyes bent on his form; and well, so, for they would have shaken his heart and relaxed the bow-tension of his muscles, of which he had full need to parry the quick thrusts of Cranston's rapier.

No thought struck the masquers that this sword-play was aught more than a part of the show. Presently all grew still, spelled by that fascination of naked steel which, in the theatres, entrances pit and boxes alike; which, in the silent room of the suicide, often reveals a razor in the blood next morning; which, on the field, makes armies stand still from fighting to see the waving and circling and hewing of the falchions of their leaders in single combat. So that now, even had the masquers known the deadly earnestness with which the two combatants were fighting, no one would have broken the spell by interfering in the dangerous, beautiful scene.

Cranston held his left hand aloft, presenting only his right side to his opponent, as fencers use; but Rübetsahl, wielding his weapon with both hands, like the old rugged Ritters of his native land, stood full-breast to the foe. In at this broad bosom, searching the life lurking there, darted the rapier time and again, a baffled but insatiable lightning.* Like an angry serpent's tongue, it leapt back and forth. *Coup de reverse!* No; the broad blade received it slanting, and the narrow one glanced harmless. *Flanconnade!* No; the broad blade wound about the narrow, like one serpent twining about another. Feint, *dégagement*, cut, in *tierce*, in *cercle*, in *octave!* No, still no; the broad

* [The MS reads, "searching its lurking life, time and again, like those lightnings that searched the forest of ——[1] for the guilty lovers hiding there." The appended footnote reads, "[1] Robert Browning's."—Ed.]

blade was there to receive them always, a polished, ubiquitous-hovering shield.

Strange, that the thin and doubtful music of two metal blades clashing against each other should so enchant three hundred men and women! No one uttered a sound; they drew breath, even, with an effort to be still.

Queen Felix, who had drawn back to give room for the swing of Rübetsahl's arm, only now began to suspect the fearful reality of what, at first, she had supposed, with the rest, a sham. She felt rise within her a purer and queenlier blood than that of the Guinevere she personated; the arch of her neck became more regal; her head rose aloft; her nostril distended itself, and she looked on with a proud smile, in full confidence that bold Lancelot would lose.

Flemington, who, with Ottilie and Gretchen, alone knew the true nature of this tragedy veiling itself in sport, could not now have interfered if he would. Everywhere within that magic circle gleamed the two blades, in quick parry and thrust, either of which would have taken the life of one in their way.

All this time, the little brook that runs by the arbor-hill of Montvale, kept singing its tiny " road-melody," as it journeyed on toward the great Wave of Death, accepting cheerfully and making merry over the few moon-rays that struggled through thick overhanging leaves to light its way.

All this time, the grace of moonlight lay tenderly upon the rugged majesty of the mountains, as if Desdemona placed a dainty white hand upon Othello's brow.

All this time, the old priestly oaks lifted yearning arms toward the stars, and a mighty company of leaf-chapleted followers, with silent reverence, joined in this most pathetic prayer of those dumb ministers of the hills.

And all this time, the white stars said with silvery voices, "*Benedicite*: peace down there! and struggle to give more light to your fellow, not to take away his light! "

All of which remarks of the shiny preachers were, one may judge, unheard by Cranston or Rübetsahl, or any of the masquers. For, presently, Cranston began to grow tired under the unaccustomed weight of hauberk and helmet; and Rübetsahl, who had hitherto acted entirely on the defensive, saw himself able to put an end to the conflict. A mighty struggle, which crowded a month's arguments and replies into a second, flashed through his mind.

Shall I kill this man?

He deserves it.

Shall I not kill him?

It would be generous.

Any man can mete justice, especially when it comprehends his own revenge. The noble man scorns justice and spares. Justice is blind; blindness is not good. Mercy is Justice with the hood off her eyes.

Some one in the crowd whispered a word to his neighbor, and broke the fascination. A hum went about and began to grow; the crowd swayed and grew uneasy. Cranston, enraged at his declining strength, and fearful of interference, determined to risk all on a stroke. He drew his rapier far back over his head, for a feint-cut and *dégagement*, his favorite thrust; but, quick as lightning, Rübetsahl made a great stride forward, his sword glittered in circle about his head, making him look like a god with a halo, and, stretching clear over Cranston's shoulder, he struck the backward-extended rapier in the centre, sending it spinning in a hundred diamond-bright gyrations to the opposite wall, against which it struck and fell.

"Take thy life, and use it better, Sir Lancelot of the Lake!" said he, as he struck, with his head so close that his breath was hot in Cranston's face.

But the force of Rübetsahl's blow and the weight of his huge sword were so great that he was swung entirely round, by sheer momentum. As he strode forward, Ottilie had fallen upon her knees and leaned far into the circle, with arms outstretched. Suddenly she felt a sharp fire leap along her arm, as the point of Rübetsahl's whirling sword penetrated the flesh and ran a long gash from elbow to wrist; and fainted, as the excited crowd rushed in between the two combatants, like a furious wave between two ships.

"Hold, men!" shouted Flemington, standing over Ottilie and pushing back vigorously, "a lady is hurt. You trample her to death!"

"Who is it?" cried a hundred people, anxious for sister or

wife or daughter. Two or three shrieks, from women overcome by excitement and terror, sounded shrilly through the din.

"I've lifted her up, Aubrey. You and John push ahead through the crowd, and make way for me to bring her into the air. She has fainted."

"Permit me, sir!" said Rübetsahl, grasping the lifeless form which Flemington bore. He had recognized Ottilie as her domino fell off. Supposing that some brother or husband claimed his right, Flemington cheerfully yielded his burden, and joined the pioneers who were pressing a way through the crowd.

Quickly Rübetsahl bounded down the steps, and deposited Ottilie upon the rustic bench there, near the door. Gretchen glided past him, sat down on the bench, and supported Ottilie's head on her bosom. A moment after, John Briggs was up from the spring with a glass of cool water, which he dashed in the fainting girl's face.

Presently the gray eyes opened.

"It is only a scratch, Gretchen, and I fainted. Give me your arm. Let us go back into the hotel. I thank you very much, gentlemen!" she said, to the anxious men bending over her.

In a moment she was gone.

She had not looked in Rübetsahl's eyes.

CHAPTER XIII

My vast pity almost makes me die
To see thee laying there thy golden head,
My pride in happier summers, at my feet.

[Tennyson,] *Guinevere*

Snug.—Doth the moon shine that night we play our play?

Bottom.—A calendar, a calendar! Look in the almanac: find out moonshine, find out moonshine. *Midsummer Night's Dream*

Ladies and Gentlemen: In consequence of the sudden sickness of my operator, I have to run this moon, to-night, myself.

A. Ward, Showman

JOHN CRANSTON paced to and fro in the dark shade of an oak. A swirl of black shapes whirled in a hideous round through his brain: revenges, angers, self-reproaches, vague remembrances, vaguer bitternesses. As he paced, he tottered and came near falling.

" 'Gad, I'm weak," said he to himself, " and well might be. Don't think I slept any last night; more by token, was drunk or crazy—God knows which!— and got knocked down to cap it all!" He laughed the bitterest laugh of man. " I'll go sleep a little, and think about the pistols in the morning."

Meanwhile, the band in the ball-room played its most enticing waltzes, in vain. The masquers had lost heart for it, and only one of two couples remained, endeavoring to get up some spasmodic enthusiasm in a dance.

Flemington and his two friends stood under the big oak, looking at the silvery mountain-crest, rising above its jet-black base in the shade.

" Damned be he who first cries ' Go to bed! ' " exclaimed Flemington. " Gentlemen, I'm for a smoke and a long stroll in the moonlight. Black must be the soul of that man that would so affront our Lady Moon, yonder, as to put himself under cover at this time o' such a night. What d'ye say?"

" It's a *nem. con.* business, Flem," said Aubrey. " I'll go. Just wait a minute, tho', till I run up and get on a pair of boots, for these miserable sandal-soles are so thin that I'd as lief walk on my bare feet. Especially the left one, somehow," and he looked at his feet inquiringly. His face grew blank, and his companions burst into a loud laugh. He had loosened his thong while dancing, and in pressing through the crowd, the sandal had fallen off entirely; but the noble Roman, all unconscious of his great loss, had continued to stalk about, one shoe off and one shoe on, with far more ostentatious dignity certainly than his ancient prototype ever possessed.

"Thought the ground was unusually obtrusive on my left foot," said he, and ran off for his boots.

"Think I'll get on a pair of pants, myself," observed Briggs. "These ribbons round my leg make it feel like I had been holding a protracted session in the stocks."

They were not long gone.

"Which way?" asked Flemington.

"I vote for the half-way spring, up there on the mountain. The view from the rock that juts out there must be charming to-night," said Briggs.

They took the road which winds up the mountain. This road, just beyond the "half-way spring," a mile and a half from the hotel, forks, one branch leading over to Thalberg, the other to Cade's Cove, where Ottilie had resided some months.

"It's rather difficult," observed Flemington, puffing his cigar meditatively, "to imagine that this old prim earth, which now seems so demure and starchy and modest in her moonlight night-cap, is plunging along, on a scared nightmare, at the rate of I-forget-how-many-thousand miles a second!"

"What a wake she must make—hang the rhyme!" said Aubrey. "Jove! Wouldn't it be pleasant, now, to fly up close to her, on a pair of long, rakish wings, and get sucked into the boiling ether-foam behind her, and then fold yourself up like a lazy bird, and let her draw you along for a million miles or so!"

"And then flash out of the whirlpool, and run over and chat with somebody in the sun, and watch Maj. Orion sit in Cassiopeia's Chair and pull off his big military Boötes!" suggested Briggs.

"Pleasant enough," replied Flemington, "if one only had the—the—transportation-facilities!"

"A bad business," continued Aubrey, "this same want of

transportation-facilities i' this world. A fellow feels so heavy and clogged like, when he thinks about wings and buoyancies, and such like other-world advantages. If one's body were only as light and as strong as one's thought, now! I'd like, for instance, to catch hold of that straight moon-ray yonder that shoots through the leaves, and pull up by it right to the moon, hand over hand, like a sailor on a rope! "

" Or to start from a high peak on the night-side of the world, and make five strokes of your wings, and then curve them backward like a keen eagle, and swoop down into the sun and flit about in his fire, like a moth in a candle-flame! " said Flemington.

" And, when you got tired, stretch yourself on the bright top of a cloud, and float through the red, green, and gold of a sunset; for you could find a sunset somewhere any time you wanted one! " quoth Briggs.

" Aye," responded Flemington, " the old royal sun does fare right gallantly through the heavens, with a dainty dawn trumpeting silverly in front of him, and a sunset retinue in scarlet and gold crowding behind him! "

And then the three grew still, and walked and puffed their little smoke-clouds in silence.

While they are so—here, 24,999! slip along this steep acclivity and align yourselves upon the curving edge of the mountain-road, and take a look at these men by moonlight. It is a better light to see a soul by than sunlight. For sunlight, as an economical gas-saving arrangement, is a good thing and promotes business— but it puts out the stars! these, dark night discloses, and sacred moonlight purifies them white. As with stars, so with souls. Flemington has a genius, you observe, for commanding; Aubrey a genius for obeying; John Briggs a talent for everything, and no genius for anything. Flemington is independent; Aubrey sympathetic; John Briggs impulsive. Under given circumstances, Flemington would think the best thing to be done; Aubrey would recognize the weight of his opinion; and John Briggs would *do* something right or wrong immediately. If you were associated with Flemington, his originality would attract you to himself,—with Aubrey, his sympathy would direct your attention introspectively to yourself,—with Briggs, his unselfishness would send your thought away, both from him and you, to something else. Flemington is tall and graceful, with dark eyes; Aubrey never yet knew what to do with his hands, and has hazel eyes; and John Briggs —John Briggs—dear me, I have forgotten whether John Briggs was graceful or not, or what was his height or his color of eye; in fact I don't think I ever knew, or even thought of looking to see, nor would you, if you had known glorious, unselfish, fine John Briggs. Further information as to the parentage, birth, and early life of Flemington and Aubrey can be obtained upon application to this author; as for John Briggs, I do not think he had any parentage or birth, but the probabilities are strong that, as a man might send a dutiful son without a tutor to do Europe, so God put Briggs down on the earth, confident that he would return Home much improved in his knowledge of foreign life and manners!

The three friends were now arrived at the spring. The water bubbles into its basin, tinkling; the spring is born to music. It gushes from the solid rock, out of which the road is hewn, flows across this, and pours a tiny stream down the steep channel-way it has worn for itself. On this outer edge of the road, nearly opposite the spring, the rock juts out and overhangs a sheer precipice of some hundreds of feet. It is fine vantage-ground for a view, being clear of undergrowth and trailing vines that obstruct the sight on other parts of the road. Herefrom went up silently the three smoke-wreaths.

Far away to the left stretched the still procession of the peaks, like pilgrims halted in a curving line, when the foremost has reached a river. The furthest of these hill-pilgrims had reached the Tennessee. In front, if daylight shone, would have been a brave sweep of circular horizon, with its sky fitted in, like a broken piece, to the whole notched and serrated edge of the land; but, to-night, the dark trees under the mountain grew lighter and lighter until they reached the bright trees that were in moon-range, and these bright trees quickly became, further off, a mere silvery indistinctness which blended with silver mists and blotted out the horizon-line, so that on the rock there one seemed to stand in mid-heaven upon a vast slope that shot down away into unfathomable space.

At this moment, the noise of horses' hoofs was heard upon the rocky road. Soon, two voices sounded in the still air as the riders turned an abrupt corner a few yards below the spring. The voices were of women, and the talk was in German.

" O, Fraulein, let us go back to the hotel! It is too far to ride so late; and unaccompanied, too. I wish we had not started."

" No, no, no, Gretchen. I must go. I could not stay there. Gretchen, you forget! He is there! My God, no! "

" But, Fraulein, I am all bloody with helping you on your horse. Your arm should be bound; the wound is still bleeding. See! You reel in your saddle. Ah, mercy! " shrieked Gretchen, as Ottilie leaned far back with weakness, and, forgetting the curb, made her horse rear fearfully close to the precipice. She would have fallen; but Flemington bounded into the road and seized the bridle, while in the same instant Briggs caught the fainting girl in his arms.

This time the swoon was a deathly one, and did not yield easily.

" No wonder! " said John Briggs. " Look here! "

He pulled apart the pieces of cut sleeve, and disclosed the arm. Pearly white shone the upper portion, but the lower was dark with blood that still flowed from a long, lengthwise gash.

" Great God! Will she die, here? It is terrible! Keep throwing the water in her face till I run to the hotel and bring up a physician! "

Flemington turned and nearly ran into a carriage and horses, which had approached unperceived by the excited men round Ottilie. The carriage stopped.

" What's the matter, James? " said a cheery man's voice inside.

" Road blocked up wid people and horses, sah! Somebody hurt, I b'lieve, sah! "

A gentleman and lady emerged from the carriage, two horsemen who had been riding behind it alighted, and all came up.

" Ah! " said John Sterling, " it is our poor lady who was wounded in the ball-room. Let me see, gentlemen. I'm somewhat of a physician. It is not a bad wound," he added, examining the arm. " No artery is cut, though blood has flowed profusely. We'll bind it up. Lend me your handkerchief, Felix, and tear mine into strips. Fan her face, Phil, with your hat, and let some one chafe her hands. She'll recover in a minute."

Cheery words of John Sterling's, that went to Gretchen's heart!

Rübetsahl stood still, with folded arms, intently regarding the white face of his old beloved. As Ottilie, under the vigorous treatment of John Sterling, recovered life, her eyes unclosed full into Rübetsahl's. An expression of infinite yearning and infinite appealing gathered in them, and then they closed again, while a tear slid down one lash, glittered, and fell.

Tall Rübetsahl shook through all his frame.

He did not love her, now, and could not, henceforth. His soul was filled with a " vast pity " for her; and love admits no pity, on either side: it demands awe, which is pity's opposite, on both sides. Rübetsahl felt this. It was for this lost love, which had left only pity behind it, that he shook through all his frame. For it is impossible that King Arthur, breathing a vast pity over Guinevere's low head, should, in the same breath, have sworn,—

> I love thee still,
> Let no one dream but that I love thee still! *

Pity presupposes an ugly inferiority in the pitied; but Love demands a beautiful equality of preëminence in both the loved.

Over this thrice-dear dead love, upon whose grave lay pity like a flower, Paul Rübetsahl mourned and mourned, as he stood there gazing upon Ottilie.

" She is recovering. How far is it to your home, madame? " said John Sterling.

" About four miles, Herr! " answered Gretchen.

" Then my house is nearest. We will take her there. Gentlemen, assist me to get the lady into my carriage. Felix, you and the lady's friend ride with her inside. I'll take her horse."

" By the way, Flem," said Philip Sterling, " I can't let old college days go without one talk. What are you going to do, to-morrow? "

" Thought I'd pack up and go home next day. Season's about over anyhow."

" Don't think of it. You'll miss the best part of our year. The autumn is glorious here! I'll make a better proposition.

* [Tennyson, " Guinevere."—Ed.]

You and the boys there ride over, to-morrow, to Thalberg, and spend a week or more with me. Got plenty of room. We can hunt and fish a little. And I'll show you what father calls Valley Beautiful. What do you say, Aubrey?"

"Good!"

"Briggs?"

"Splendid!"

"It's all arranged then. Come early. Good night!"

"Good night, Phil,"—from the three. And so the footsteps passed one way, and the clang of hoofs receded, the other.

The spring bubbled its birth-music and flashed its little stream down the rock, a breeze woke up a minute and rustled the vine-leaves and went to sleep again, a dreamy bird uttered a faint half-whistle half-sigh in his sleep, and the mountain presently became as still as the stars.

CHAPTER XIV

Morn in the white wake of the morning star
Came furrowing all the orient into gold.

[Tennyson,] *The Princess*

THE SUN must needs be of an impudent fancy. He alone had boldness to look on fair Godiva at Coventry: and on the morning after the masque-ball at Montvale, he sent peering ray-glances into every chamber-window that opened eastward in our half of the earth. One of these light-bolts struck John Cranston full in the face, and woke him from the deep sleep that had followed two days of exhausting excitement. As if he had been uninterruptedly pursuing the train of thought in which he had fallen asleep, Cranston immediately commenced to discuss within himself the situation.

"If I challenge him, he'll choose swords again; and, by the rood! however reluctantly I confess it, I've got evidence to show that he can beat me at that.

"So, on swords, I lose.

"If he chose pistols, I might kill him; but then inquiry would be aroused, the contemptible quidnuncs would investigate, and the whole affair would be trumpeted forth by the enterprising scoundrels.

"On pistols, I lose again.

"What a fool I am," he suddenly exclaimed, rising up in bed, "not to see that I have lost already! Old Sterling will never pardon what occurred in his house; nor—nor Felix either. The whole thing stands about so,"—knitting his brows and falling back upon his pillow: "first, the gratification of revenge; said gratification is, however, in the first place doubtful, and in the second place, if successful, will lose me my reputation for life and kill John Cranston, senior: second, the postponement of the revenge till such time as I can call this man out on some other pretext which will not involve the discovery of my——affair at Frankfort. For which, God knows! God knows! I'm sorry enough. How white her face was!"

John Cranston's face became half blank, as faces will, when, in endeavoring to avoid a thought, one does one's best to think of nothing. But he was a man of short arguments and quick conclusions.

" I'll go home and wait," concluded he; and did so, that day.

The sun sent another ray into the window of a room in the second story of John Sterling's house. It fell and dwelt lovingly upon the sleeping eyes of Ottilie. Large, diaphanous half-globes, blue-veined, dainty, were these white-lidded eyes. Have you ever seen two grand magnolia petals fallen on the ground, convex side up?

Ottilie rose, and walked to her window. From the tranquil river below were rising a thousand rings of mist, which lengthened into soft ellipses, or broke and curled into fantastic curves, or stretched away into wavering, streaming pennants, all glittering suddenly as they floated into range of the straight sun-rays.

" The river prays to God! " said Ottilie; and, obeying an inexplicable impulse, she fell upon her knees and burst forth into an agony of tears.

She had not wept in a year; nor prayed either, except to the trees and the stars.

Rübetsahl saw his sun-ray coming. He had not slept all night. He had been silently sitting by his grave, and watching the pale flower that lay upon it.*

And poor John Briggs, being in No. 93 of the west wing, got no sunbeam. All the night his dreams had hovered vaguely, yet full tenderly, about Ottilie, like clouds gathering round a star.

* [The MS adds: " He had been saying to himself, ' Do I still love her: or this other one? ' "—Ed.]

CHAPTER XV

The love of nature seems to have led Thomson to a cheerful religion; and a gloomy religion to have led Cowper to a love of nature. The one would carry his fellow-men along with him into nature; the other flies to nature from his fellow-men.

S. T. Coleridge [, *Biographia Literaria*]

Nevertheless, that great epoch cannot fail to arrive when the whole family of mankind, by a grand universal resolve, will snatch themselves from this sorrowful condition, from this frightful imprisonment; and by a voluntary abdication of their terrestrial abode, redeem their race from this anguish, and seek refuge in a happier world with their Ancient Father.

A class of Nature-philosophers refuted by Novalis *

THAT DAY at Thalberg, when dinner was over, the sun had only a half-hour for this side of earth, having an appointment with the Antipodes at half-past six.

" Gentlemen," said John Sterling to Flemington and his two friends, as they rose from table, " you saw the silver side of my valley when you were riding over this morning. Come with me, and I'll show you and these ladies the golden side; for it is like the old shield in the story, only I don't know that any foolish knights ever quarrelled over it. Phil, have chairs brought out on the balcony. Shall we lead the way? " He offered his arm to Ottilie.

In laughing procession they filed out, and established themselves upon a fair broad balcony that looked westward and overhung the slope which swept down with all its trees and boulders to the river.

"Our womankind are all used to cigar-smoke, Flem," said Philip, handing them round. " You don't object to it? " addressing Ottilie.

" O, what a question,—to a German! At home,"—ah, my God! Home? What a word is this for me to speak! thought

* [The words quoted are Carlyle's translation from von Hardenberg's *Lehrlinge zu Sais* (*Pupils at Sais*) in his essay " Novalis." Another quotation from the same appears on the following page.—ED.]

Ottilie—" the house was always full of smoke from a half-dozen pipes of as many German kinsmen of mine. I made a virtue of necessity and liked it in self-defense."

Who grumbles that such a dinner should end in nothing but—smoke? You're a dyspeptic; it wasn't smoking hurt you, sir; it was the want of exercise, which if you had taken, you might have smoked as much as you pleased!

Be still about this Thalberg smoke. It ascended towards heaven; and drew their thoughts buoyantly upward.

The Thalbergers began to discourse upon high topics.

" How easy is it,"—observed Philip, " when one looks on a scene like this, to answer the arguments of those wild disputants in Von Hardenberg's book? ' Intercourse with the powers of Nature,' says one party, ' with plants, animals, rocks, storms and waves, must necessarily assimilate men to these objects. This assimilation,' they go on to say, ' this metamorphosis and dissolution of the divine and the human into ungovernable forces, is even the spirit of Nature, that frightfully voracious power. Is not all,'—they ask, with an earnestness which only makes one smile, here; ' is not all that we see even now a prey from heaven, a great ruin of former glories, the remains of a terrific repast? ' "

" I don't feel," said Flemington, with a long-drawn luxurious puff, " as if I were relapsing into barbarism, just at this particular moment. Though, sure enough, it must have been in some wild hurly-burly of Nature's youth, when she piled up these huge hills so high, and tossed them about so carelessly."

" Yes," said Rübetsahl, " but look! she's sorry she did it! She's done her best to smooth it over! She has covered these same mountain-evidences of folly with picturesque rocks and loving mosses; with stately trees and saintly flowers; with glittering springs that invite people to drink, and with hospitable ferns that allure people to rest. She has converted the boisterous sins of her youth into the enchanting virtues of her age. Her wild oats have blossomed into mountain-roses and tiger-lilies! "

" That's true," chimed Aubrey; " whereas Nature was an earthquake, now she is a flower. Let men tremble with a sublime terror at her old destructions; they can thrill with a sublimer love at her later creations."

" And yet," interposed John Sterling meditatively, " if one

attempt to fly from his sins into Nature, expecting to drown the memory and sting of his transgression in her terrors and her beauties, one fails unless he remembers this: that Nature is nothing as an end; that Nature is everything as a means.* Nature is finite in herself; she is infinite in her suggestions. We must not fly to her, but to the great Christ she helps us see. Perhaps the mysterious idea of Divinity is like a sentence written backward; we make it out easiest by reflecting it in a mirror. As such a mirror, Nature is a glorious revealer to the sorrowful soul; an infinite-tongued preacher of the Son who is our Father. I do not know the metaphysics; but as a practical man, hunting something to live by through day and night, Sundays and all, I do not want other proof of Christ and his purifying faculty through love, than that fair pageantry out yonder," he concluded, pointing to the brilliant west.

Ottilie looked at the far, glowing mountains with wistful eyes. With wistful tone, "What you say, sir," said she, "is charming. But, alas, does not every one carry into Nature an eye either bleared, or long-sighted, or short-sighted, or somewise defective? Is not this vast mirror to some a concave one; to some a convex one; to some a cracked one, distorting, all ways, the sentence one wishes to read? Does not each heart interpret Nature its own way, so that to the sad heart this great dew-drop glitters like a tear, while to the joyful heart it seems a diamond at a feast? One of your own poets calls the moon Queen of Heaven, blessing all lovers; another swears the moon is the Eye of Hell recording the crimes of men!"

"Young lady," replied old John solemnly, "these vagaries of trembling human hearts only exhibit more clearly the sympathy, the *sun-pathos*, the feeling-with, of Nature. The mirror will correct itself and mend itself for any persistent and serious eye. I think, through all phases of wavering distortion, the heart will find behind Nature love as well as terror, and will spring to the most powerful of these, which is love."

"And so," cried Philip, "who can believe all this humbug of Macaulay, that the advance of imagination is inverse to the advance of reason, and that poetry must decline as science flourishes? ** It is true Homer was at one end, and Newton at

* [Numerous passages in Lanier's Ledger discuss Nature's role in human life, as well as other ideas advanced in this chapter.—Ed.]

** [Macaulay, "Milton."—Ed.]

the other, of a time. But how long a time intervened between Humboldt and Goethe; how long between Agassiz and Tennyson? Moreover and what is more, one can scarcely tell whether Humboldt and Agassiz were not as good poets as Goethe and Tennyson were certainly good philosophers! And nothing surprised me more than that even fine Jamie Hogg must needs fall into this folly and say, 'Let philosophers ken causes, poets effecks'; * but"—

"Hold on, Phil!" interrupted John Briggs. "Honest Hogg, when he said that, had just come in out o' the cold to a warm fire; the poor fellow was sleepy. He didn't mean it. I hardly think, now, you ought to bring that up against Jeems!"

"Well, I won't. But I feel mighty savage against Macaulay!" replied Philip, rolling up his coat-cuffs.

"You're right, Phil," said Flemington. "One can trace, through the whole literary development of our day, the astonishing effect of the stimulus which has been given to investigations into material nature by the rise of geology and the prosperity of chemistry. To-day's science bears not only fruit, but flowers also! Poems, as well as steam-engines, crown its growth in these times."

"So!" said John Sterling, "the nineteenth century has taken a stroll into the woods and fields, and good is come of it. For every time has its mythology of Nature. The Gheber found, or rather placed, a God in the sun; a strange God, nor human nor divine. The Greek put fauns and hamadryads in the woods, not divine, and yet not human, for they did not suffer; they had no human hearts. Our poets, God bless 'em! have given to all natural forms that they shall suffer and love as we suffer and love. They have not conquered and made slaves of the rocks and trees; but they have won them over to be friends, neighbors, and citizens; which culminated when Robert Browning declared of a stone church in Italy, that it—

> Held up its face for the sun to shave! **

The earth, through our poets, is no longer dead matter. She has a soul, and it dreams of God, and one can see this dream in any lake!"

* [In *Noctes Ambrosianae*, No. XLII, April, 1829, North and Hogg discuss at length philosophy and poetry.—Ed.]

** ["Old Pictures in Florence."—Ed.]

"Hurrah for matter," quoth Briggs, "mysterious, spirit-hiding matter! I move that the freedom of the city of the universe be presented to this new citizen by a committee consisting of humanity at large!"

"What you say has occurred in poetry has also taken place, I think, in music," said Felix Sterling. "Why do they talk of pre-Raphaelitism, and not also of pre-Beethovenism and pre-Miltonism? These all mean surely nothing more than the close, loving, broad-minded study of Nature; and meaning this, they mean just what Raphael and Milton and Beethoven must have done. The beauty of our time is, that science has enabled us to do so better than they could! Beethoven is to Chopin as a wild mountain is to a flower growing on it; as the sombre booming of the sea in a cave is to the heavenly murmur of a rivulet in a glen. So Milton to Tennyson and all the sweet house-hold poets of our day; so Angelo to Bierstadt. Those were grand, but these are beautiful; those were magnificent, these are tender; those were powerful, these are human!"

"Wherefore," said John Sterling, "matter is not so bad, after all. Verily it is true that matter does imprison our souls; and it is absolutely impossible that these souls can communicate directly with each other. We may talk, sing, write, paint, carve and build; we express our soul, so; but we must use matter each time. We may even, to adopt the most intangible method, gaze into the eye of our beloved, speaking many things silently; yet this requires still an eye, which is matter. Each soul is prisoner in his cell. Yet we can paint on the wall, and it will remain! We can use that mysterious cypher we call language, and the wall will send it along! We can sing, and the wall will convey the song to our brother in the next cell! And so, albeit there is for souls no 'kissing through the bars' of matter, yet matter is a good jailer, and conveys our messages to our fellow-prisoners, and even suggests better messages than we could frame without!"

"And will never cease!" broke in Philip. "Poetry will never fail, nor science, nor the poetry of science. Till the end of time will deep call unto deep, and day utter speech unto day, and poets listen, with eavesdropping ears, to catch and sing to men some melodies from that sounding song-rhetoric of the lights and the waters!"

Philip disappeared, as if to hide a blush. Presently a prodigious rumbling was heard.

"Is that thunder?" said John Sterling. "Surely those clouds over yonder are too far for that!"

The rumbling increased, like an approaching earthquake.

It burst upon the wondering Thalbergers.

"Easy there, Ned. So! Now lift, boys, all, and get it over the threshold. Roll it along out there, so he can sit with his face to the west. There!"

It was the piano, which four stout negroes had rolled from the music-room out on the balcony.

"Ladies and gentlemen," said Philip, distributing manuscript parts of music, "profiting by a suggestion of my wise sister there, I have arranged a glorious thing of Chopin's here, not for an orchestra, as she wished, but for voices. We'll have a vocal orchestra. Sister Felie, here's the contralto part. I know you sing,"—to Ottilie,—"for I heard your soprano swelling up to-day from somewhere in the house. You and Felie will do splendidly in that duet there that commences the piece. To it there's a four-voiced accompaniment: Flem, you take the bass and Briggs the tenor—here's your part; and mother'll sing one part while I play the other on my flute. Pity you and I don't sing, Aubrey! Mr. Rübetsahl, will you preside, as the show-bills say, at the piano; just throb that bass along, you know, where it's too low for the voice; and play a full accompaniment for this second air, here. Stand up, everybody! All ready? Now; one, two, three, four, five, six;" and they started, everybody infected by the music-full soul that sparkled in his eye and fired his quick movements.

The duet rose and fell, rose and fell again, continually reaching up and continually falling down, like a human soul with its high aspirings and its terrible rebuffs. So rise we, so sink we; one moment gods, another moment beasts.

Then, with a startling modulation, and a short pause during which the singers scarcely dared to breathe, they commenced a full-chorded chorus, sung in strict time, with little *rallentando* or *crescendo*, a solemn, pathetic movement, full of sweet invitation and calm urging, repeating itself in a dozen keys, approached by new, yet simple modulations: it was like religion, importuning men every day. Now came two strains which were utterly indescribable, save by their effect. They were full of majesty and simple sweetness. They bore to you soft breaths from sunshiny woods, mingled with hum of purling waters of life and murmur of angel-talk; yet, in the midst of all, hinting by wild suggestions of a mystery that cannot be solved and a love that cannot be measured. The whole piece was like life and its end. It started with human yearnings and human failures; the second part brought religion, and the third part spoke of heaven.

And so, the last notes floated out over the rocks, over the river, over the twilight, to the west. The echoes liked the music, and long after it was over, kept humming little snatches of it, calling to each other to admire, and answering with tiny bravos.

A breeze came like a courier and told all the trees and the river that the great Night would shortly pass that way; whereat the leaves did stir a moment, and the waters ruffled, as making ready for the King.

Who came, and sat, and administered his tranquil reign over quiet mountain and quiet valley; and over Thalberg House, not quiet, being full of young and passionate hearts of men and women, some sleeping, some waking, all dreaming.

BOOK II

CHAPTER I *

Thou shalt not kill.
Love your enemies.
Father, forgive them: they know not what they do.

Christ

THE EARLY spring of 1861 brought to bloom, besides innumerable violets and jessamines, a strange, enormous, and terrible flower.

This was the blood-red flower of war, which grows amid thunders; a flower whose freshening dews are blood and hot tears, whose shadow chills a land, whose odors strangle a people, whose giant petals droop downward, and whose roots are in hell.

It is a species of the great genus, sin-flower, which is so conspicuous in the flora of all ages and all countries, and whose multifarious leafage and fruitage so far overgrow a land that the violet, or love-genus, has often small chance to show its quiet blue.

The cultivation of this plant is an expensive business, and it is a wonder, from this fact alone, that there should be so many fanciers of it. A most profuse and perpetual manuring with human bones is absolutely necessary to keep it alive, and it is well to have these powdered, which can be easily done by hoofs of cavalry-horses and artillery-wheels, not to speak of the usual method of mashing with cannon-balls. It will not grow, either, except in some wet place near a stream of human blood; and you must be active in collecting your widows' tears and orphans' tears and mothers' tears to freshen the petals with in the mornings.

It requires assiduous working; and your labor-hire will be a

* [In the MS version of this and the following chapter are several references to contemporary persons and events which Lanier suppressed in the printed novel (see Introduction, pp. xxxv-xxxvi).—ED.]

large item in the expense, not to speak of the amount disbursed in preserving the human bones alive until such time as they may be needed, for, I forgot to mention, they must be fresh, and young, and newly-killed.

It is, however, a hardy plant, and may be grown in any climate, from snowy Moscow to hot India.

It blooms usually in the spring, continuing to flower all summer until the winter rains set in: yet in some instances it has been known to remain in full bloom during a whole inclement winter, as was shown in a fine specimen which I saw the other day, grown in North America by two wealthy landed proprietors, who combined all their resources of money, of blood, of bones, of tears, of sulphur and what not, to make this the grandest specimen of modern horticulture, and whose success was evidenced by the pertinacious blossoms which the plant sent forth even amid the hostile rigors of snow and ice and furious storms. It is supposed by some that seed of this American specimen (now dead) yet remain in the land; but as for this author (who, with many friends, suffered from the unhealthy odors of the plant), he could find it in his heart to wish fervently that these seed, if there be verily any, might perish in the germ, utterly out of sight and life and memory and out of the remote hope of resurrection, forever and ever, no matter in whose granary they are cherished!

But, to return.

It is a spreading plant, like the banyan, and continues to insert new branch-roots into the ground, so as sometimes to overspread a whole continent. Its black-shadowed jungles afford fine cover for such wild beasts as frauds and corruptions and thefts to make their lair in; from which, often, these issue with ravening teeth and prey upon the very folk that have planted and tended and raised their flowery homes!

Now, from time to time, there have appeared certain individuals (wishing, it may be, to disseminate and make profit upon other descriptions of plants) who have protested against the use of this war-flower.

Its users, many of whom are surely excellent men, contend that they grow it to protect themselves from oppressive hailstorms, which destroy their houses and crops.

But some say the plant itself is worse than any hailstorm; that its shades are damp and its odors unhealthy, and that it spreads so rapidly as to kill out and uproot all corn and wheat and cotton crops. Which the plant-users admit; but rejoin that it is cowardly to allow hailstorms to fall with impunity, and that manhood demands a struggle against them of some sort.

But the others reply, fortitude is more manly than bravery, for noble and long endurance wins the shining love of God; whereas brilliant bravery is momentary, is easy to the enthusiastic, and only dazzles the admiration of the weak-eyed since it is as often shown on one side as the other.

But then, lastly, the good war-flower cultivators say, our preachers recommend the use of this plant, and help us mightily to raise it in resistance to the hailstorms.

And reply, lastly, the interested other-flower men, that the preachers should preach Christ; that Christ was worse hailed upon than anybody, before or since; that he always refused to protect himself, though fully able to do it, by any war-banyan; and that he did, upon all occasions, not only discourage the resort to this measure, but did inveigh against it more earnestly than any thing else, as the highest and heaviest crime against Love—the Father of Adam, Christ, and all of us.

Friends and horticulturists, cry these men, stickling for the last word, if war was ever right, then Christ was always wrong; and war-flowers and the vine of Christ grow different ways, insomuch that no man may grow with both!

Chapter II

King Henry.—How now, good Blunt? Thy looks are full of speed.

Blunt.—So hath the business that I come to speak of.
Lord Mortimer of Scotland hath sent word
That Douglas and the English rebels met,
The eleventh of this month, at Shrewsbury:
A mighty and a fearful head they are,
If promises be kept on every hand,
As ever offered foul play in a state.

King Henry IV [, *Part I*]

BUT THESE sentiments, even if anybody could have been found patient enough to listen to them, would have been called sentimentalities, or worse, in the spring of 1861, by the inhabitants of any of those States lying between Maryland and Mexico. An afflatus of war was breathed upon us. Like a great wind, it drew on and blew upon men, women, and children. Its sound mingled with the solemnity of the church-organs and arose with the earnest words of preachers praying for guidance in the matter. It sighed in the half-breathed words of sweethearts conditioning impatient lovers with war-services. It thundered splendidly in the impassioned appeals of orators to the people. It whistled through the streets, it stole in to the firesides, it clinked glasses in bar-rooms, it lifted the gray hairs of our wise men in conventions, it thrilled through the lectures in college halls, it rustled the thumbed book-leaves of the school-rooms.

This wind blew upon all the vanes of all the churches of the country, and turned them one way— toward war. It blew, and shook out, as if by magic, a flag whose device was unknown to soldier or sailor before, but whose every flap and flutter made the blood bound in our veins.

Who could have resisted the fair anticipations which the new war-idea brought? It arrayed the sanctity of a righteous cause in the brilliant trappings of military display; pleasing, so, the devout and the flippant which in various proportions are mixed elements in all men. It challenged the patriotism of the sober citizen, while it inflamed the dream of the statesman, ambitious for his country or for himself. It offered test to all allegiances and loyalties; of church, of state; of private loves, of public devotion; of personal consanguinity; of social ties. To obscurity it held out eminence; to poverty, wealth; to greed, a gorged maw; to speculation, legalized gambling; to patriotism, a country; to statesmanship, a government; to virtue, purity; and to love, what all love most desires—a field wherein to assert itself by action.

The author devoutly wishes that some one else had said what is here to be spoken—and said it better. That is: if there was guilt in any, there was guilt in nigh all of us, between Maryland and Mexico; that Mr. Davis, if he be termed the ringleader of the rebellion, was so not by virtue of any instigating act of his, but purely by the unanimous will and appointment of the Southern people; and that the hearts of the Southern people bleed to see how their own act has resulted in the chaining of Mr. Davis, who was as innocent as they, and in the pardon of those who were as guilty as he!

All of us, if any of us, either for pardon or for punishment: this is fair, and we are willing.

But the author has nought to do with politics; and he turns with a pleasure which he hopes is shared by the Twenty-four-thousand-nine-hundred-and-ninety-nine, to pursue the adventures of Paul Rübetsahl and company in

CHAPTER III

Prince Henry.—I have procured thee, Jack, a charge of foot.

Falstaff.—I would it had been of horse. Well, God be thanked for these rebels. *King Henry IV* [, *Part I*]

ON ONE of the last days of April, '64, six soldiers in gray, upon six horses in all colors, were riding down the road that leads from Surrey * Court House toward the beautiful bay into which the James spreads itself before it is called Hampton Roads.

It was yet early in the morning. The sun was rejoicing with a majestic tenderness over his little firstling—April.

Our six horsemen were in gay conversation; as who would not be, with a light rifle on his shoulder, with a good horse bounding along under him, with a fresh breeze that had in it the vigor of the salt sea and the caressing sweetness of the spring blowing upon him, with five friends tried in the tempest of war as well as by the sterner test of the calm association of inactive camp-life, and with the world's width about him and the enchanting vagueness of life yet to be lived—the delicious change-prospect of futurity—before him?

As they rode on, the beauty of the woods grew, nearing the river. The road wound about deep glens filled with ancient beeches and oaks, and carpeted with early flowers and heart-leaves upon which still dwelt large bulbs of dew; so enchanted with their night's resting-place that they slept late, loth to expand into vapor and go back home in the clouds.

Lieutenant Flemington spurred his horse forward and turned him round full-face to the party.

"Gentlemen, there's some mistake about all this!" said he, as the men stopped, laughing at a puzzled expression which overspread his face: "for whereas, this honorable company of six has been for three years or more toilsomely marching on foot with an infantry regiment—but now rides good horses: and whereas, this honorable company of six has been for three

* [The standard spelling is "Surry."—ED.]

years feeding upon hard-tack and bacon which grew continually harder and also less and wormier—but now devours Virginia biscuit and spring-chickens and ham and eggs and—and all the other things that came on, and went off, the table at mine host's of the Court House this morning: "—

"Not to speak of the mint-juleps that the big man-slave brought in on a waiter before we got out o' bed," interposed Briggs.

"And whereas, we have hitherto had to fight through a press of from two to five hundred men to fill our canteens when we marched by a well—but now do take our several gentlemanly ease and leisure in doing that same, as just now when the pretty girl smiled at us in the big white house yonder, where we

Went to the well to get some water:

and whereas, we have hitherto draggled along in pantaloons that we could put on a dozen ways by as many holes, have worn coats that afforded no protection to anything but the insects congregated in the seams of the same, have had shirts that—shirts that—that—at any rate we *have* had shirts—but now do fare forth prankt in all manner of gorgeous array such as gray jackets with fillimagree on the sleeves of 'em, and hussar-breeches, and cavalry-boots, and O shade of Jones of Georgia! * with spurs to boot and clean white collars to neck: and whereas, we have been accustomed to think a mud-hole a luxury in the way of beds, and have been wont to beg Heaven, as its greatest boon to man, not to let the cavalry ride over us without waking us up to see 'em do it—but now do sleep between white sheets without fear of aught but losing our senses from sleeping so intensely: and whereas, finally, all these things are contrary to the ordinary course of nature and are not known save as dim recollections of a previous state of existence in itself extremely hypothetical, therefore, be it resolved and it is hereby resolved "—

"Unanimously," from the five.

"That this—figure—at present on his horse and clothed with these sumptuous paraphernalia of pompous war, in *not* B. Chauncey Flemington, that is to say (to borrow a term from the

* [Burlesque hero of *Major Jones's Courtship* by William Tappan Thompson. —Ed.]

German metaphysics) is Not-Me, that this horse is not *my* horse, this paraphernalia not *my* paraphernalia, that para-ditto not *your* para-ditto, that this road is *no* road, and the whole affair a dream or phantasmagory sent of the Devil for no purpose but to embitter the waking from it, and

"Resolved, further, that we now proceed to wake up, and exorcise this devil. Cain Smallin, of the bony fingers, will you do me the favor to seize hold of my left ear and twist it? Hard, if you please, Mr. Smallin!"

Cain seized and twisted: whereat went up a villainous screech from the twistee.

"Mark you, men, how hard the Devil clings to him!" quoth Briggs.

"Herr Von Hardenberg says, 'when we dream that we dream, we are near awaking,'" * said Rübetsahl, "but I am not awake and I surely dream that I do dream!"

"I remember," said Aubrey, "that Hans Dietrich did dream, upon a time, that the elf-people showered gold upon him, but woke in the morning and found his breeches-pockets full of yellow leaves. *À fortiori*, this in my canteen, which I dimly dream was poured in there for home-made wine by an old lady who stopped me and blessed me the other side the Court House this morning—this, I say, in my canteen, should now be no wine, or at least, if these present events be a dream, should be sour wine. I will resolve me of this doubt!"

The canteen rose in air, its round mouth met Aubrey's round mouth, and a gurgling noise was heard; what time the five awaited in breathless suspense the result of the experiment. The gurgling continued.

"I think Mister Aubrey must ha' fell into another dream, like," quoth Cain Smallin, "an's done forgot he's drinkin', an' the rest of us is dry!"

"Ah-h-h-h!" observed Aubrey as the canteen at last came down. "Gentlemen, this is as marvellous like to good wine of the blackberry as is one blue-coat to another. Albeit this be but a thin and harmful wine of hallucination, yet—I am a mortal man! at least I dream I am, wherefore I am fain exclaim with the poet

Thus let me dream, forever, on!

* [Quoted in Carlyle, "Novalis."—Ed.]

" I think," modestly interposed Philip Sterling, " that I might perhaps throw a little light on the subject; at any rate, the number of experiments will increase the probability of our conclusions drawn therefrom. Now, as I passed down the road, in this dream, I observed a still where they make apple-brandy; and propounding some questions as to the *modus agendi* to a benevolent-looking lady who stood in the house hard by, she, if I dream not, begged that I would accept this bottle, which I now uncork, I think, and which, if all end well, will enable me to say, in the words of the song,

I see her still * in my dreams.

But if it should be wild-wine of the Devil, or newt's-eye and frog-toe porridge, or other noxious *jigote* of hags and witches—stand around to receive me as I fall. I waive the politeness which requires I should offer this bottle first to my fellow-dreamers here, Mr. Briggs and Mr. Smallin, in consideration that the compound might kill, and I were loth the country should lose two such valuable lives. I request that I be decently buried and news sent home, if it prove fatal, as I fear. I drink! Friends, adieu, adieu! "

" Why, this," quoth Briggs, " is surely much adieu about nothing! "

The bottle went up to the mouth, like its friend the canteen, and stayed, like its friend. While it hung in mid-air—

" Good Heavens! " exclaimed Aubrey, " the poison is taking effect! He has not strength to remove it from his mouth! "

" Gentlemen, all is over! " said Rübetsahl, and groaned, and, seizing Philip, dragged him to the green bank of the road, when the draggee fell back in true stage-fashion, not forgetting to spread his handkerchief upon the hillock where he laid his dying head: " I would not die," muttered he, " with my hair full of cockle-burrs! "

" Danged ef this 'ere ham ain't mighty nigh as good as fresh ven'zun! " quoth sturdy Cain Smallin, who had dismounted and seated himself on a stump, while his lower jaw worked like a trip-hammer reversed, to the great detriment of a huge slice

* [In the MS Lanier labels the pun by inserting after " still " the words, in parentheses, " where they make apple-brandy."—Ed.]

of bread and ham which he had produced from his capacious haversack. " 'Pears like as if I never was so horngry sence I was froze up over on old Smoky Mount'n, one Christmas. I b'leeve I hain't done nuthin' but eat sence we was detailed f'om the rig*iment*, t'other side o' Richmond! You better b'leeve now— Gentle*men!* " he exclaimed suddenly, " look at yan nigger down the road! He travels as peert as ef he was a-carryin' orders to a rig*iment* to come down into the fight double-quick. Hornet must ha' stung his mule; or sumthin'! "

At this moment a negro dashed up on a mule whose pace he was accelerating with lusty encouragement of switch, foot, and voice.

" Halt there, *caballero* hot with haste and coal-black with speed! " cried Flemington. " What's the matter? "

" Good God, Marster, de Yankee niggahs is playin' de devil wid old Mistis down de road yonder! Dey done hung old Marster up to a tree-limb to make him tell whah he put de las' year's brandy an' he nuvver tole 'em; an' I seed 'em a-histe-in him up agin, an' I run roun' to de stable an' tuk out ole Becky here an' cum a-stavin'; an' I 'lowed to myse'f I'd save *one* mule for ole Marster anyhow ef he lives, which I don't b'leeve he's a-gwine to do it nohow; an— "

" Mount, men! " Flemington jumped into the saddle. " How far is it to the house? What's your name? "—to the negro.

" Name Charles, sah: Charles, de ca'ige-driver. Hit's about a half ur three-quarter thar, f'om here."

" Have they got out a picket; did you see any of them riding this way while the others were in the house? "

" Yaas, sah; seed one cumin' dis ways as I cum de back-way, out o' de lot! "

" 'Twon't do to ride any further, then. Get off your mule, Charles. Boys, dismount and tie your horses in the bushes here, off the road. We'll go round this back-way. Lead the way; and keep under cover of the hedge and the fence, yonder, everybody, so they can't see us."

While the words were being spoken the command had been executed, and the party struck into a rapid walk down a path which led off from the road in the direction of the river. Presently they crossed a fence; and stopped to peep through the rails of another, running perpendicularly to the path. A large house, part brick, part wooden, embowered in trees, appeared at a short distance.

" Dat's de place! " whispered Charles, the carriage-driver.

Flemington had already formed his plans.

" Men, they're all inside the house, except the picket out in the road yonder. I'm going to creep up close to the house just behind that brick garden-wall there, and see how things look. The rest of you keep down this side o' the fence, and get just behind the long cattle-stable in rear of the house. Wait there till you hear me shoot; then dash up to the house,—'tisn't twenty yards—and every man for himself! Come with a yell or two. Cain, you come with me. Here goes over the fence: quick! "

The minutes and the men crept on, like silent worms. Flemington and Smallin gained their wall, which ran within a few feet of the house, unperceived.

" I'll stop here, Cain. You creep on, close down, old fellow, until you get to the front fence yonder, and wait there till I shoot. Then come on like a big rock tumbling down Old Smoky! "

Under cover of a thick vine which ran along the top of the wall, Flemington cautiously raised his head and peeped over.

An old man was lying on the grass-plat, with a rope-noose still hanging round his neck. Over him bent a young girl. She was dashing water in his face and chafing his hands in the endeavor to restore the life which, by his bloodless face and the blue streak under his eyes, seemed to have taken its departure forever. Near them sat a corpulent old lady, on the ground, passive with grief, rocking herself to and fro, in that most pathetic gesture of sorrowing age.

Inside the house was Bedlam. Oaths, yells of triumph, taunts, and menaces mingled with the crash of breaking crockery and the shuffling of heavy feet.

Just as Flemington raised his head above the wall, four stout negroes staggered through a wide door which gave upon a balcony of the second story, bearing a huge old-fashioned wardrobe which they lifted over the railing and let drop. A wild shout went up as the wardrobe crashed to the ground and burst open, revealing a miscellaneous mass of the garments that are known to the other sex.

"Mo' good clo'es!" cried the four, and dived back into the door for new plunder.

Through the parlor-window, just opposite Flemington, appeared a burly black, with rolling eyes and grinning mouth, seated at the piano. With both fists he banged the keys, while he sang a ribald song at the top of a voice rendered hideously husky by frequent potations from a demijohn that stood on the centre-table. Suddenly the performer jumped from his seat.

"Damn ef you'll ever play on dat pianner agin, you Becky Parven!" said he, and seized an axe and chopped the instrument in pieces.

The raiders—unauthorized ones, as Flemington knew—had evidently found the brandy. They were already infuriated by it. It was with difficulty that Flemington could refrain from firing long enough to allow the rest of the party to gain their position.

Suddenly a huge negro, dressed in the tawdriest of uniforms, which he had just been decorating with all conceivable ornaments tied to whatever button offered a support to dangle from, rushed out of the house towards the group in front, exclaiming,—

"By de livin' God, I'm de Cap'n and I'm gwine to do de kissin' fur de comp'ny! *You* needn't to shake, old lady Parven, I'm a'ter dem red lips over yonder!"—pointing to Rebecca Parven.

Flemington could withhold no longer. He fired; the black captain fell, an answering yell came from the stable-yard, he leaped the wall and rushed towards the house, meeting Aubrey, who exclaimed hurriedly,—"The rest ran into the back-door, Flem; I ran round for fear they might be too many for you in front, as they came out."

Almost simultaneously three shots were fired inside the house, and eight or ten negroes in blue uniform rushed through the front door and down the steps. In their ardor Flemington and Aubrey gave no ground. The foremost negro on the steps fell, his companions tumbled over him, the whole mass precipitated itself upon Flemington and Aubrey, and bore them to the earth.

At this moment the black commander, whom Flemington's bullet had merely stunned for a moment, scrambled to his feet, and seeing the other three of Flemington's party running down the steps, called out, "Jump up, boys; de ain't but five of 'em, we can whip de lights out'n 'em, yit!" Brandishing his sabre, he ran towards Flemington, who was just rising from the ground.

The surprised negroes took heart from the bold tone and action of their commander, and commenced an active scramble for whatever offensive weapons lay about. In the undisciplined haste of plunderers they had thrown down their arms in various places inside the house, the necessity of caution being entirely overwhelmed by the more pressing one of arm-room for the bulky articles which each was piling up for himself. To prevent them from grasping the axes and farming implements about the yard, besides two or three guns and sabres that had been abandoned by the most eager of the plunderers before entering the house, now required the most active exertions on the part of the Confederates whose number was actually reduced to four, since Flemington was entirely occupied in repelling the savage onslaught of the colored leader.

To increase their critical situation, nothing was heard of Cain Smallin; and they could ill afford to lose the great personal strength, not to speak of the yet unfired rifle, of the mountaineer, in a contest where the odds both in numbers and individual power were so much against them.

Affairs grew serious. Flemington, for ten mintues, had had arms, legs, and body in unceasing play, to parry with his short unbayoneted carbine the furious cuts of his antagonist. He was growing tired; while his foe, infuriated by brandy and burning for revenge, seemed to gather strength each moment and to redouble his blows. The others were too busy to render any assistance to their lieutenant. John Briggs had just made a close race with three negroes for an axe that lay down the avenue, and was now standing over it endeavoring with desperate whirls of his carbine to defend at once the front, flank, and rear of his position.

Flemington felt his knees giving way, a faint dizziness came over him, and in another moment he would have been cloven from skull to breast-bone, when suddenly John Briggs called out cheerily,—

"Hurrah, boys! Here's help!"

All the combatants stopped to glance towards the gate that opened from the main road into the short avenue leading to the house. True! On the other side the hedge appeared a cloud of dust, from which sounded the voices of a dozen men,—

"Give the nigs hell, thar, boys!" shouted a bass-voice. "Here we come; hold 'em thar, Flem!" came in treble, as if from a boy-soldier. "You four men on the right, thar, ride round 'em, cut 'em off from the back-yard!" commanded the stentorian voice of Cain Smallin.

The tide of victory turned in an instant, and bore off, on its ebb, the colored raiders. Their commander hastily jumped over the garden-wall and made huge strides towards the woods, his followers scattering in flight towards the nearest cover.

Too weak to pursue his frightened opponent, Flemington sat down to rest, gazing curiously towards the reinforcing voices.

"Open the gate thar, you men in front!" came from the advancing dust-cloud. The gate flew open; in rushed a frightened herd of cows, sheep, horses, mules, hogs, and oxen, in whose midst appeared the tall form of Cain Smallin. Armed with a huge branch of a thorn-tree in each hand, he was darting about amongst the half-wild cattle, belaboring them on all sides, crowding them together and then scattering the mass, what time he poured forth a torrent of inspiriting war-cries in all tones of voice, from basso-profundo to boy-soprano. On comes he, like an avalanche with a whirlwind in it, down the avenue, all unconscious of the success of his stratagem, stretching out his long neck over the cows' backs to observe the situation in his front, and not ceasing to dart to and fro, to belabor, and to utter his many-voiced battle-cries.

"'Gad, he don't see a thing!" exclaimed Briggs; "his eyes are mud-holes of dust and perspiration! He'll run over the old gentleman there, boys: let's get him into the porch;" and the four had barely lifted the still unconscious man up the steps when the cattle-cavalry thundered by, splitting at the house like a stream on a rock, and flowing tumultuously each side of it towards the back-yard.

"Hold up, Cain! Hold up, man!" shouted Flemington; "the enemy's whipped and gone!"

Mr. Smallin came to a stop in his furious career, and, covered with the dust and sweat of grimy war, advanced at a more dignified pace to the steps where his party was resting.

"You see, boys," said he, wiping his face with his coat-sleeve, "I was a right smart time a-comin', but when I did come, I *cum*, by the Livin'! Phe-e-e-w!" continued he, blowing off his excitement. "Reckin you thought I was a whole brigade, didn't ye? An' I'm blasted ef I didn't make mighty nigh as much rumpus as any common brigade, sure's you're born to die! Ye see, I was creepin' along to'rds the road out yan, an' I seed all them critters penned up in a little pen just 'cross the road over aginst yan gate, an' I 'lowed to myself 'at the niggers had jest marched along the road an' druv along all the cattle in the country for to carry 'em back across the river. An' so I thought if I could git them bulls thar—mighty fine bulls they is, too!—git 'em right mad, an' let the whole kit an' bilin' of 'em in through yan gate down to'rds the house, I mought skeer somebody mighty bad ef I didn't do nothin' else; an' so I jest lit in amongst 'em thar, an' tickled 'em all right smart with yan thorn bushes till they was tolubble mad, an' then fotch 'em through the gate a-bilin'! I've druv cattle afore, gentlemen!" concluded Mr. Smallin, with a dignity which was also a generosity, since, while it asserted his own skill, it at the same time apologized for those who might have attempted such a feat and failed from want of practice in driving cattle.

CHAPTER IV

> And if a sigh that speaks regret of happier times appear,
> A glimpse of joy that we have met shall shine and dry the tear.
>
> Quoted by Charles Lamb *

IN A BATTLE, as far as concerns the individual combatants, the laws and observances of civilization are abandoned, and primitive barbarism is king *pro tem.* To kill as many as possible;—this, at the actual shock of arms, is the whole duty of man. If indeed there be generals of genius managing the thing behind the lines, it is not less barbarism, but only more powerful barbarism; it is genius manœuvring the interests of brute strength; it is Apollo tending swine.

When the battle is over, to emerge from this temporary barbarism is difficult and requires a little time. Kind Heaven! To see a beautiful woman, to hear her soft tones of voice, to say pleasant things to her, seems *so* strange, just after you have uttered those strange, hoarse cries that men *do* utter, not knowing why, in battle;—just after you have killed a man, and perhaps felt the sickening warmth of his blood, and turned away from the terrible odor that rises like a curse from the wound. The young men were all moody, and, in spite of their exertions to appear unconstrained, continually relapsed into a half-sullen silence, as they sat at Mrs. Parven's elaborate dinner.

Dinner? So. They had poured some brandy into the mouth of old Mr. Parven, he had recovered, and, though he could not speak, had smiled to the good wife at his bedside to reassure her. Lighter of heart, Mrs. Parven had instinctively bent herself to hospitable deeds, had assembled her dusky handmaidens, had bustled up-stairs and down-stairs and in the kitchen, had removed the wreck of furniture, had restored order out of chaos, had, in short, issued commands whose multitude made Napoleon's feat of three thousand despatches in an hour sink into pale insignificance.

While they were shaking hands, before mounting to pursue their journey, a mournful tone pervaded the forced liveliness

* [The lines are quoted in Lamb's letter of June 13, 1796, to Coleridge.—ED.]

of the young men's congratulations to Mrs. Parven upon the good fate which had brought them up in time to save the house. And even while good Mrs. P. was calling out, in her loud, hearty voice, to the scouts, inviting them to ride up frequently and dine with her, she was saying to herself, " God help us! It is but the beginning of the raids; * next time, the raiders will be more infuriated, and we may have no friends at hand. God help us! "

And Rebecca, smiling upon Aubrey as he rode away, was moved by those timid apprehensions which love creates in tender hearts, and said to herself, over and over again, " When will I ever see him again? "

* [In the MS the marauding negroes are not soldiers, but runaways under the protection of Federal forces across the James. Further raids are expected from these runaways and from the crews of Federal gunboats in the river.—Ed.]

CHAPTER V

> *Edgar.*—Let's see his pockets. These letters—
> May be my friends. He's dead: I am only sorry
> He had no other deaths-man.—Let us see:—
> Leave, gentle wax: and, manners, blame us not;
> To know our enemies' minds we rip their hearts—
> Their papers is more lawful. *King Lear*

A TRAVELLER UPON the river-road from Surrey Court-House to Smithfield, towards the last five or six miles of his journey, will skirt the beautiful expanse of Burwell's Bay at two or three hundred yards from the water's edge. From all points of this stretch the water is visible, but the view changes frequently, according to the width and direction of the vistas through the trees fringing the bold bluff that overhangs the beach. About midway of this part of his journey he will meet a road crossing his own at right angles, running directly to the edge of the bluff. If he canters along it a few hundred yards he finds it descending the steep bank, quartering, so as to make the slope gentler. It is nevertheless steep, and the horse will instinctively turn back, not believing that his rider is going that way. Tempted however by the smooth, white shell-beach, which his eye follows for mile after mile, curving in and out the green bluff, and whose hard surface is a delightful contrast to the deep sand through which he has been plodding; tempted by the cool breeze that blows in his face (for this is a May-day), of which the trees on the main road deprive him; invited down there by the freshness of the white foam from a tiny surf that escalops the beach like a lace edging, changing every moment its dainty pattern;—he urges his horse to the descent. With much dubious shaking of his long head, with a dogged I-told-you-so-if-you-get-your-neck-broken expression, with much careful and deliberate reaching out and planting down of the forefoot, the horse will start, and will arrive upon the beach at the bottom, with a deprecatory motion of his under lip which says plainly enough, You needn't say a word about it, sir, it was my prudence in the forefoot business that got you down safe; mingled with which comes a side-long turn of the large eyes in sheepish acknowledgment that the thing wasn't so very steep after all!

The breeze invigorates horse and rider, the green waves break and glossy curves glide smoothly up as if on glass, the traveller bursts into a song and straightens up in his saddle, the horse feels the reins tighten and canters off with a swing and a bound, the bluff face shows a million green mosses and trickling springs, great oaks hold out their arms from the top in a perpetual attitude of blessing, the eye ranges freely down Burwell's Bay, across Hampton Roads, to the Chesapeake, out between the capes, on, to the broad waters,—it is charming for a mile or two.

It is the first day of May, 1864, and this hypothetical course which has just been marked out is being actually pursued by an ordinary looking traveller upon an ordinary looking horse. Suddenly he becomes aware that his horse is sinking over fetlocks in soft sand. He looks around; the bluff has receded inland, a long marsh is between him and it, full of marsh grass, of mourning cypresses, of black water and black mud, and, at the further end of it, the bluff is crowned with scraggy and desolate pines. The beach is now, for a few yards, only a narrow strip of sand between the near end of the marsh and the bay. The horse snorts, his feet sink deeper; as he draws them up the holes fill with water and crumble in. But it is no use to turn; fortunately the tide is out, the quicksand is somewhat dry; the horse plunges forward, and arrives, covered with perspiration, and trembling in every nerve, on hard beach again. The broken line of the bluff now recommences, with its fringe of oaks. In the face of the cliff appears an opening filled with undergrowth. A blind road turns off from the beach into it. The traveller wishes now to leave the treacherous beach and regain his main road. He turns into the grassy path, round an angle of the bluff, and instantly is in a Garden of Eden.

He finds himself in a small dell which is round as a basin, two hundred yards in diameter, shut in on all sides. Beeches, oaks, lithe hickories, straight pines, roof over this dell with a magnificent boscage. In the centre of it bubbles a limpid spring. Shy companies of flowers stand between the long grasses; some of them show wide startled eyes, many of them have hidden away in cunning nooks. Over them, regarding them in silent and passionate tenderness, lean the ebony-fibred ferns; and the busy mosses do their very best to hide all rudeness and all decay behind a green velvet arras. The light does not dare shine very brightly here; it is soft and sacred, tempered with green leaves, with silence, with odors, with beauties. Wandering perfumes, restless with happiness, float about aimlessly; they are the only inhabitants here.

Our traveller has not seen a sign of human life.

Suddenly he stops, recoils, and turns pale with the surprise of it.

He has seen a sign of human death. A corpse, in blue uniform, saturated with water, lies before him in the path. It has evidently been just dragged from the waves. A line of moisture extends to the water's edge through the opening in the bluff; it is where the stream dripped through the wet clothes.

Our traveller gazed around him, he could not see a man or a trace of one. Good God! Can the spirit of death inhabit the balm of this May-air in this little Heaven? Does the Devil dwell also in this rosebud of little glens? Grave-openers get sometimes, one may imagine, a mixed odor composed of the death-smell from inside the grave, mixed with the perfumes of roses growing on it. Our traveller seemed to inhale this odor. The air grew thicker, the silence seemed full of noises as of ghosts flitting about, the horse started at a falling leaf, our traveller spurred him and cantered off. He emerged from the dell, followed a path through an old field, opened a gate, and found himself once more in the road which he had quitted to ride on the beach.

From the time that this traveller descended to the beach, until he entered the dell, that is, for a distance of two miles, an eye was watching him closely and noting every movement.

Upon the edge of the bluff, a few feet above and beyond the point where the blind road enters the dell, is a sort of niche or shelf made by the uprooting of a tree from the face of the cliff. It is thickly covered with bushes and grasses and trailing vines. In this niche lies a statue, which has seemingly fallen upon its face. In front of its eye is a long field telescope, resting upon two forked twigs driven in the ground. If we watch this statue, it comes to life. Two hands appear from beneath it: they lift the glass from its rests, and place it upon two others, driven so as to point it in a different direction.

This far-reaching eye was not the only one which had been watching our traveller. He had only passed the corpse a few minutes, when a tall form rose from behind a thick vine near the path. Another clump yielded another form, and so on until four men had emerged. They assembled around the corpse.

"Poor Fed," said Philip Sterling, who, nothwithstanding three years full of battles, could never keep from being solemn over dead men. "The old remorseless waves must have been taken with a spasmodic fit of repentance. It is not usual that the sea is so just. She renders this time to Cæsar the things that are Cæsar's. She floats to the shore its own dust. Let's bury him, boys."

"Wait a while, Phil," said Rübetsahl, in a sterner tone. "Let's see if there are any letters or papers in the pockets. This is the very officer who commanded the party that attacked us last night, on the other side. Do you see that long nail on the little finger of his right hand? Here's a sign-manual he made with it on my neck. I knocked his pistol out of his hand while we were fighting there in the water; he then gripped my throat, and that nail there kept digging in till I thought it would cut the artery."

While he was speaking, Rübetsahl had turned the pockets inside out. A leathern pocket-book, the inevitable photograph of wife or sweetheart, and a penknife, were brought to light.

Rübetsahl opened the pocket-book. It contained a few dollars in greenbacks, an official order from "H'd Q'rs., Newport News," and a letter, apparently crumpled and thrust in hastily.

"I'm wondering," said Rübetsahl, "how those fellows got wind of our expedition last night. I'm going to read this man's letter, to find out, maybe. I beg his pardon, and if I don't see any thing to the point in the first two lines I won't go further."

Rübetsahl carefully spread out the damp folds. The letter inclosed a note which ran thus:—

"Lieut. Zimmerman, Com'dg, &c.

"Inclosed is a letter handed me to-day by a neighbor. He does not wish to be mixed up in the business and asks my advice. The writer of the letter is a connection of his. Of course, as a loyal citizen, I cannot leave this letter and its information to pass unnoticed, and therefore send it to you immediately.

" Hoping you may capture the troublesome party mentioned,

" I am," &c.

Rübetsahl raised his brows, and proceeded to read the letter. It had evidently cost the writer some pains.

" To Mister Jeems Horniddy, My deer Cuzzin Jeems: hope you air well and these few lines will find you enjoinin the saim. I lef ole Tennessy some munths ago, I was brought from thar with mi hands tied as you mought say. The Cornscrip brought me. I was hid whare I thot the Devil hisself couldn find me, but ole man Sterlin he cum and showed whar I was and they took me and sent me to the rigiment. He foun out whare I was hid by a darn ongentlemunly trick, a-peirootin thu the bushes as he is always a-Dooin. An if I dont root him out for it I hoap I may go too hell damn him and I have deserted from the rigiment and cum down hear to smithfield whare than aint no cornscrip. Thar is sum scouts down hear and ole Sterlins son is wun of thum, and so is brother Cain I thot he had moar sense and I am agwine to fule em to death i am agwine to make em put me across the river and then see em captivated every wun of thum brother Cain and all and what did they drag me from hoam and fambly for? which I havent been married to her moar than a year and a rite young babi and they a starvin and me not thar.

" An so git some yanky soldiers and be reddy at Bullitt Pint a tooseday nite nex week and that night I'll git the scouts to set me over in thar boat an as sune as I jump out on the beech you can fire into em or what you pleeze.

" And as for ole man Sterlin I am gwine to root him out I am not gwine to leeve enuff of him to sware bi. This confedracy is gone up and ole Bob Lee he is the King of it and I am tole many respectubble and wulthy fambilies in Richmound gits the only meat they do git bi bool-frawgs which they fish for thum in pawns and they aint no mo Salt Peter and so be reddy a tooseday night and my love to all which i hoap to see you all in a short time from

" Your aff. cuzzin

" GORM SMALLIN "

" n. b. bee reddy."

"Where's Cain, this morning?" asked Rübetsahl when he had finished the letter.

"Gone to the Point, to look after the horses," replied Philip.

"Glad he wasn't here to hear that letter."

"He's got a big heart, and this exposure of his brother's treachery would break it," said Aubrey. "But you boys haven't told me a word about the fight you had on the other side last night. You all slept so hard this morning when I came in from picket that I wouldn't wake you, until Flem saw this dead man floating out there in the water and called to me to get you up and bury it."

At this moment Flemington came down from his niche in the bluff, to inspect the dead body.

"Flem, the boys had a little brush last night. Sit down and let's hear about it. Phil, you go watch the glass, as you were there and don't want to hear it told," continued Aubrey. "Go on, Briggs."

"Oh, there isn't much to tell. You know we left you and Flem on guard about ten o'clock. We had a fine run across, but just as we got to the other shore, the wind hauled clear round and blew right out of the mouth of the creek. We lowered the sail and had just got out the oars, when a large skiff came dashing out of the shadow of the trees and bore down on us, aiming to run us right under. I sounded with my oar, found the water wasn't more than knee-deep, and jumped out of the boat. The rest followed, and as the skiff came by somebody knocked over her helmsman with his gun."

"Modest John!" interposed Rübetsahl. "He did it, himself, boys, and it was a neat trick too!"

—"Knocked over the helmsman of the skiff. Of course she came to instantly. Her crew jumped out and fired a volley at us. We had held our fire, till then, for fear of alarming the pickets on the shore; but it wasn't any use now, so we blazed away and closed with 'em. Well, we made a very lively little splash in the water. After a while I looked around and didn't see anybody but Rübetsahl, Cain, and Phil. I heard two or three of the enemy, though, come out of the water and run along the shore. We didn't lose much time in getting in the boat, I assure you. Wind was fair for this shore, we put up the sail and came home in a hurry. Dead and wounded none; missing none; total none. Enemy routed. Flem, read this document," Briggs concluded, all in a blush at talking so long.

"Boys, Cain mustn't know this," said Flemington when he had hastily glanced over the letter. "It'll break his heart!"

"Exactly what I said," exclaimed Aubrey. "But how can we manage it? We must certainly capture this fellow Gorm. It won't do to let him get off, now; and he can find plenty of boats that he can steal and go across in, any time."

"What harm can he do, if he does get across?" said Briggs. "The enemy already knows that we visit the shore there, at night. Gorm Smallin can't tell them any more. He don't know our camp."

"He suspects it, tho'," said Phil Sterling from the niche. "You saw the horseman who came by just now, when we all dodged? That was Gorm Smallin, and he was taking that ride for no other purpose than to discover our camp. If I had known as much as I do now, I would have arrested him: but perhaps it is well enough we didn't betray our hiding-place."

At this moment a man who had been crouching beneath a clump of vines a few yards from the group around the body, stealthily crept to the top of the hill and walked rapidly away.

"Ye have betrayed yer hidin'-place tho', and Gorm Smallin's too smart for any of ye, any day!" said he, as he moved off.

Gorm Smallin had executed a flank movement upon the scouts of the Lower James.

CHAPTER VI

Russet yeas and honest kersey noes.

Love's Labor's Lost

CAIN SMALLIN was the most indefatigable of scouts. He was always moving; the whole country side knew him. His good-natured face and communicative habits procured for him a cordial welcome at every house in that quiet country, where as yet only the distant roar of the war had been heard, where all was still and sunny and lonesome, where the household-talk was that of old men and women, of girls and children, whose sons and brothers were all away in the midst of that dimly-heard roaring. In this serene land a soldier's face that had been in front of cannon and bullets was a thing to be looked at twice, and a soldier's talk was the rare treasure of a fireside. The gunboats in the river, upon which these neighbors looked whenever they walked the river bank, had ceased to be objects of alarm, or even of curiosity. They lay there quietly and lazily, day after day, making no hostile sign; and had lain so since Norfolk fell. And as for the evening-gun at Fortress Monroe—that had boomed every sunset for many a year before the war.

On his way to the Point which terminates between Burwell's Bay and Smithfield Creek, and which afforded store of succulent grass and clover for the horses, Cain Smallin passed the house of a neighbor who had particularly distinguished himself in kindness to our little party of scouts. The old gentleman was seated in the open doorway, in midst of a pile of newspapers.

"Good mornin'! Mr. Smallin. Couldn't stand it any longer, you see, so I sent Dick away up to Ivor yesterday to try and get some papers. Here's another stinger in the *Examiner*.* Sit down here; I want you to read it."

"Thank'ee, sir, don't care if I do rest a leetle; tollubble warm walkin' this mornin'," replied the mountaineer, and fell to reading—a slow operation for him whose eye was far more accustomed to sighting a rifle than deciphering letters.

* [A Richmond newspaper severely critical of the Confederate government. —ED.]

"Massy me!" said he, after some silence, "our men's desertin' mighty fast, up yan, f'om the army. Here's nigh to a whole column full of 'Thirty Dollars Rewards' for each deserter. Let's see if I know any of 'em."

Cain's lip moved busily, in what might well have been called a spell of silence. Suddenly he dropped the paper and looked piteously upward.

"May be I spelt it wrong, le'm me look again," muttered he, and snatched the paper up to gaze again upon that dreadful Thirty Dollar column.

It was there.

"THIRTY-DOLLARS REWARD

"Deserted from the — Regiment, —— Volunteers, GORM SMALLIN, who enlisted," &c., &c.

Cain Smallin dropped his newspaper and strode hastily out of the door, unheeding the surprise of his host.

He walked rapidly, and aimlessly. The cruel torture would not permit him to rest; his grief drove him about; it lashed him with sharp thongs. Across fields and marshes, through creeks and woods, with bent head, with hands idly hanging, with unsteady step, he circled. A tear emerged from his eye. It stopped in a furrow, and glistened. Occasionally he muttered to himself,—

"We was poor. We ain't never had much to live on but our name, which it was good as gold. An' now it ain't no better'n rusty copper; hit'll be green an' pisenous. An' who's done it? Gorm Smallin! Nobody but Gorm Smallin! My own brother, Gorm Smallin! Gorm,—Gorm." He repeated this name a hundred times, as if his mind wandered and he wished to fix it.

The hours passed on and still the mountaineer walked. His simple mountain-life had known few griefs. This was worse than any sorrow. It was disgrace. He knew no sophistries to retire into, in the ostrich-fashion wherewith men avoid dishonor. He had lost all. Not only he, but all whom he loved, would suffer.

"What will the Sterlin's say? Old John Sterlin'; him that stuck by us when corn was so scurce in the Cove? an' Philip!

him that I've hunted with an' fished with an' camped with, by ourselves, in yan mountains? And Miss Felix! Miss Felix!"

The man dwelt on this name. His mind became a blank, except two luminous spots which were rather feelings than thoughts. These were, a sensation of disgrace and a sensation of loveliness: the one embodied in the name Gorm, the other in the name Felix. He recoiled from one; he felt as if religion demanded that he should also recoil from the other. He suffered more than if he had committed the crime himself. For he was innocence, and that is highly tender and sensitive, being unseared.

At length the gathering twilight attracted his attention. He looked around, to discover his locality. Leaping a fence he found himself in the main road, and a short walk brought him to a low house that stood in a field on the right. He opened the gate, and knocked at the door. "Here's whar he said he'd stay," he muttered. Gorm himself came to the door.

"Put on your hat, Gorm!"

The stern tone of his voice excited his brother's surprise.

"What fur, Cain?"

"I want you to walk with me, a little piece. Hurry!"

Gorm took down his hat and came out.

"Whar to, brother Cain?"

"Follow me," replied Cain, with a motion of displeasure at the wheedling tone of his brother.

Leaving the road, he struck into a path leading to the Point from which he had wandered. As he walked his pace increased, until it required the most strenuous exertions on the part of his companion to keep up with his long and rapid strides.

"Whar the devil air you gwine to, Cain? Don't walk so fast, anyhow; I'm a'most out o' breath a'ready!"

The mountaineer made no reply, but slackened his pace. He only muttered to himself: "Hit's eight mile across; ye'll need your strength to git thar, may be."

The path wound now amongst gloomy pines, for some distance, until suddenly they emerged upon the open beach. They were upon the extreme end of the lonely Point. The night was dark; but the sand-beach glimmered ghastly white through the darkness. Save the mournful hooting of an owl from his obscure cell in the woods, the place was silent. Hundreds of huge tree-stumps, with their roots upturned in the air, lay in all fantastic positions upon the white sand, as the tide had deposited them. These straggling clumps had been polished white by salt air and waves. They seemed like an agitated convention of skeletons, discussing the propriety of flesh. A small boat rested on the beach, with one end secured by a " painter " to a stake driven in the sand.

" Little did I think, when I found it in the marsh this mornin' an' brought it thar, thinkin' to git it round to camp to-night, what use I was gwine to put it to," said Cain Smallin to himself.

As he led the way to the boat, suddenly he stopped and turned face to face with his recreant brother. His eyes glared into Gorm's. His right hand was raised, and a pistol-barrel protruded from the long fingers.

" Gorm Smallin," he said, with grating voice, " have ye ever know'd me to say I'd do anything an' then not to do it? "

' I—I—no, I haven't, Cain," stuttered the deserter, cowering with terror and surprise.

" Remember them words. Now answer my questions, and don't say nothin' outside o' them. Gorm Smallin, whar was you born? "

" What makes you ax me sich foolish questions, Cain? I was born in Tennessy, an' you know it! "

" Answer my questions, Gorm Smallin! Who raised you, f'om a little un? "

" Mother an' father, o' course."

" Who's your mother and father? what's ther name? "

" Cain, air you crazy? ther name's Smallin."

" Gorm Smallin, did you ever know any o' the Smallins to cheat a man in a trade? "

" No, Cain; we've always been honest."

" Did ye ever know a Smallin to swar to a lie afore the Jestis? "

" No."

" Did ye ever know one to steal another man's horse, or his rifle, or anything? "

" No."

" Did ye ever know one to sneak out f'om a rightful fight? "

" No."

"Did ye ever know one to"—the words came like lightning with a zigzag jerk—"to desert f'om his rigiment?"

The flash struck Gorm Smallin. He visibly sank into himself like a jointed cane. He trembled, and gazed apprehensively at the pistol in his brother's right hand which still towered threateningly aloft. He made no reply.

"Ye don't like to say yes this time!" continued Cain. "Gorm Smallin, altho' I say it which I'm your brother,—ye lied every time ye said no, afore. *You* has cheated in a dirty trade; *you* has swore to a lie afore God that's better than the Jestis; *you* has stole what's better'n any rifle or horse; *you* has sneaked out f'om the rightfullest fight ye ever was in; *you* has deserted f'om your rigiment, an' that when yer own brother an' every friend ye had in the world was fightin' along with ye.

"Gorm Smallin, you has cheated me, an' ole father an' mother an' all, out of our name which it was all we had; you has swore to a lie, for you swore to me 'at the colonel sent you down here to go a-scoutin' amongst the Yankees; you has stole our honest name, which it is more than ye can ever make to give to your wife's baby; you has sneaked out f'om a fight that we was fightin' to keep what was our'n an' to pertect them that has been kind to us an' them that raised us; you has deserted f'om your rigiment which it has fought now gwine on four year an' fought manful, too, an' never run a inch.

"Gorm Smallin, you has got your name in the paper 'ith thirty dollars reward over it, in big letters; big letters, so 'at father's ole eyes can read it 'ithout callin' sister Ginny to make it out for him. Thar it is, for every man, woman, *and* child in the whole Confederacy to read it, an' by this time they *has* read it, may be, an' every man in the rigiment has cussed you for a sneak an' a scoundrel, an' wonderin' whether Cain Smallin will do like his brother!

"Gorm Smallin, you has brung me to that, that I hain't no sperrit to fight hearty an' cheerful. Ef ye had been killed in a fa'r battle, I mought ha' been able to fight hard enough for both of us, for every time I cried a-thinkin' of you, I'd ha' been twice as strong an' twice as clear-sighted as I was buffore. But —sich things as these"—the mountaineer wiped off a tear with his coat-sleeve—"burns me an' weakens me an' hurts my eyes that bad that I kin scarcely look a man straight forrard in the face. Hit don't make much diff'ence to me now, whether we whips the Yanks or they whips us. What good'll it do ef we conquer 'em? Everybody'll be a-shoutin' an' a-hurrahin' an' they'll leave *us* out o' the frolic, for we is kin to a deserter! An' the women'll be a-smilin on them that has lived to git home, one minute, an' the next they'll be a-weepin' for them that's left dead in Virginy an' Pennsylvany an' Tennessy,—but *you* won't git home, an' *you* won't be left dead nowher; they cain't neither smile at you nor cry for you; what'll they do ef anybody speaks yer name? Gorm Smallin, they'll lift their heads high an' we'll hang our'n low. They'll scorn ye an' we'll blush for ye.

"Hadn't ye better be dead? Hadn't I better kill ye right here an' bury ye whar ye cain't do no more harm to the fambly name?

"But I cain't shoot ye, hardly. The same uns raised us an' fed us. I cain't do it; an' I'm sorry I cain't!

"You air 'most on yer knees, anyhow; git down on 'em all the way. Listen to me. God A'mighty's a-lookin' at you out o' the stars yan, an' he's a-listenin' at you out o' the sand here, an' he won't git tired by mornin' but he'll keep a-listenin' an' a-lookin' at ye to-morrow all day. Now mind ye. I'm gwine to put ye in this boat here, an' you can paddle across to yan side the river, easy. Ef ye'll keep yer eye on yan bright star that's jest a-risin' over Bullitt Pint, ye'll strike t'other shore about the right place. Ef ye paddle out o' the way, the guard on yan gunboat'll be apt to fire into ye; keep yer eye on the star. Ye'll git to the beach on t'other side, an' lay down under a tree an' sleep till mornin'—ef ye *can* sleep. In the mornin' ye'll walk down the road, an' the Yankee pickets'll see yer gray coat an' take ye to Head-quarters. The officer at Head-quarters'll examine ye, an' when you tell him you air a deserter he'll make ye take the oath, an' ef he know'd how many oaths ye've already broke I think he would'n' take the trouble! Howsumdever, I'm gwine to do the same foolishness, for it's all I kin do. Now when ye take the oath the officer'll likely make ye sign yer name to it, or write yer name somewhar. Gorm Smallin, when ye write that name ye *shall* not write your own name; ye must write some other name. Swar to it, now, while ye air kneelin' buffore God A'mighty! Raise up yer hands, both of 'em; swar to it, that ye'll write some other name in the Yankee deserter-book, or I'll shoot ye, thar, right down!"

Cain had placed the muzzle of his pistol against his brother's forehead.

The oath was taken.

"Don't git up yet; kneel thar. Hit would'n' be right to put any other man's name in the deserter-book in place o' yourn, for ye mought be robbin' some other decent fambly of ther good name. Le'ss see. We must git some name that nobody ever was named afore. Take a stick thar an' write in the sand, so you won't forgit it. The fust name don't make no diff'ence. Write Sam'l."

It was written in great scrawling letters.

"Now write J, an' call out as you write, so you won't forgit it. For I'm gwine to captur' that deserter-book an' see ef your name's in it. Write J, an' call out."

"J."

"O."

"O."

"X."

"X."

"O."

"O."

"B."

"B."

"B, agin."

"B, agin."

"le, -bul!"

"le, -bul!"

"Sam'l Joxo—Joxy—I cain't call it, but you can write it—hit'll do. Git it by heart."

Cain paused a moment.

"Now git up. Git in the boat. Gorm Smallin, don't never come back home, don't never come whar I may be! I cain't shake hands with ye; but I'll shove ye off."

Cain loosened the head of the boat from the sand, turned her round, and gave a mighty push, running with her till he was waist deep in the water. He came out dripping, folded his arms, and stood still, watching the dusky form in the receding boat.

Gorm Smallin was a half-mile from shore. Suddenly he heard his brother's voice, across the water.

" Gorm! "

" Hello! "

" Joxo—Joxobabbul! " cried Cain Smallin at the top of his voice, bending down to read the inscription on the sand.

CHAPTER VII

Edward.—Dazzle mine eyes, or do I see three suns?
Richard.—See! see! They join, embrace, and seem to kiss,
As if they vowed some league inviolable;
Now are they but one lamp, one light, one sun?
In this the heaven figures some event.

King Henry VI [, *Part III*]

Prince Henry.—Go, Peto; to horse, to horse! for thou and I have thirty miles to ride ere dinner-time.

King Henry IV [, *Part I*]

AT TWO o'clock on the morning of May 5th, 1864, Philip Sterling relieved John Briggs on guard. The morning was clear and still, the Bay was fast asleep, the stars were in an ecstasy, the enchanted trees seemed to fear that a stir would insult the night and prevent the day from coming.

"It's beautiful, Phil, beautiful, beautif—beaut"— and John Briggs was asleep. He had accomplished it in one time and three motions, as the tactics say. He had spread out a blanket, fallen down on it, and slept. His comrades were sleeping soundly in all wonderful attitudes, as they lay under a magnificent oak close to the edge of the bluff.

The spot was a few yards from the niche which has been described. The scouts had chosen it as a night-post, since it offered a fair view of the Bay, and presented a sward clear of undergrowth, along which the sentinel could pace and relieve the tedious vigil of the night. As Philip Sterling walked back and forth, a large and luminous star appeared rising over the low point at Newport News. He glanced at it and sighed, and fell to dreaming of another star that had risen upon him when Ottilie came wounded to Thalberg.

Half an hour later, his attention was suddenly attracted to this star, he knew not why. He watched it closely. It had not ascended, but was now shining *between* him and the dim line of trees at Newport News. It had become triple; three stars shone like illuminated globes in front of a pawnbroker's shop.

Behind these his eye caught another golden light, then a red one, then golden and red ones, close together as dots on a page, stretching in a long curve around Newport News and appearing on the other side of it, until the land rising inland hid them from sight. It was as if a glittering crown of stars had fallen down out of the generous heavens and encircled the dark land. It was as if an interminable serpent, with golden and red scales, lay in an infinite coil upon the top of the sea, and was slowly unwinding his folds and stealthily ringing himself about the earth.

The fascination of these silent lights which moved so rapidly yet so insensibly, which shone so serenely in the tranquil water, which had sprung up so magically out of the darkness, kept Philip Sterling for some moments in a dream. Rather by some instinct of a scout, than with any definite idea, he stooped down over Flemington and shook him.

"Get up, Flem," said he. "Queen Mab's coming up the river!"

"Ah—ah—ugh—umph!" observed Flemington, yawning fearfully. "Phil," he continued, without opening his eyes, "present my complim—that is, if the enemy's not within a few inches give him the bayo—I mean, wait till you can see the white of his—Yes, Phil, wait till then—I'm a little sleepy—umph"— and he fell back and snored.

Philip shook more vigorously.

"Get up, Flem. No fun, boy. The Bay's full of gunboats!"

Flemington caught the last word and sprang to his feet. He glanced down the Bay.

"Butler, Phil, by the Rood! Butler at last!"* Flemington could scarcely restrain a shout. Down in the river, there, silently approached the danger which he and his men had been sent here to announce.

Cain Smallin's long legs lay extended promiscuously along the sward. Flemington placed himself between them, as between the shafts of a wheelbarrow, and, seizing hold of the feet for knobs, dragged the living machine furiously round

* [Major-General Benjamin F. Butler's advance with the Army of the James was synchronized with Grant's Wilderness campaign. Until Beauregard brought reinforcements from the south the Confederates in Petersburg were hopelessly outnumbered.—Ed.]

amongst the sleepers, and ran over and crushed four dainty, childlike dreams. The wheelbarrow creaked.

"Thunder and lightnin' and—hello!" growled the mountaineer, sitting upon the sward, breathless, and gazing with wide eyes at the thousand lights in the water below. "I thought, Bi 'gemini, a b'ar had me an' was a-rollin' me down old Smoky Mount'in for pastime!"

"Whillikens!" groaned Aubrey, in a voice that came as if from afar, he writhing under Rübetsahl and John Briggs piled across him in a miscellaneous mass of humanity. "Briggs, which of these numerous legs—which I don't see, but am conscious of—is mine? Wish you'd just feel along, old fellow, and find out which is my leg; one will do—I merely want to use it to get up with!"

"Phil," said Flemington, who had been scanning the line with his glass, and counting the lights, "mount, and ride to Petersburg in a hurry. I see the signal-men up the river yonder are sending up the news, but a fog might stop 'em, or something. It'll be better to go yourself. Briggs, ride with him; it'll be lonesome. Saddle up, boys; and don't mind about killing your horses; ride 'em till they drop and then 'press' some more. Tell the general that forty vessels were in sight when you left, and that I'll send another courier with details in the morning, soon as I can see by daylight a little. The signal-line will be broken up of course, but I'll keep him posted with couriers. Wait a minute till I make another count." He swept down the line of lights with his glass. "Forty-five of 'em, now; can't swear to it, it's so dark, but one or two monitors, I think, in front. Off, boys! Good-by, and come back as quick as you can. We'll have some lively times down here!"

In ten minutes Philip Sterling and John Briggs were spurring lustily towards Petersburg.

The foremost lights had now passed the spot where Flemington and his comrades lay, and were far on their way towards a bold bend in the river, fifteen miles above, which sweeps around the long projection of Hog Island, and incloses the water-view. Fifteen miles above and fifteen miles below—there were thirty miles of lights, and still new ones kept rapidly gliding into view from behind the dim shore-line far down the river.

"Paul, it looks as if somebody had roused all the *Ignes Fatui* in the world, and they were all going on a pilgrimage to some vast marsh in the west," said Flemington, meditatively gazing on the slow-passing lights.

"Or like a stately Polonaise, with flames for the dancers of it," added Rübetsahl.

"I was just imagining," said Aubrey, "a hundred angels, each with his star on forehead, floating in a wavy file behind General Michael yonder, in front, triple-starred; executing, perhaps, a brilliant flank movement on old Lucifer and his army in the black bend up there!"

"Waal, now," interposed the sturdy mountaineer, "I cain't find it in my heart to look on them bloody Yankee gunboats, an' call 'em angels 'ith stars upon ther heads. To me, now, hit 'pears more like they was a hundred devils, an' every man of 'em was totin' a piece o' brimstone in his hand, ready sot a-fire, for to blow up Richmond and Petersburg with!"

"You see, Cain," said Flemington, "if the Yankees, even in the act of attacking us, show us a pretty sight, why, in Heaven's name, let's take it!—even if we don't say thank'ee, gentlemen; nor fight any the less for this unintentional beneficence! Indeed, I don't like the gift any more than you: '*timeo Danaos*' *—if you'll excuse me, but it's *too* pat! I fear Beauregard hasn't reached Petersburg yet; likely as not Butler will gobble it up before he *can* reach there!"

"Nary time, gobble it up!" sturdily rejoined the mountaineer. "Ef Beauregard don't git thar in time, God A'mighty will! *He*'ll hold 'em in check untwell Beauregard does come up; an 'ith *them two* together, hit 'pears to me likely 'at we kin about tan out anything the Yanks kin bring up Jeems's River!"

* [Virgil, *Æneid*.—Ed.]

Chapter VIII

—One that hath been a courtier;
. . . . . And in his brain,
Which is as dry as the remainder biscuit
After a voyage, he hath strange places crammed
With observation, the which he vents
In mangled forms. Oh that I were a fool!

As You Like It

IN THE early morning of May 7th, John Briggs and Philip Sterling lay sleeping peacefully in No. 78 of that charming old Virginia hotel which stands like a reservoir to receive the stream of passengers flowing into it from the great channel of the Petersburg and Weldon railroad.

Simultaneously entered into this room two visitors, one from heaven and the other from the hotel-office.

These were a sun-ray which flashed in through the window, and a black waiter who opened the door half-way and inserted his dark and dignified phiz therethrough.

The sun-ray, retaining its *penchant* for windows, continued its course and entered into Philip Sterling's soul by the windows of it. It shone on his eyes, passed through, and produced upon the soul inside some vague impression that darkness was gone and light was about; under which impression Philip Sterling threw open the shutters of his soul-windows. The black waiter, on the contrary, true to his instincts, retained his *penchant* for doors,—since, if eyes be the windows, surely ears are the doors, of the soul.

"Glad to see you sleep so comfuttuble, sah! Compliment to de house, sah! Bin knockin' ten minutes or mo, sah! Note for you; gemplim waitin' at de door on de hoss send compliments, an' tell de boys he in a hell of a hurry, sah!"

Philip placed his mouth at the ear of John Briggs and blew strenuously. In his sleep the blowee was straightway nightmared with the dream that all the winds of heaven had drawn to a focus in his ear, where they did yell and hound him on through the world.

"Get up, John. Note from the major. Wants us to ride

with him immediately, before breakfast. Horses saddled, at the door," said Philip, reading from the note.

As John Briggs was pulling on his right sock, his eyes fell on the open note lying on the table.

"I see," said he, laughing, "the major retains his affectionate propensity for calling us pet names, Phil. Did you notice the sweet term of endearment wherewith he commences his yepistle? '*You damned lazy hounds*,' quoth he, '*I want you!*' &c., &c.

Oh that I had but time, while these boys are dressing, to submit a little dissertation upon "*Individual Character as displayed in pulling on socks and breeches o' mornings, together with a View of Humanity at the Moment of Emergence from the general Couch of Slumber*," but who hath time to say aught while a Confederate soldier was dressing,—a matter of two minutes and less! Moreover the horses wait down-stairs and Major M—— is fuming, being the most restless of mortals. Yet, oh that I had time!

"Mount, boys!" cried the major, as the two young men descended the steps. "Haygood's out on the railroad, and he's going to have a devilish hard time of it this morning."

As they rode down the street, John Briggs whistled long, like a boatswain i' the calm.

"Phe-ee-ee-w!" observed he. "Phil, I'm hungry! I could eat dog. I could masticate adamant. I could deglutite a fortress, or a chain-shot, or the major's conscience, there,—and I'll stop, for that's the hardest simile extant. Methinks I see the early pies, borne on the heads of the daughters of Afric. Hast in thy purse, my friend, aught wherewithal a gentleman might buy—a pie?"

"That have I," said Philip proudly,—"and thereby hangs a tale. I drew two months' wages t'other day. It was twenty-two dollars. I met three friends, and we four drank: one gill, of *such* whiskey, apiece. Four drinks at five dollars *per* drink, is twenty-dollars. The residuum and sweet overplus of my two months' wages thou beholdest there!" he said, and flaunted a two dollar bill like a triumphal flag upon the breeze.

"Here, Dinah," quoth Briggs, "give us a pie. Dinah, these be pale and feeble pies,—how much for one of 'em?"

"Two dollars, sah!'

" Now an I had had Golconda in my pocket, she had surely said Golconda was the price of a pie: which is, in the vernacular, she would ' size my pile! ' What, Dinah! This large bill, this most rare and radiant sweet bill, with the pathetic inscription thereupon! '*Six months after the ratification of a treaty of peace, I promise to pay!*' quotha! As who should say, ten days after death I will disburse!— Here, Relentless! receive the pathetic inscription! and give me a pie: and now my money is gone, my future is black as thou, Dinah—till pay-day."

In silence rode they on. " Methinks," presently said Briggs, meditatively biting into the last half of his pie,—" methinks I see within this pie "—

" What is it, John; a fly, or a cockroach? " tenderly inquired the major.

" Or a lock of hair? " suggested Phil.

" Gentlemen, it is a most monstrous thing,—it is worse than flies and larger than cockroaches and it strangleth more chokingly than hair: for it is—the degeneracy and downfall of my country! Hear me! Philip Sterling, do you remember, oh, do you remember how, when we passed herethrough two years ago, you and I did straggle into Ledbetter's bakery, and sat down at a marble-topped table and took a pie and a glass of milk? Compare that time with this! Sir,"—appealing to the major as he rose into the pathetic-sublime,—" the crust of that pie (at Ledbetter's two years ago) was dark with richness! The crust of it was short, ladies and gentlemen; short as—as the major's nose, there; short as rations; short as life compared with eternity; in short, it was as short as pie-crust. It did melt upon the tongue sweetly; languidly dissolving into a vague deliciousness, as the sweet day dissolves into mysterious twilight. Moreover, between these dainty crusts our am'rous tongues discovered liberal largesse of th' integrant fruit,—peach, and other the like confections, sugared and spiced, which with the creamy milk did mingle and marry-in rarely, patly, like ' two souls with but '—and so forth; like ' perfect music set to noble words '; * like dreamy star-light shimmering into dreamy dawn-light i' the early morn. Thinking of those pies I have much contempt for Apicius, Heliogabalus & Co.

" But alas, and woe is me, Alhama!

* [Tennyson, *The Princess*.—ED.]

"I contrast this pie with those pies.

"I observe with pain and smearing, that molasses, otherwise sorghum, hath entirely superseded sugar.

"I observe that this crust hath a weakly-white and wan aspect, and a familiar tang it leaveth as it departeth, admonisheth my secret soul of bacon-fat that went to the making of it, *vice* lard, deceased.

"And as for the spices, they have shared the doom of Ilium and of the buried past; *fuit*; they are not.

"And I do remember that those large pies were vended to the happy at the rate of twenty-five cents each, whereas these small pies bring two dollars: stated generally, the price proceedeth upon the inverse ratio to the size.

"Sir, and gentlemen of the jury! aside, my lords, from the moral degradation evinced by this low pass to which the once pure pie is come,—how can men be raised to fight upon such villainous coward's-pabulum as this?

"Is this, O ye delegates of the diet of worms, is *this*"—holding up the last ragged mouthful between finger and thumb—"to be the sweet reward and guerdon of the battle-grimed veteran, just come from the big wars? Forbid it, Mars!—which is to say, cook better ones, mothers!" concluded the speaker, and meekly, in absence of mind, swallowed the last piece.

"*Eheu, Pius Eneas!* I"—

"Hold your gab, boys! Listen!" interposed the major.

Stopping the horses a moment, they heard the sound of a cannon booming in the direction of Richmond.* Another and another followed. Presently came a loud report which seemed to loosen the battle as a loud thunder-peal releases the rain, and the long musketry-rattle broke forth.

"Haygood's having a rough time of it. Let's get there, hearties! It'll be three more of us, anyhow," said the major, sticking spurs to his horse.**

They approach the outskirts of the storm of battle.

* [The MS supplies the detail that "they were now three miles from the city, upon the Richmond turnpike." The ensuing combat, therefore, is that with Butler's main force (north of Petersburg) rather than one with his cavalry raiders (south and more distant).—ED.]

** [In the MS Lanier began a new paragraph here: "A rapid gallop up four miles brought them in sight of the battle-field." He then drew a line through these words. Thus ends Fragment B. Fragment C begins with Chapter IX.—ED.]

There lies a man, in bloody rags that were gray, with closed eyes. The first hailstone in the advancing edge of the storm has stricken down a flower. The dainty petal of life shrivels, blackens: yet it gives forth a perfume as it dies; his lips are moving,—he is praying.

The wounded increase. Here is a musket in the road: there is the languid hand that dropped it, pressing its fingers over a blue-edged wound in the breast. Weary pressure, and vain,—the blood flows steadily.

More muskets, cartridge-boxes, belts, greasy haversacks, strew the ground.

Here come the stretcher-bearers. They leave a dripping line of blood. "Walk easy as you kin, boys," comes from a blanket which four men are carrying by the corners. Easy walking is desirable when each step of your four carriers spurts out the blood afresh, or grates the rough edges of a shot bone in your leg.

The sound of a thousand voices, eager, hoarse, fierce, all speaking together yet differently, comes through the leaves of the undergrowth. A strange multitudinous noise accompanies it,—a noise like the tremendous sibilation of a mile-long wave just before it breaks. It is the shuffling of two thousand feet as they march over dead leaves.

"Surely that can't be reserves; Haygood didn't have enough for his front! They must be falling back: hark! there's a Yankee cheer. Good God! Here's three muskets on the ground, boys! Come on!" said the major, and hastily dismounted.

The three plunge through the undergrowth. Waxen May-leaves sweep their faces; thorns pierce their hands; the honey-suckles cry "Wait!" with alluring perfumes; guarded oak-twigs wound the wide-opened eyes.

It is no matter.

They emerge into an open space. A thousand men are talking, gesticulating, calling to friends, taking places in rank, abandoning them for others. They are in gray rags.

"Where's Haygood?"

He is everywhere! On right flank cheering, on left flank rallying, in the centre commanding: he is ubiquitous; he moves upon the low-sweeping wing of a battle genius: it is supernatural that he should be here and yonder at once. His voice suddenly rings out,—

"Form, men! We'll run 'em out o' that in a second. Reinforcements coming!"

"What's the matter with the Yanks? Look, Phil!" says Briggs.

The Federals, having driven the small Confederate force from the railroad, stop in their charge as soon as they have crossed the track. Behind their first is a second line. As if on parade this second line advances to the railroad, and halts. "Ground arms!" Their muskets fall in a long row, as if in an armory-rack. The line steps two paces forward. It stoops over the track. It is a human machine with fifty thousand clamps, moved by levers infinitely flexible. Fifty thousand fingers insert themselves beneath the stringers of the road. All together! They lift, and lay over, bottom upwards, a mile of railroad.

But, O first line of Federals, you should not have stopped! The rags have rallied. Their line is formed, in the centre floats the cross-banner, to right and left gleam the bayonets like silver flame-jets, unwavering, deadly; these, with a thousand mute tongues, utter a silent yet magnificent menace:

"Charge! Steady, men!"

The rags flutter, the cross-flag spreads out and reveals its symbol, the two thousand sturdy feet in hideous brogans, or without cover, press forward. At first it is a slow and stately movement; stately in the mass, ridiculous if we watch any individual leg, with its knee perhaps showing through an irregular hole in *such* pantaloons!

The step grows quicker. A few scattering shots from the enemy's retiring skirmishers patter like the first big drops of the shower.

From the right of the ragged line now comes up a single long cry, as from the leader of a pack of hounds who has found the game. This cry has in it the uncontrollable eagerness of the sleuth-hound, together with a dry harsh quality that conveys an uncompromising hostility. It is the irresistible outflow of some fierce soul immeasurably enraged, and it is tinged with a jubilant tone, as if in anticipation of a speedy triumph and a satisfying revenge. It is a howl, a hoarse battle-cry, a cheer, and a congratulation, all in one.

They take it up in the centre, they echo it on the left, it swells, it runs along the line as fire leaps along the rigging of a ship. It is as if some one pulled out in succession all the stops of the infernal battle-organ, but only struck one note which they all speak in different voices.

The gray line nears the blue one, rapidly. It is a thin gray wave, whose flashing foam is the glitter of steel bayonets. It meets with a swell in the ground, shivers a moment, then rolls on.

Suddenly thousands of tongues, tipped with red and issuing from smoke, speak deadly messages from the blue line. One volley? A thousand would not stop them now. Even if they were not veterans who know that it is safer at this crisis to push on than to fall back, they would still press forward. They have forgotten safety, they have forgotten life and death: their thoughts have converged into a focus which is the one simple idea,—to get to those men in blue, yonder. Rapid firing from the blue line brings rapid yelling from the gray.

But look! The blue line, which is like a distant strip of the sea, curls into little waves; these dash together in groups, then fly apart. The tempest of panic has blown upon it. The blue uniforms fly, flames issue from the gray line, it also breaks, the ragged men run, and the battle has degenerated to a chase.

John Briggs and Philip had started side by side. But the swaying line, the excitement of the chase in which the fastest man, either pursuing or pursued, was the happiest also, had drawn them asunder.

Briggs overtook a color-sergeant.

"Surrender!"

"B'lieve I will. Got me!"

"Hurr—!" It is probable that John Briggs finished this exclamation with a sigh of ineffable delight. For he was at this moment, in the Jean Paul sense, promoted. A random bullet entered his mouth; and, with that eagerness to escape which argues the soul's great contempt for the body, through this small aperture leaped out John Briggs' ascending spirit.* Philip

* [In his Ledger (p. 254) Lanier attempted to versify this episode:

"John's dead: and yonder goes his soul.
It flashes through the battle-smoke,
As if a lost sun-ray upbroke
And went back to the sun."

—Ed.]

was not near to congratulate him upon this heavenly brevet, conferred purely for gallantry on the world's field. But when the day of separated friends comes, then what shakings of the hand, then what felicitations poured on fine John Briggs, that he won his bay so well and with so much less pain of life than we!

Philip was wild with the fascination of victory. It was an enchantment that urged him on. He saw nothing, knew nothing, to right or left; a spell in front drew him forward. He was far ahead of the line. Something behind a smoke called out,—

"Surrender!"

Philip raised his gun. His left arm suddenly felt paralyzed and he was half-blind with pain. The next moment a form which loomed before his hot eyes like a blue mountain, lifted a musket to what seemed an immeasurable height in the sky, which dazzled him like an infinite diamond. The musket descended with a sidewise deflection and fell upon his eye as if a meteor had crashed into it. He felt himself falling, and fainted.

Chapter IX

I think there is a fatality in it,—but I rarely arrive at the place I set out for. Sterne [, *A Sentimental Journey*]

PHILIP STERLING attempted to open his eyes. One of them unclosed, but the other refused to do him that good turn: it had swollen fearfully.

"John," said he faintly, without turning his head, "believe I'm hurt a little."

"Humph?" replied a gruff voice.

Slowly and wearily, Philip turned upon his side. A Federal soldier stood near him. Through an opening he saw strange trees and hills whirling past him in a wild gigantic dance.* As his eye moved from point to point, his slow ideas gradually shaped themselves into the conclusion that he was lying upon the deck of a steamer in rapid motion.

The surprise of this idea stimulated him. He rose to a sitting posture, remained so a moment, then caught hold of a stanchion and assisted himself to stand. The delicious breeze of the May-morning blew upon his fevered head, cooled him, and strengthened him.

To Philip, a tree was always equal to a dream; a hill was but a surface that slanted his soul upwards; a dell was only a vase that brought forth its own flowers, and every stream held truth, white-bosomed, like a naiad, in its depths. To-day he had all these. The hours flew past him as rapidly as the trees on the banks. At four o'clock they rounded the curve which leads into Burwell's Bay. Philip watched the shore with intense yet furtive eagerness. He wished to discover some trace of his comrades; but he feared to attract the attention of the officers standing about the deck lest they also should discover some sign of the hostile scouts on the shore.

Presently the face of the continuous bluff grew familiar to him. At this moment an officer who had been also curiously regarding the shore, called out,—

"Lend me your glass a minute, quartermaster!"

* ["See Tennyson's *Orpheus*" (notation in margin of MS). Probably a slip for "Amphion."—Ed.]

The quartermaster aye-aye'd-sir, handed him the glass, touched his hat, and resumed his beat.

"Thought I saw a man dodging about amongst those trees over yonder," said the officer, adjusting the glass to his eye. He looked steadily towards the shore for some moments.

"Well, by old Gideon!" exclaimed he, without taking the glass from his eye; "a cosy spying-nook as ever I saw, and be damned to 'em!"

"What is it, chief?" inquired several voices.

"A real Johnny Reb over there, stuck in the face of the bluff like a sand-martin, bi-God, in a hole! Got his spy-glass and all, too, and gazing away at us as if he was reading a newspaper! Let's give him the news, what d'ye say?"

He ran to the gun on the starboard quarter.

"Bear a hand; we'll run her out ourselves. How's she charged?"

"Shell, sir; two seconds."

"Too much. Run in a grape-pill over it. 'Tisn't four hundred yards from here to the impudent rascal yonder. Now then. Let me aim her. So."

"Fire!"

Philip's heart thrilled and sickened.

The channel makes inward at this point. It is not more than a quarter of a mile from the shore. The shell and the grape-shot howled and screamed in an agony of delight, like bloodhounds long held and just unleashed when a few springs bring them on the victim.

The chief raised his glass.

"Damned if he isn't gone up," said he, "or gone down, more likely. Can't see anything of him."

"Good God!" thought Philip, "who's killed? Was it Flem, or Paul Rübetsahl, or honest Cain, or Aubrey?"

Vague ideas ran through his mind. They were something like this; life—death—friendship—strange—how does God have the heart to allow it—don't understand—insane if I think—wait—wait!

The steamer touched at Newport News wharf. Two passengers came aboard, of whom one was in blue and the other in dirty gray. This was all that Philip noticed as he glanced at them and fell back into his sorrowful reflections. If he had looked more closely, he would have discovered that the man in gray looked at him twice, the last time with a grin of triumph which soon darkened into an expression of hatred and revenge.

Philip must needs moralize.

"The skies," said he to himself, "smile, no matter who frowns. They are unmindful of men. And so are the waters. Two years ago these very waves floated our *Merrimac* proudly; there are the masts of the frigate she sunk that day. Now they float, full as proudly, the hostile keels of our enemies.

"Ah, Nature has no politics. She'll grow a rose as well for York as Lancaster; and mayhap beat both down next minute with a storm!

"She has no heart; else she never had rained on Lear's head.

"She has no eyes; for, seeing, she never could have drowned that dainty girl, Ophelia.

"She has no ears; or she would hear the wild Sabian hymns to Night and prayers to Day that men are uttering evermore.

"O blind, deaf, no-hearted Beauty, we cannot woo thee, for thou silently contemnest us; we cannot force thee, for thou are stronger than we; we cannot compromise with thee, for thou art treacherous as thy seas: what shall we do, we, unhappy, that love thee, coquette Nature?"

This inquiry of Philip Sterling's received immediate answer, —from the lips of a dead man. For at this moment he heard some one saying in a low voice,—

"Toes up, boys!"

He looked towards the sound. A wounded prisoner had just died. Philip stepped to his cot.

Winged victory, in the likeness of a smile, dwelt upon the dead man's face. This still smile contained the ineffable repose of a marble statue, and something more, namely, the potential energy and smooth irresistible activity of a victorious soul. Spiritual force, confident, calm, untrammelled,—this is the meaning of such a smile on such a face.

Philip perceived it.

He stood at the bow of the boat looking seaward until she ran alongside the wharf at Fortress Monroe.

Chapter X

York.—Upon thine honor, is he prisoner?
Buckingham.—Upon mine honor, he is prisoner.
King Henry VI [*, Part II*]

AT A WOODEN building which bore sign "Provost Marshal's Office," our prisoner sat down in midst of some frightened-looking men, and one or two women, who seemed to be following similar instructions to those given to Philip by his guard:—

"Wait here till you hear your name called."

The guard stepped into a room adjoining the ante-chamber where the prisoners sat, delivered a written paper, and retired after a short colloquy with the clerk at the desk.

Philip was evidently to be shortly disposed of; his turn came first.

"Philip Sterling!" called out the clerk. *Mein Himmel,* Federal conquerors, how greasy, sleek, and complacent was the voice of this clerk in your provost's office there! It was the tone of the spider *after* the fly has walked into his little parlor.

"That your name?" inquired the greasy voice, as Philip stood up.

"Yes."

Without further ado, a spruce attendant in citizen's dress, unarmed, stepped from the next room, politely (aye, politely; he was a good man—that spruce attendant—let him here receive benedictions!) requested Philip to walk with him, and led the way along a plank sidewalk, which divided an irregular, crooked street from a line of crooked, irregular buildings. Philip's impression, as he walked, was a miscellaneous idea of grayish sand, of whitewash, and of the want of it, of granite bastions, of earthworks of a casemate,—through whose one embrasure peered a cannon like an *ennuyée* prisoner through his window,—of parapets over which also peeped black cannon-faces, as if the cannon had climbed there to see over, and were holding on by their hands and knees,—of a wilderness of smoke-stacks and masts,—of a strange gassy odor. He turned once to look back. Chesapeake smiled to him, like a maiden inviting him to stay. He disregarded the invitation, as in duty bound, and followed his guide through a sally-port. They emerged from the inner mouth of the dark passage into a brick-paved court. A tall grenadier, in blue with red trimmings, stood at the angle of the wall, bearing at his belt an immense key.

With a half-smile, Philip's conductor made a sign silently. The red-trimmed faced about, turned a key which was in the lock of a wooden door opening out from the wall, and disclosed a huge iron grating which he unfastened with the key at his belt. It creaked open wide enough to admit a man.

" Step in! " growled the key-bearer.

Philip stepped in.

Instantly the iron grating clanged, the sound reverberated through the brick-walled court, the wooden door came to with a heavy thud, and Philip found himself in darkness, amidst a Babel of oaths, songs, groans, chain-clankings, jars, unmeaning cries, and intermingling echoes.

He had closed his eyes in order to accustom them more quickly to the darkness. When he opened them he saw at first a semicircular line of sparkles gathered around him. A moment elapsed before he perceived that these were human eyes, the shadowy forms of whose owners he could barely trace at the distance of a few feet from him. The noises had suddenly ceased. The occupants of the cell had discovered the new-comer and were peering curiously into his face.

Suddenly a furious clanking and rolling of heavy metal issued from a low-arched corridor, which communicated between the main cell and some subterranean recess. The dusky crowd around Philip opened. Through the opening appeared a tall, thin man, with long hair and beard, and glimmering cat-like eyes. He was dancing a progressive jig toward Philip; his saltatory performances being apparently little impeded by a chain which connected both his legs to a large cannon-ball, that darted about in all kinds of gyratory movements by reason of the vigorous and eccentric jerks of the legs about which its chain was wound. As he approached, his arms and hands lashed the air with fierce and threatening gestures.

Suddenly he made a bound which placed him immediately in front of the new prisoner. Philip was in the act of drawing back to defend himself, when he saw the strange dancer place his hand on his heart and bend in a profound bow, until his peaked face almost touched the floor.

" Sir," said the shadow, " permit me to inquire if you intend to remain in this house for some time? "

" I must confess, I think it extremely likely," replied Philip.

"Ah! Then I hope I shall be able to offer you better accommodations than is possible to-night. You perceive,"—with a stately apologetic wave of the hand—" how crowded I am at present. My guests come faster than they go; but I hope I may do better for you to-morrow. For this time, at least, allow me to point out to you what I consider the softest bed in the establishment. Walk this way, sir! " The host stepped a pace toward the wall.

" There, sir! " he continued, with a magnificent gesture of one hand, while he pointed to the dirty bricks of the floor with the other. " I, myself, having a constitutional aversion to sleeping with the whole Democratic party, have retired to an inner apartment. But you will find these bricks good bricks, soft bricks as ever you slept on in your life, sir. I have tried them. You will repose in the honored consciousness of sleeping, sir, where *I* have slept! "

In this cell the sweet light was niggard of her cheer. Day dawned there about noon, glimmered an hour or two, and the night came on before sunset.

Philip was weary. He stretched himself upon the soft spot indicated by his singular landlord, and clasped his hands under his head for a pillow. But he could not sleep yet. The noises recommenced with their pristine fury. A man would rise and start across the floor. Suddenly he would yell like a fiend, and, as if the inspiration of a howling dervish had rushed upon him, would set up a furious jig in which feet, arms, legs, and head strove in variety and wild energy of movement. To this the invariable accompaniment was the rattle of chains connecting ankles or wrists, or dragging balls,—sometimes both. A double shuffle and a terrible oath would complete the performance, and the man would proceed upon his errand across the room. It was as if some infernal deity had his altar in the centre of the floor, at which each must perform his hideous devotions before he could pass.

Upon each side of Philip a man lay stretched along the floor.

The face of one, in which the eyes rolled restlessly, was turned towards him.

"Who was the man that danced up to me just now?" said Philip to the eyes.

"Oh, hell! he's a fellow that's been in here some time."

The eyes looked down, and Philip following the direction, saw two legs elevated at an angle of forty-five degrees. The ankles were linked together by a chain.

"Them things," continued Philip's companion, while the feet dangled to and fro so as to rattle the chain-links, "is apt to make a feller sorter how-come-you-so 'bout the head, if a feller wears 'em too long. He"—jerking one foot toward the corridor into which the host had retired, "he's dam nigh crazy."

"You are not Confederate soldiers?"

"No, not much. Yanks, all of us. Don't you see the blue blouses? But you ain't got owl-eyed yet!"

"Why in the world do they confine you so rigidly? It is worse than their prisoners fare!"

"Oh, we're extra fellers. Bounty-jumpin', stealin', fightin', murderin', desertin', and so foth! That feller with the brass buttons there, he's a paymaster; 'counts not square, or the like o' that. Jugged him. The feller inside that skeered you, he's been waitin' some time for 'em to take him out and shoot him. Sentenced!"

Philip remained quietly watching the dusky figures that stormed about the cell. Gradually the noises receded, the shadows flitted silently, the coarse web of the darkness lightened into an airy scarf that inclosed him, and day dawned for Philip in a peaceful dream.

It was about eleven o'clock at night when, oppressed with a vague sense that some alien earth-light was struggling through the pure heaven-light of his dream, Philip turned and sighed and woke. A man was standing over him with a lighted candle, but quickly passed on when he saw that he had roused the sleeper.

Philip raised up on his elbow and looked around. The room was still, except in one spot, where, on a sort of platform constructed of a couple of planks resting on two camp-kettles, sat four man, of whom one was shuffling a pack of cards whose recondite symbols were nearly obliterated with grease and dirt.

On his right lay two men close together conversing in a low tone. The card-players talked as the game went on.

"—In *that* lock-up" was saying one, emphasizing the "that" by slapping his card on the plank. "Now, when they *do* put a gentleman in the lock-up, *I* say, treat him *like* a gentleman!"

"'Xactly so!" chimed another. "Some places, they does. There's some lock-ups where they hands your vittles through the bars o' the gratin', a mou'ful at a time, and you has to take it with your mouth. I don't call that no decent way to treat a gent'man. I *has* been in lock-ups," continued the "gent'man," swelling with the pleasing recollection, "where they brung your vittles to you reg'lar and handed 'em to you, slice and hunk, and you could eat 'em then or whenever you dam please!"

At this moment Philip's attention was attracted to the conversation on his right. It had grown louder: one of the speakers was talking rapidly and excitedly.

"—An' when I *do* git thar," he was saying, "jest let 'em stand f'om under, for I'm a-gwine to root 'em out lively now, sure!"

"But how the devil will you get to Tennessee from here? You'll have to go back the way you came, won't you?"

"Never ye mind about that: I'll git thar. I mought ha' forged a pass an' ha' went to Lynchburg, an' f'om thar I could ha' snaked it thu' the bushes to home, easy. But I thought to myself I mought make a few greenbacks afore I started; it's all Yankee-land, you know, in Tennessy, now. I knowed whar ther was some scouts on Jeems's River, an' I knowed they was a-devillin' you folks powerful, an' I thought I'd come over an' help you all to ketch 'em; an' I 'lowed 'at your officers mought gimme a leetle to make it wuth my trouble."

"Well; how did you come out?"

"Durned ef they didn't want to shoot me fur a spy, a'ter I'd done deserted! Ye see, out o' foolishness, or somethin'—I—I scarcely knows what made me do it,—I didn't give 'em my own name when they tuk me up on this side, thar, at Newport News. 'Stead o' that, I give 'em some dam rigmarole or other, jest spellin' it to 'em, you know, sorter promiscus like, an' some of 'em said they be darn ef that was any man's name on this yeath, an' said I was tryin' to fool 'em; an' as luck would have it, I seed a man thar 'at I had knowed in Tennessy afore the war, an' he got 'em to send me down here untwell he could see the general an' git me off. Major Cranston,—know him?"

"Yes. He's on duty here."

"A clever man, certin! Know'd me in a minit, an' axed me about a gal in Tennessy, an' shuk hands an' gimme a drink o' mortial good whiskey, an' said he'd see me in the mornin'. An' when he does git me off, an' I git to the Cove," continued Gorm Smallin, rising to a sitting posture in his anger, which seemed always to become inflamed at this idea, "jest let ole Sterlin' git up an' git! He holped 'em to send *me* off to the army whar I never had no house to keep off the rain,—an' I be dam ef *he* shall have ary one! He holped 'em put me whar the bullets was whizzin'; I'm gwine to make *him* hear one whiz, a ole sneakin', meddlin',"—

"You infernal scoundrel!" cried Philip, and leapt like a tiger upon Gorm Smallin, clutching his throat. His opponent wound his arm about Philip, and endeavored to turn him under. Like two serpents they writhed and agonized. Philip's inferiority in strength was for a time compensated by the indignation which swelled his veins and corded his muscles.

"Fight! Fight!" cried a voice.

The four card-players tumbled off their platform and ran to see the fun, bringing their light. The other inmates roared and gathered round. It was delightful: it was a godsend to them; they shouted encouragement to the varying fortunes of the combatants.

"Stick to him, little un!" cried one.

"Why don't you mash his mug?" screamed another.

"Hold yer light higher, I can't see 'em," plaintively begged a third.

"Bet rations on the big un!" said a speculator.

"Thump him, bump him. Hoo-oo-oo-ray!" yelled an ecstatic enthusiast.

Gorm Smallin had the advantage of weight and muscle. He succeeded in getting his throat loose, and grasped Philip's with one hand, while he fumbled in his pocket with the other. He drew out his knife, caught the blade between his teeth, opened it, and lifted it high over the powerless boy in his grasp. He was in the act of striking,—when the butt of a musket came down heavily upon his uplifted hand, crushing the fingers and dashing the knife to the floor. Sickened with pain, Gorm relaxed his grasp, and Philip staggered to his feet.

" Should think you Confeds had had enough o' fightin', outside o' here," growled the corporal, who, with the sentinel on duty, hearing the commotion in the den, had rushed in unnoticed by the excited by-standers. " Sentinel, walk your beat inside for the rest of your watch, and keep a light burning. If anybody else gets to fighting, just take a hand yourself with the butt o' your musket,—or the bullet in it, I don't care much which."

The prisoners resumed their beds, laughingly discussing the fight. Philip attempted to pace the floor, but his wearied feet refused and he lay down. In spite of the restlessness of aroused tenderness, of unappeased anger, of bitter repining against that most maddening of all feelings to a man—helplessness, his exhaustion prevailed and he slept, at first fitfully, at length soundly.

Chapter XI

Item, A capon	2*s.* 2*d.*
Item, Sauce	4*d.*
Item, Sack, two gallons	5*s.* 8*d.*
Item, Anchovies, and sack after supper . .	2*s.* 6*d.*
Item, Bread	*ob.*

King Henry IV [*, Part I*]

WHEN PHILIP awoke, the dungeon was as light as it ever became, with the light of day. His enemy of the night had fled with it; and for this reason, if no other, Philip would have hailed the holy light with Miltonic fervor.

If he had known the full extent and sincerity of Gorm Smallin's designs, and how, as they were brooded over, they grew always more diabolically vindictive, he would have preferred the presence of the plotter, since that only disgusted him, to an absence which menaced the safety of those whom he loved better than himself.

At this moment, however, Gorm Smallin was as happy as any Gorm Smallin could be.

Early in the morning a sentry had called his name at the grated door, and conducted him out of the cell, where Cranston met him. After witnessing the solemn ceremony of his taking the oath of allegiance, Cranston had conveyed him aboard the steamer for Norfolk, to the narrow streets of which ancient town a short and pleasant passage quickly brought them.

As they stepped upon the wharf, Mr. Smallin threw his burning soul into one short interrogatory.

" Major," said he, " whar mought a body git a leetle mite o' somethin' to eat, here? "

" That's a fact," said Cranston; " you must be hungry after living on those slim rations at the fortress."

" Waal," replied Mr. Smallin, guardedly, " I don't mean to say nothin' agin them rations o' yourn back yan: but I will say, fur I never was one o' them that's afeard to speak ther mind, that a leetle mite o' breakfas' right now 'ud do a body a power o' good! "

" Well, let's turn across, here. Yonder's the 'United States

Restaurant,' over there. I remember when we came in here, first, it was the Confederate States Restaurant: you can still see the C O N under the one coat of paint with which the proprietor scratched out his old patriotism."

"A dam rascal!" observed Mr. Smallin, indignantly. "Changed his flag, did he?"

"Yes;—or rather his colors, like a chameleon. While the ground was gray, he was gray; but the ground changed to blue, and the groundling became a Yankee."

"A mortial sight o' feed and truck o' one sort and another thar, in the windows! Hit makes me hongrier and hongrier the nigher I git to 'em!"

They entered the restaurant, passed through an anteroom which was fitted up as a bar (so delicately intimating that drinking comes before eating, as well in the order of time as of dignity), and approached a long and indescribably greasy pine-table which ran down the centre of the eating-room.

"Now then, Mr. Smallin!" said Cranston, as they took their seats on a bench which ran alongside the table, and which was as like it in all its features (*can* grease be called a feature?) as if it were an infant table nestling by the side of a maternal one, "what'll you take to eat?"

Who, with any the slightest knowledge of the habits of the Confederate army in '64, does not know what Mr. Smallin took to eat?

"A cup o' kauphy," said he, "fust and fo'most!"

The war disclosed the fact that kauphy (which, with that independence we have preserved in some matters, we still call so, though the spelling nowise justifies it) was more thoroughly interwoven with our existence than any other institution. Our social life was "like an island in the sea," * and the sea was a sea of coffee. This beverage was to us as Malmsey to Clarence, as Falernian to Horace, as the Pierian Spring to poets. We made libations to the coming day in coffee, at breakfast; we sped the parting day with stirrup-cups of it, at supper; we drowned ourselves in it, in the last full ecstasy of good dinners.

As heathens worship their grotesque ideals through grotesque

* [Bailey, *Festus*; the allusions in the next sentence are to Shakespeare's *Richard III* and Horace's *Odes*.—Ed.]

idols of wood and stone, so we, genuine coffee being invisible as any spirit during the war, made hideous images of it and paid our devotion to these, morn, noon, and night. We made decoctions of pease, of potatoes, of pea-nuts, of meal, of corn, of okra, of butter-beans, of rice, of acorns, of heaven knows what else. These we sugared (with sorghum-syrup), and these, our cows having been slaughtered after the manner of beef-cattle in the scarcity thereof, we drank milkless, and called them kauphy.

A cup of genuine coffee!

This in the Southern States, in the year 1864, was alike the Dream of soldiers and of statesmen, of old men and of matrons, of children and of slaves.

Happy Gorm Smallin! He realized this dream.

The waiter brought in the ideal, on a tray. Mr. Smallin sugared and stirred and drank.

"What else'll you have?" said Cranston, quietly laughing as he saw how the coffee, meandering through the great desert of Smallin, did forthwith cause the same to smile and blossom as the rose.

"What—else?" slowly repeated Mr. Smallin. Question of questions! How should he tell, he, who so long had wanted everything and had nothing, to eat?

Mr. Smallin would have preferred time to think on it, but his pent appetite brooked not delay; it rose and poured over the feeble dam he tried to erect, and he floated upon the stormful current. He eagerly seized the first chance to guide himself into a haven.

"Major," said he with solemnity, as if he were an acolyte questioning a venerable father upon the sacred mysteries, "what air *you* goin' to take?"

"Nothing!!"

Kind Heaven, it was a blow like to the blow wherewith King Richard did fell the stout friar of the greenwood chapelle! *

It was as if Mr. Smallin's bush, by which he was pulling in to bank, suddenly gave way by the roots, so that he floated out again, despairing, into the stream. Nay, more. That a man, with good serviceable white teeth gleaming through his mous-

*[Scott, *Ivanhoe.*—Ed.]

tache, a man with a mouth and appurtenances thereunto pertaining, a man with the ordinary passions of humanity,—that a *man*, in the time of the war, should sit at table, in sight and smell of the very things,—and take nothing to eat; this was a trifle too much for Mr. Smallin. His mind recoiled from the contemplation of such a phenomenon, and he resolutely closed his eyes upon this " devilish suggestion " which made his brain reel.

With a tremor, as if the devil had flitted by while his eyes were shut, he opened them. At which auspicious moment, sublime luck, even as the goddess in the old Virgilian battle, arrayed herself on hesitating Smallin's side. At the other end of the table Mr. Smallin saw a thrilling sight.

Four rough sailors, not long ashore, sat there making great ado over their grub. Of these, one's face showed dim through a cloud of smoke from a hot dish of stewed oysters, like the face of your future husband in one of those charming visions conjured up by the great second-sight necromanceress, Madame —— from Paris; another was attacking, with wild energy and marvellous sagacity in the avoidance of bones, a plate of fried hog-fish; a third could not see his plate by reason of a huge beefsteak thereupon, and was making successful endeavor to *see* his plate; and a fourth had just finished squaring, with great nicety of eye and accuracy of handling, a slice of ham that had been sent in circular, and upon which reposed, as yet untouched by this dallying gourmand, three of those most pitiful of all flat squelched objects in nature and art—fried eggs.

" Here, you! said Mr. Smallin to the waiter, keeping his eye fixed upon the other end of the table as if he were reading his Bill of Fare: " Fetch me a dish o' eysters, hot! an' some fish, some o' them, some—pirch, hit looks like f'om here; an' some beefsteak, 'ith butter on it, an' pepper a plenty! an' some ham and eggs, an' saw the ham out'n bone an' all, like yan slice: an'—an'—waal, fetch *them* fust; an' some bread;—an' some mo' kauphy! " he shouted as the astounded waiter vanished into the dark regions where the kitchen lay *perdue.*

And now again burned the ardent soul of Smallin, and again, as if to cool it, he plunged it into a question.

" Major," said he, " how long, mought you think, 'll take him to git 'em ready? "

Cold, cold indeed, was the water that Cranston offered.

"I should think," replied he, meditatively, "about three quarters of an hour!"

An expression overspread the face of Mr. Smallin which can only be described by a paradox—it was a visible groan. This, not long lingering, died away and dissolved into a plaintive look of settled melancholy, during which Mr. Smallin sat and idly struck his horn-jointed fingers upon the table, in his abstraction finishing his kauphy at a draught.

But long-suffering hath an end.

As peace out of grimy war, as sweet spring out from the Merlin-beard of winter, as Æneas from Avernus' smoky pit, issued at last the waiter from the dark regions, bearing gifts which Mr. Smallin did not fear.

Utterly disdaining that his cohorts (Mr. Smallin was a captain of ten—fingers) were not by any means gleaming with purple and gold, Mr. Smallin came down like the wolf on the foal, with dire intent to utterly mangle and crunch the several vivers.*

Sternly, single-souledly, Mr. Smallin devoted himself to the great work before him. He did not, would not, could not talk.

"How long since you were in Tennessee, Smallin?" asked Cranston, seeing him fairly started, impatient for news of those who had made so deep impression on his life, and full of bitter thoughts, of love which fed on absence, of half-formed designs.

"Some—time," chewed out the cormorant, without looking up.

"Was Mr. Sterling living when you left?"

"Umph, humph."

"Was Miss—were the two young ladies still at his house?"

"Umph—b'lieve they was."

"Damned glutton!" ejaculated Cranston.

"Yaas,—umph, humph," abstractedly remarked Mr. Smallin, while egg No. 3 ran partly down his chin, leaving yellow footprints upon that sand, which must have been anything but heartsome signs to egg No. 4.

Cranston gave it up, but his tormentor kept at his work.

* [The punnish allusions are to Byron, "The Destruction of Sennacherib." The MS, at this point, quotes the penultimate line of Poe, "The Conqueror Worm."—Ed.]

Once, and suddenly, the Ravenous surceased a moment.

"Major, hit's the month of May now, hain't it?"

"Yes."

"'Feard it's too soon for 'em," said Dalgetty,* in a melancholy soliloquy. "Howsomedever; here waiter! Got any chickens: young uns?"

Of course the waiter had chickens.

"Fetch one; fry him—in batter," guzzled the bibulous voice, resounding sepulchrally from inside the coffee-cup.

But to this trembling soul came its doomsday. At length Dalgetty could no more.

Cranston saw that this man who had sat down at table a sour-faced, half-bowed, scowling son of darkness, arose from it erect, complacent, to all appearance a son of the morning—if it could be imagined, even by a poet, that sons of the morning wound up their ambrosial breakfast with that luxuriant, loud, and resounding eructation wherewith Mr. Smallin trumpeted the fullness of his—satisfaction. Who might believe that out of mere dead flesh of beasts, which hath been also burned, could arise such moral dignity and sweetness as Mr. Smallin's face now displayed beamingly? Indeed, in this moment Mr. Smallin had forgot his revenge. Such flowers from such decay!

Might not the statistics of crime be also called statistics of hunger?

True, Falstaff and Fosco had plenty of sack and plenty of tarts and cream. Yet, the one took purses from mere dread of thirst, the other lied and apostatized from dread of hunger.**

That the Confederate army starved, and yet was a confessedly virtuous and patriotic army,—let men give them credit.

The souls of these men did not reside in the stomachs thereof. The soul of this deserter did. Cranston had determined to see Felix Sterling once more. He would procure leave of absence as a spy in the Confederacy. Mr. Smallin would guide him. To buy Mr. Smallin—this came first. Cranston made a quick bid.

"Smallin," said he, when he had gotten that smiling individual into a room at the hotel, "don't you want to go home?"

"Thar's jest whar I'm a-gwine."

* [Character in Scott, *The Legend of Montrose.*—Ed.]

** [Allusions to characters in Shakespeare, *King Henry IV, Part I,* and Wilkie Collins, *The Woman in White.*—Ed.]

" How much will you take to get you and me there, through the Confederacy?"

It was not in the nature of Smallin to bite so quickly at bids as at bread.

" You want to go thar, too?"

" Yes."

" Waal, Major, I should think 'at about a hundred dollars in greenbacks mought do a'most any thing now, in that section!"

" Very good. The money's yours when we get there. Make the arrangements. If you betray me, Smallin," he coolly continued, " here's a little dog that'll trail you through every ravine in your mountains till he bites you. Feel his teeth!"

Cranston placed the cold muzzle of a pistol against Gorm Smallin's forehead.

Which action awoke disagreeable memories, and spoiled the fine lingering aroma of Mr. Smallin's dinner. He smiled very faintly, and did not reply.

He muttered to himself something very like Joxabobble.

Chapter XII

Ef thar is enny gentleman in this bull-pen, he will, &c., &c.
Extract from Bulletin-board, Point Lookout Prison

TO GO into a prison of war is in all respects to be born over. For, of the men in all the prisons of the late war, it might be said, as of births in the ordinary world,—they came in and went out naked. Into the prison at Point Lookout, Maryland, were born, at a certain time, of poor and probably honest parents, twelve thousand grown men. Their inheritance with which they had to begin life *de novo* was the capability of body or soul wherewith each happened to be endowed at the moment of this second birth. And so, in this far little world, which was as much separated from the outer world as if it had been in the outer confines of space, it was striking to see how society immediately resolved itself into those three estates which invariably constitute it elsewhere.

For there were here, first, the aristocrats, who lived well but did not labor; second, the artisans, who lived well by laboring; third, the drones, who starved by not laboring. Moreover one could find here all the subdivisions of these great classes which occur in the regions of crowded civilization. For instance, of the aristocrats, there were the true-gentlemanly sort, the insulting-obtrusive sort, the philanthropic sort, the fast sort; of the artisans, there were the sober-citizenly sort, the mind-your-own-business-and-I-mine sort, the gloomy, brooding-over-oppression sort, the cheerful workers, the geniuses, together with those whose labor was spiritual, such as the teachers of French, and arithmetic, and music, including those who lived by their wits in the bad sense; and of the drones, the kind who swear that the world owes them a living, but who are too lazy to collect the debt; the sentimental-vulgar kind, whose claims are based upon a well-turned leg or a heavy moustache, and are consequently not appreciated by a practical world; the self-deprecatory sort, who swear that Nature has been unkind in endowing them, and who then *must* starve for consistency's sake or forswear themselves; and lastly, the large class of out-

and-out unmitigated drones, who, some say, serve the mere purpose of inanimate clay chinked into the cracks of this great log-cabin which we all inhabit, and who, poor men! must endure much bad weather on the wrong side of the house.

Was there then no difference between life in the prison and life in the world?

It is to be answered,—none, generically; the difference was one of degree merely.

For instance, if our every-day world had a catechism, its first question, What is the chief end of man? might be answered, "The chief end of man is either end of Pennsylvania Avenue." Whereas this question in the prison-world catechism would be answered, "The chief end of man is the West End";—which at Point Lookout was (for the pleasure of the paradox-loving) at the eastern extremity of the Peninsula.

In the one case the aim was to be President or Congressman, with honor and luxury; in the other, the aim was to get into a cracker-box cabin, where rain and vermin were not free of the house, as they were in the tents in which ten out of the twelve thousand resided.

So, the stature of the men and the burning of their passions remained the same inside the prison as out of it, only the objects of these passions and exertions were immeasurably diminished in number and dignity. To Philip Sterling this was the terrible feature in the prison-changed behavior of his old army friends. They did not crowd to shake joyful hands with him and hear the news from outside, but met him with smiles that had in them a sort of mournful greasiness, as if to say: Ah, old boy, mighty poor eating in here! Their handshakes were not vigorous, their souls did not run down and meet Philip's at the finger-tips. How could they? These same souls were too busy in devising ways and means to quiet the stomachs and intestines,—a set of dependents who show their born inferiority to the soul by always crying out to it when they are in distress, and by always endeavoring to dethrone it when they have waxed fat on its labor.

Some such thoughts crossed Philip's mind, as on the loveliest morning of May, a few days after his night in the cell at Fortress Monroe, he found himself inside the great gate of the prison at

Point Lookout. He had recognized and spoken to some friends as they passed by, but had not yet left the rank in which his squad of seventy fellow-captives had been drawn up after being marched into the prison.

A Federal sergeant told them off into smaller squads. Philip stood in the last.

—" Four, five, six, seven, eight," finished the sergeant. " Plenty o' room in eleventh division. Corporal, Eleventh! "

" Here, sir."

" Here's your squad. March 'em down."

" Forward," said the corporal, placing himself with the front file.

Passing a row of small A tents presently, the corporal looked at his book.

" Tent fifteen; think there's four men in it. Let's see." He thrust his head into the low opening. " How many in here? "

" 'Bout a million, countin' lice and all! " responded a voice, whose tone blent in itself sorrow, anger, hunger, and the sardonic fearlessness of desperation.

" Guess *they* want another man in, if *you* don't," said the corporal, with a pleasant smile. " You, Number Four, what's your name? "

" Philip Sterling."

" Bunk here. Rest, forward,"—and the corporal passed on with his squad, writing, as he went, the name in his book.

A long, cadaverous man sat outside the door of Philip's tent, sunning himself. He was bare to the middle, but held a ragged shirt on his knees, toward which he occasionally made gestures very like those of a compositor setting type.

" 'Fords me a leetle amusement," said he, looking up with a sickly smile toward Philip. " Jest gittin' well o' the feever: cain't git about much yet! "

Sick at heart, Sterling made no reply, but entered the tent. Just inside the entrance stood a low bench, which held a rat-tail file, a beef-bone, a half-dozen gutta-percha buttons, a piece of iron barrel-hoop, two oyster shells, and a pocket-knife. Cross-legged on the ground before it, sat a huge individual, who was engaged in polishing, with a rag and the grease of bacon, a gutta-percha ring which he held with difficulty on the tip of his little finger.

For this man's clothes, those three thieves, grease, dirt, and smoke, had drawn lots; but not content with the allotment, all three * were evidently contending which should have the whole suit. It appeared likely that dirt would be the happy thief.

" Wash 'em! " said this man one day when the Federal corporal had the impudence to refer to the sacred soil on his clothes —" wash 'em? corp'ral! I'm bound to say 'at you're a dam fool! That mud's what holds 'em together; sticks 'em fast,—like! Ef you was to put them clo's in water they'd go to nothin' jest like a piece o' salt! "

As inside of these clay-clothes a stalwart frame of a man lived and worked, so, inside this stalwart clay-frame lived and worked a fearless soul, which had met death and laughed at it, from the Seven-days to Gettysburg, but which was now engaged in superintending a small manufactory of bone trinkets and gutta-percha rings, the sale of which brought wherewithal to eke out the meagre sustenance of the prison ration.

Sterling threw down his blanket.

" This corner occupied? "

" Wa'al—yes, a leetle, you may say. I should judge thar was about some sebben or eight thousand livin' thar now. You needn't mind *them* tho'; they won't keer ef you sleep thar," observed the huge ring-maker.

" They are very kind, indeed."

" Sorry I cain't offer you a cheer; jest now loaned out all the cheers."

Sterling squatted tailor-wise upon his blanket, placed his chin in his hand, and prepared to go into a terrible sentimental review of the utter loneliness of his position. Suddenly, however, the ludicrous phase of the situation came over him. He smiled, then chuckled, and at last burst into a long, uproarious laugh.

The eye of the ring-maker twinkled. His lip quivered. He thrust his head though the opening of the tent and ejected from his mouth a surprising quantity of tobacco-juice. It was his manner of laughing. Beyond this he made no sign.

" Hello, Sterling, where are you? " shouted a cheery voice outside.

* [With these words Fragment C (the last part of the MS) ends.—Ed.]

Philip showed a merry face through the door, and recognized an old " Ours."

" By the poker, but you are merry for a man that's just come to Point Lookout! As a general thing we may say here,

My cue is villainous melancholy.*

And of all men in the world *you,* who were always a sort of melancholy Jacques! Have you, like him, heard a fool moralling on the times?" he continued, shaking Philip's hand, and directing their walk toward the head of the division.

" Aye, that have I," replied Sterling.

" We must get you out o' that hole in the 11th div. some way. Let's see; I think I saw an advertisement yesterday on the bulletin-board yonder, of a fellow in the 3d that wanted to sell out. Let's walk up and see."

The bulletin-board was surrounded by a thick crowd, to whom a lucky man on the inside was reading, in a loud voice, a long list of names from a paper tacked to the plank.

" Letters from Dixie," said Sterling's friend.

They placed themselves on the outer edge of the circle, and gradually moved in toward the centre.

" Do you notice a man over on the other side of the crowd yonder, pushing and struggling this way, with his gaze fixed on you?" said Sterling, to his friend. " His eye has a snaky glare in it. He hasn't lost sight of you for ten minutes. Got something against you, hasn't he?"

" He is my Nemesis. Every morning at nine o'clock, I come to the bulletin-board. Every morning at nine o'clock he meets me here, and demands of me a"—

" What?"

" A chew of tobacco! He commenced it two months ago. He has not missed a morning since. One day I attempted to dodge him. I sought cover behind every tent successively in the encampment. My meanderings must have been between five and ten miles in length. I thought I had succeeded. Breathless, but with a proud smile of triumph on my countenance, I walked slowly down the street, when he emerged dignifiedly from behind the next tent, and with disdainful composure inquired

* [Shakespeare, *King Lear*; the allusion in the next sentence is to *As You Like It*.—Ed.]

if I had ary chaw of terbacker about my clo'es. Since then I have resigned myself. He is a fate!"

"The Fates, then, have learned to chew tobacco, also! *eheu!* what would Pius Æneas have said to see them using spittoons in Hades?"

They were now at the board. It was covered with a thousand strips of paper, bearing in all manner of chirographies a thousand items of information. Mr. A. had changed his residence from No. 3, 4th division, to No. 7, 10th division; Mr. B. had a corner to let in his shop, "splendid stand for the unwanted bean-soup trade"; J. Shankins had a blanket "which he would swop it fur a par of britches, pleese caul at," &c.; the negro minstrels, in big red letters, announced "an entire change of programme, at 5 o'clock, G. M. Admission ten cents. No Confederate money received at the door"; L. Crabbe advertised to meet the eye of his brother, M. Crabbe, who, if in the prison, would call at, &c.; Jaines Haxley inquired "ef any gentleman in the 64th regiment seed his son with his own eyes killed at the Sharpsburg fite"; a facetious individual, blushing to reveal his name, and therefore writing over Anonymous, perpetrated the enormous joke of "Help wanted, to assist me in eating my rations. None need apply except with the most unexceptionable reference"; to which was appended the replies of a hundred different applicants for the situation; a sardonic gentleman inquired "if Dixie and the Yanks was still a-havin' high words. Let dogs delight," * &c., &c.; J. Shelpole had drawd a par of shues, but one of thum was number six an' wun was No. 10, and "wished to know ef enny gentleman had a shue, size number 10, pleese call at," &c., &c.

"Here it is at last!" said Sterling. The legend ran, "Fur privit reesons," (—"to wit," interposed Phil's companion, "a plug of tobacco, or the equivalent thereof in bread, bean-soup, cash, or other commodities,") "the undersined will swop places, fur a little boot, with eny gentleman in the 11th division. Pleese call at, &c, 3d division. Call soon and git a bargin.

"Sined J. THREEPITS"

"He's your man, Phil. Let's go right up and see him."

* [Watts, *Divine Songs*.—ED.]

"But how do you do it? when my corporal calls the roll"—

"All you've got to do is to answer to the euphonious appellation of Threepits, while Mr. T. will respond to the call for Sterling. The corporal won't know the difference. I can't deny but Mr. Threepits, in the matter of names, will slightly get the advantage in the swap. But it's a very good thing here to have two names; inasmuch as you stand two chances, when the exchange-lists are read out, to go back to Dixie. You must take care, however, that both of you don't answer to the same name, —a circumstance which has several times occurred, and caused no little pleasure to the sharp-witted authorities, as affording a pretext to remand the disappointed prisoner back to his hole."

Chapter XIII

Bot.—There are things in this comedy of Pyramus and Thisby that will never please. First, Pyramus must draw a sword and kill himself; which the ladies cannot abide.

Snout.—By'r Lakin, a parlous fear!

Midsummer Night's Dream

IN MID-MAY, near sunset, as John Cranston and Gorm Smallin mounted the rocky apex of Chilhowee Mountain, and turned a corner, so as to overlook Valley Beautiful, a question occurred to the former of these two individuals, which might far more appropriately have commenced his journey than ended it.

" What the devil," said Cranston, aloud, " have I come here for? "

He drew rein and sat still on his horse, thoughtfully gazing downward toward where Thalberg hung on the slope like a fruit on a tree.

" Danged ef I know, bless *your* heart! " doggedly remarked Gorm Smallin.

Cranston had early conceived a half disgust for his travelling companion, which, in the irritability of a soul not at ease with itself, had been more than once displayed amid the frets of their journey. Up to this time Mr. Smallin had been too much absorbed by the constant fear of detection and the adoption of precautions thereagainst, to notice this ill-concealed contempt of his employer; but now, when he was out of the long reach of the Confederate provost, when he was upon his native heath, when he had his hundred dollars in his pocket, and when he was in sight of his triumph, the mountaineer deemed that the circumstances justified him in asserting, at least to a prudent degree, the rights of man.

" Raälly, now," continued Gorm Smallin, " I *cain't* see, come to think of it, what in the name o' sense you *air* a-gwine back thar fur. Ef a man mought judge from some powerful cur'ous tales that's come to him, a man wouldn't think *you*'d be gwine back thar in a hurry. Seems as if I recomember havin' hearn 'em tell how "—Gorm Smallin sent a sidelong glance toward Cranston's face, as a mariner might look into the sky, to find out if the weather-signs would authorize him to proceed farther; and apparently satisfied himself of clear weather—" how a big fellar thar one night slapped you down in the parlor right afore the women! "

Cranston's treacherous calm, like that of the great deep, tempted the adventurous Smallin too far.

" An' how," continued Gorm, " you left thar betwixt two day-lights, and nervver cum back fur yer trunk, even! "

In a thin, languid, prolonged voice Cranston said only "Ah-h! " Then, quick as lightning, turned and struck Smallin on the cheek such a blow as sent that adventurous individual gyrating to the ground. Cranston's face was of the livid hue that makes the sea-horizon seem deadly, just before a storm. He leapt from his horse, drew his pistol, ran to his prostrate tormentor, and was in the act of firing right into his face, when, as if an invisible hand had dealt him a blow on the forehead, he threw back his head, fired his pistol in the air, glanced undecidedly about him for a moment, then sprang up the huge boulder that crowns the peak, and sat down, leaning his back against it, looking westward straight into the sun.

A dun-blue cloud, that seemed like a huge bruise on the pearly cheek of the sky, hung over the distant end of the line of peaks. From behind it, the sun shot crimson streaks like veins up the sky; but presently came down out of the cloud, making its edge an insupportable crimson brilliancy, and like a red, flaming heart, throbbed out infinite, pulsing floods of glittering blood-light over world and heaven.

And then the cloud moved down on the sun as he touched the far summits, and lay over him like an eyelid, from under which the fierce Polyphemus-eye of the sun glared back into Cranston's eye along the level peak-line.

It was like the blood-shotten eye of a wild beast, scowling vengeance after you have hurt him, as he retreats to his jungle.

Suddenly, with a great bound, the red sun leapt into the sea.

Cranston turned and looked into the eastern heaven, and lo, Brown Dusk, winged o' one side with a sigh and o' t'other with a smile, and whispering her secret to herself, came trailing up and lit a star in the east.

And then she floated down and walked airily into the valleys, like a kindly, smiling nurse, and whispered the sparrow to sleep on his twig, and put to bed the wren on her sedgy couch. And then she wandered by a curving ravine up the mountain, and came and stood about Cranston on the high rock.

Bad spirits are charming because they are daring. The evil ones in Cranston's soul could not resist the temptation to show that they were not afraid even in this exquisite presence of the Dusk. They came out and showed themselves to Cranston clearly, in his soul. They hovered before his soul's eye, and flouted their wickedness in his face. His impurities, his angers, his weaknesses, his bitter passions, marched past him. It was like a field-day down Below there, when the Devil reviews his troops. Their martial music was monotonous. It was the uttered word " Never." From somewhere this word uttered itself in Cranston,—" Never! " It is impossible that any human soul should confront this idea calmly. Cranston grew sick-hearted. A cascade of " Nevers " kept falling, falling in the hearing of his soul, whose monotony did not lull him but only sated him. Never—what? Let no man imagine it was the " conviction of sin " which tortured him. He loved Felix Sterling; he knew she was pure and high; he knew he was not. He knew that Felix was queen of herself. He had not been king of *his* self. Could he be king of her?

Never!

His infinite yearning was that his life might have been so white, that he could have stripped the flesh off his soul, and bared that to the sight of men and angels, and sworn in their hearing, while he clasped Felix, " I love her, and I am worth her, and by love!—the deepest oath—she is mine forever! "

" Never, never! " rhymed the evil spirits.

" Ah, I could not endure *now*, even if she were mine, to see her head here "—said Cranston to himself, and smote his breast—" here, where other heads have lain, and whence they have been pushed away, by wearied hands. Good God, my soul's all scarred and dented and dulled, and hers is smooth and white as her cheek, and glitters trenchantly as her eye when I played for her! What for? why is it? "

Cranston sprang upon his feet and tossed out his arms in a wild questioning gesture over the precipice.

" Why," said he, with upturned face, " you that made the world and the men in it, whatever they call you,—God, or

Christ, or Jove, or what not,—why have you made me so? Why didn't you make me strong and unselfish and white-souled like her? Why didn't you stretch out your finger and stop me from the acts which have rendered me incapable of winning this woman, or even of gaining any thing but the bitterness of self-accusation, and the consciousness of a foul imposition of *me* upon her too worthy—if I *could* win her? The world condemned and despised the man who saw his worst enemy sleeping and would not run to save him from a serpent that had coiled round his neck. The serpent was allowed to strike, and the man allowing won universal obloquy. But *you*—you, God—you allow every day your men and women to poison themselves with poisons that seem to them sunshine-wine. You stir not to prevent them, and you smile serenely with your skies and your stars over the convulsions of your children. Why didn't you keep me clean and pure like her?"

"Why?" he continued, with a crazied iteration, audibly.

"Why?" shouted he, at the top of his voice, up to the stars.

"Adzactly," muttered Gorm Smallin to himself. In view of all the circumstances, Mr. Smallin had concluded to waive for the present the rights of man in favor of the mights of man. Pursuing which policy he had arisen, and taking the bridle of the horse in his hand, had walked down the steep road descending the mountain, and was now in a path branching to the right from the road, some distance below the summit. Indistinctly he heard the last wild shout of Cranston. "Adzactly," said he; "ye may call thar till ye rot, for all the comin' back *I*'ll do, to show ye the way. I *did* think I'd ride with ye clur to Tolberg, and then come back to my cabin by myself; but I'm derned if ye hain't saved me the trouble! I'm glad enough to git shet of ye any way." With which consolation Mr. Smallin pursued his journey in silence and deep meditation. Through the May woods came upon him, rustling, sweet home-influences, as he neared the spot where, some months before the conscription bore him off, he had cleared some ground, built his cabin, and installed his young wife mistress. Here, and then, he had felt his breast expand with that strange responsibility-idea which crowns us kings when we are young, but bends us into slaves when we are old. He pictured the opening door of the cabin when he should knock presently. Sary, God bless the gal! would rush into his arms. The clasp, the strain, the thrill,—all these came to him. They would sit, and give and take the news. With lordly air he would deposit on the brackets over the head of his bed the magnificent silver-mounted rifle which Cranston in a generous burst had given him. Lord of the place,—this idea made Gorm Smallin straighten up involuntarily,—King of it,—aye, tittering ladies and gentlemen,—a mere Hesse Darmstadt of a kingdom, yet nevertheless a veritable kingdom, and I, Gorm Smallin, king of it; a mere log-cabin, yet I

Loved it better than many a better

house!

Thinking in his ruder dialect some such thoughts, Gorm Smallin emerged into the small cleared space that surrounded his cabin.

Emerged,—and stood suddenly still as a gravestone. No cabin was there. He walked waveringly forward. A black patch on the ground revealed the spot where his house had stood. He wandered slowly across this black blur on the earth. The melancholy crunch of his feet upon the cinders overcame him. His limbs trembled, he sat falteringly down upon the charred remains of his kingdom, and a tear started from each eye.

The Devil, who has tact in these matters, embraced this weak moment. "What ho, there, Old Revenge,—old Trusty,"—said the Devil, in endearing terms, to his grand vizier. "Here's a heart, with gates unbarred. Enter and possess it in my name!"

It must be confessed, his Satanic Majesty has also administrative talent, and inspires his servants with enthusiasm. The heart was entered and formally possessed. O lithe Temptation, thou swift tropical tiger of most rare exquisite spots, thou art never more dangerous than when thou hast just retired before a human eye into thy jungle, as if the eye-glance had conquered thee; for then, when the man hath twice gratulated himself, and whilst he is stooping to pluck one of thy jungle-flowers to crown his victory withal, *then* thou leapest!

Gorm Smallin on this May night had even reproached himself for his vengeful feelings against John Sterling, and abandoned them. To-morrow, other cares and old John's kind face would have dissipated them forever. But listen:—

"I heered," presently he muttered to himself,—"I heered as

the Yanks had been burnin' the houses of them that went off to the Confed'ate army. An' whose fault was it *I* went? John Sterling's! An' *he*'s got sons in the Confed'ate army, an' *his* house is a-standin' yit, for I seed it from the rock back yan; why didn't they burn *hit*? Because *he*'s rich, an' I'm poor."

Gorm Smallin rose deliberately to his feet, while it seemed to him as if liquid steel were slowly diffusing itself through his veins.

"Hit's been a rich man's war an' a poor man's fight long enough. A eye fur a eye, an' a tooth fur a tooth, an' *I* say a house fur a house, an' a bullet fur a bullet! John Sterlin's got *my* house *burnt, I*'ll get *his'n* burnt. John Sterlin's made *me* resk bullets, I'll make *him* resk 'em! An' ef I don't may God-a-mighty forgit me forever and ever, amen!"

Gorm Smallin entered the woods with his face toward Thalberg, walking slowly at first, as if he meditated, and gradually increasing his pace, as his plans grew definite, until his strides were more like long leaps than steps.

On the top of his rock lay John Cranston like a chained Prometheus. It was right that vultures should feed on Cranston's heart, as they were now feeding. He had stolen the fire of heaven, to kindle his kitchen-fires with. He had stolen a woman's love,—that lambent, lurid, hot-sweet fire of heaven,—and applied it to mere fleshy purposes. Now, when again he urged his daring head up through the sky to steal once more, in spite of the holier uses he designed for it the flame rebelled, and shot its fire-barbed arrows, and scorched and blinded and repelled him. Here was he, a sitter upon lonely rocks, and a prey to that most terrible vulture, himself.

The top of Chilhowee is a long, narrow plateau, level, except where the huge rock rises upon which Cranston sat. Along this plateau, at right-angles to the road crossing the mountain, runs an old, blind, grassy path, surrounded by rocks on either side strewn in all fanciful circles and angles. This path winds about the rock and gives into the main road suddenly.

In the deep twilight Cranston heard hoofs of horses coming along this path toward his rock, and presently began to distinguish the voices of two women in conversation. They quickly ceased, and the women rode on in silence until just under the rock. Felix said,—

"What are you thinking of, *Liebchen*?"

"I was just thinking," replied Ottilie, "that if we were in a city, amongst men, riding alone at this hour, we should be frightened to death; whereas here amongst rocks and wild beasts, we stray in the night with the most charming fearlessness. Strange, isn't it," she continued, meditating half-aloud, "that men should be more dangerous to men than all the tigers and storms?"

"So," cried Felix, "and women are as dangerous to women. Look! With your German enthusiasm, and your dear, dainty-hearted German Heine, that you read to me at the spring yonder, you've made me leave my veil and my brooch there. Sit on your horse here, dear, till I gallop back and get it. 'T won't take me ten minutes."

"Indeed, I'd rather go with you," said Ottilie, half turning her horse.

"No, you sha'n't. You look pale and tired enough now. Here! see; I've tied your horse! Walk up this winding path to the top of the rock, and see how Valley Beautiful looks by night. Obey me, my darling Ottilie!" said Felix, and kissed her, and galloped away.

Ottilie dismounted, and walked up the rocky steps.

Cranston stood erect behind an abruptly rising ledge of the rock, with folded arms.

It was quite light up there. The white rock reflected the thousand star-rays that fell upon it; and a faint halo, which was more a memory of the sun than a light, yet diffused a mild and mysterious half-twilight around the mountain-top.

As Ottilie stepped upon a broad, flat plateau, Cranston advanced a pace to meet her. Oh conventionality! He was in the act of extending his hand and saying, "How are you?" when her white face, in which he could almost see the sweet blue veins that in these days began to glimmer through the delicate skin, smote upon him like a sheet of white lightning. In an uncontrollable agony he threw himself on his face and grovelled at her feet.

Presently he heard her dress rustling, and the long train trailing softly over the rock. He raised his head. Ottilie was standing on the very verge of the ledge, where the sheer precipice sank straight down many hundred feet, with arms stretched far upward and hands clasped.

Fearful that a noise would startle her into destruction, Cranston crawled like a snake close to where she stood, and grasped the long train of her thick riding-dress.

"O God!" she said, in a voice ineffably soft, "I thank thee that this pain in my heart, which so long hath been dull as ashes and yet burnt like fire, which so long hath been leaden and yet cut sharp like steel, which so long hath refused even to throb in its monotonous ache,—O God, I thank thee for even a small variation of it which makes it sharper and hotter and livelier for one moment."

"O God," she said in a pathetic inquiring tone that went jagged into Cranston's heart,—"O God, hath not sorrow its dandy-moments, hath not sorrow its time when it would prank itself for a show to others? hath not sorrow its whim and its caprice? doth not sorrow, like a maiden, forever regard her image in the clear pool and take her maidenly pretty attitudes; and wilt Thou deny sorrow this little comfort ere it drown itself in the pool of Thine eternity? and have I not yearned that this man whom thou seest grovelling now on the rock should be here when I cast myself from this place, and hast thou not brought him here for this, kind God?"

"O God," she said, "have I not failed of life, and art Thou not done with me here, and can I do any good thing save maybe to die in this man's sight, and so perhaps strike a new regret into his soul which may save some other from my wretchedness?"

"And yet," she said, with still softer voice, "perhaps I wrong him,—*I* erred too; I will not go, with a wrong for my last act; I forgive him, and I throw him this kiss of forgiveness," and she drew down one hand, kissed it, and waved it back to where Cranston lay.

"Thou star, there," suddenly she cried, "in one second I will be waving my wing in thy sweet fire!" and threw her hands apart, and sprang.

But Cranston had clasped her about the waist, and in an instant had borne her back, down the irregular declivity. She had closed her eyes in a momentary faintness, but opened them quickly; and, lying in his arms, taunted him,—

"Coward, cruel, cruel coward! how dared you place your false arm around *me* again? How"—

"Pity, pity, pity," said Cranston hoarsely, and a great shiver went through his frame.

"Who asks *me* for pity?" She raised herself up and stood. "You? you? O,—*you?*"

"She is coming. For God's sake collect your strength. Can you sit your horse?" said Cranston, and lifted Ottilie into the saddle; "I cannot meet her, *now!*" He ran back behind an angle of the rock.

For one moment the woman's jealousy rose in Ottilie's heart. She looked at his retreating form with a scornful expression, but quickly the tight lip trembled in a bitter smile. "O Heaven!" she said, "a jest, an infinite jest: I *jealous!* I!"

"How the little night-breeze groans sometimes through these pines!" said Felix as she cantered up. "I could have sworn I heard a man talking!"

"Yes, yes. Did you find the brooch?"

"Oh yes. Let's go home; and get a good rating from father for staying so late! But he'll kiss us twice when it's over, and bless us, and put his hand on our heads; and that's worth a little scolding. Isn't it, you dear white flower-petal?" and Felix leaned over and kissed the cold lips of her friend as they rode off down towards Thalberg.

Cranston emerged from his hiding-place and followed them, afar off.

A few yards from the edge of his clearing, Gorm Smallin stumbled and fell over a small long hillock. It was a grave, with a plain head-board. The mountaineer never travels without his tin match-box. He made a light, and read on the board:—

"S. S."

"Sary Smallin!" he said to himself. "Wife dead, too?"

He strode on, with unutterable thoughts straining his soul. Presently Thalberg rose grimly before him. The house was dark on that side. The negroes were gone with the Yankees.

"*They* won't bother me," he said to himself, as he thought of it. He walked round the house. One room was lighted, on the other side. He had but time to jump behind a tree as John Sterling passed into the house.

"Hear the girls coming down the road, wife!" said the cheery voice. "Let's get 'em some supper ready. They'll eat like young hyenas!"

Gorm Smallin went back to the dark side. A low window was open. He pulled off his shoes and climbed into it. It was the same by which Cranston had left Thalberg. Disgrace left it; Revenge entered it.

Revenge is ingenious. Gorm Smallin dug a hole in the plastering with his knife, and cut through a half-dozen laths. In the space between the laths and the inner wall he deposited a charge of powder, upon which he carefully rested the corners of two or three book-leaves which he tore out of Phil Sterling's Carlyle on the table. Upon the other corners of these leaves he deposited a pile of paper, and splinters of laths split off with his knife. He then lit one end of a twig of rotten-wood and placed it in the opening, the other end resting on the powder. Deftly and quietly he locked the door on the inside, and dropped from the window. No danger of any body's seeing the fire from outside,—he said to himself, and grinned. He stole round to the very edge of a lane of light that shot straight out from the window of the music-room, among the black tree-trunks. He selected a tree, and stood behind it: then pointed his gun so that the rifle-sight was in the glare and his eye in the shade. "Mought blind me," he muttered: "shines the bead splendid, though. They'll likely set thar, a'ter the women's had supper. Hit'll do!" He took down his rifle, folded his arms upon the muzzle of it, and stood still as a statue.

Two hours Gorm Smallin stood. His hope began to fail him when John Sterling entered the music-room, Ottilie, Felix, and wife following.

"Well, girls," said he, "if it is isn't too soon after supper, let's have some music."

John Sterling paced about, noiselessly, while they sang.

Gorm Smallin's eyes must needs play unceasingly in all directions. He saw a tall form cross the lane of light from the other window. It placed itself against a tree, and fixed eyes upon Ottilie, and stood, statue-like. It was the poor Indian, Chilhowee, worshipping as he worshipped nightly. Presently another dusky figure appeared on the other side of the light-bar, and took stand, and gazed upon Felix from among the trees. Gorm made it out to be John Cranston; whereat his soul shouted with a hellish exultation.

"They'll all see Gorm Smallin's revenge!" he said to himself. Nature, probably upon the same principle that her sharks can't bite without turning over and giving time, has ordained that the revengeful man, if deliberate, must always make a little speech, at least to himself, before he commits the fatal act. Gorm Smallin began to gloat, and menace, and taunt, and chuckle, and prematurely triumph.

John Sterling sat between the girls, and his wife just behind him, with head lovingly over his shoulder. Alternately his tender hand stroked hair and cheek of all three.

"Wife and daughters," he said, "I feel, somehow, as if the world would end to-night; but I've often felt so before, when the music roused me."

"And so we needn't pack our trunks?" interposed Felix, with a roguish twinkle of the eyes.

"No. But listen," continued John with a tender solemnity—"Listen. God, help us all. Wife and children, life is Force.* Now, Force effects motion and resistance. Time and space are measures of resistance, and motion varies inversely to them, so that, resistance being abolished, Force becomes infinite and time and space nothing. Now, after death they say time and space are abolished; but as our Force does not become infinite, therefore resistance continues. What shall take the place of time and space as its measures? Your young minds may dream of it.

"Motion is change; science is the observation of the changes or motions of mind and matter. Art effects changes or motions of mind and matter. All men can see, and all men can effect, and therefore all men are *savans* and all men are artists. The good *savant* sees correctly what is low and what is high, and

* [John Sterling's speculations in the following pages are paralleled in numerous passages throughout the Ledger and echoed in Lanier's later writings. —ED.]

the good artist effects higher results from lower ones. There will come times in your life when you will find this generalization not wholly unhelpful to you.

" Now passing by the million million *savans* and artists that by day and by night through the world are seeing and doing, I wish to speak to you of some particular artists.

" Seven motions of matter belong to the painter, and seven motions of matter belong to the musician: these be the seven colors of the spectrum and the seven tones of the scale. And as the prism analyzes light into seven colors, and the string analyzes sound into seven tones, so life analyzes time into seven days of the week.

" Whereby hangeth a fancy, which being but a fancy, yet will not hurt you to dream upon it. For inasmuch as there be living motes that hover in the seven colors or float in the seven tones; so may we be living motes that hover and float through the seven days, and these seven days may be to some higher folk in the universe but seven colors, and to other higher folk but seven tones. Aye, this present life may be but a wavering ray, seven-colored, thrown from above. Runs not the spectrum from red up to violet, which is to say, advances not life from red Hades up to violet Heaven?

" And this present life may be but a seven-toned sound, struck from above. Runs not the scale from Do to Si,—from a groan to a joy-cry?

" So, *exeunt* fancies, all! Enter facts!

" The facts are: there be five channels through which the artist receives lower effects, and through which he returns forth higher ones. These be taste, touch, smell, sight, and hearing. Now, by common consent of all men, it is agreed that taste, touch, and smell, poor devils, shall be forever engaged principally as scullions and waiters for humanity, since eating, feeling, and smelling are considered as the (so to speak) mere domestic necessities of the flesh, and their pleasures rank as high only as table-pleasures, and vary according to condiments, sauces, and the quick-waning activity of the said scullions and waiters.

" But sight and hearing, as they are highest by physical measurement, are also highest by spiritual rank. For while, one moment, the eye and the ear with their less happy brethren, perform the offices of scullions and waiters, yet the next moment they may be performing the offices of genii and angels. For these have power beyond the flesh and the earth, over the spirit of man.

" As, for instance; in a morning, our ear will bring to us the sound of the breakfast gong, and our eye will cunningly superintend our steps and show us the way to the breakfast-room. Base scullions and waiters, so far, but remarkably useful! Wait, though. We sit at breakfast-table and read the paper. Eye informs us there will be a concert to-night, and Liszt will play some of Chopin's best music. Bravo, Eye! thou art advancing from thy scullionship and art already a private secretary! And bravo, again; for thou art lending a helping hand to thy poor brother Ear, and arranging fine things for him!

" Wait, though.

" Night comes; we go to the concert-room. Liszt plays; we writhe under the music like the old priestess under the divine afflatus, so that our souls prophesy good things; and we shout in glory that the man there with his piano and his wondrous fingers has made conquest over the grim kingdom of the unutterable,—has spoken the otherwise unspeakable; and as we leave the concert-room, brave Sight flashes up to the skies and lets down the star-beams, upon which, as upon a swaying golden ladder, our souls mount up to the very hem of the garment of God, we hearing, as we pass, the infinite music of the worlds singing while they spin the thread of time. And so, bravissimo, O Eye and Ear! This morning ye were but scullions and waiters; to-night ye have become fair heavenly friends, by whose airy guidance we wander through the morning glades, by the clear rivers, and across the mysterious wonder-chasms of the supersensuous Unknown Land!

" This morning ye conducted us to breakfast; to-night ye have wafted us to heaven!

" And so, dear wife and daughters, eye and ear are ever willing, either as swineherd or as Apollo, to serve and befriend the kings that paint and sing.

" But it would seem that there will be some difference of dignity between these two. For surely, the Art of to-day is music! I cannot now talk of photographs, which are *in omnium manibus.* But the art of painting has not struck its infinite roots into the domestic every-daynesses of life, as the art of music has. There are not many homes in the land where one finds a painter's palette or a camera; but where is the cottage or hovel in which one will not find either a piano, a guitar, a flute, a violin, a banjo, a jew's-harp, a whistling faculty, or a singing faculty? To go to the lowest form at once, do but look at the ten-year-old negro balancing his bucket on his head as he carries it home from spring or pump! Oh never, never would he 'tote' it safely, an he did not whistle all the time! He balanceth his burden safely, as the circus man his iron balls—to music. Every man might better balance his burden wherewith he is laden, if he kept time to music! Is any here that hath no burden, of water-buckets or of sins? If any,—forever let him hold his peace, nor whistle nor sing!"

At this moment a breeze came through the tree-tops, and swelled, and died away; making noise as if the maidenly bosom of the night heaved and panted with some fright of a dream, till the maid woke, and sighed for satisfaction that it was only a dream-fright, and rustled her night-drapery and composed herself to sleep again.

At this moment Cranston in the dark was devouring with his eyes sweet bending Felix in the light. "My queen, my queen!" he said, and yielded himself to the ecstasy of love and the luxury of gazing.

And Gorm Smallin even, after all, was growing softer-hearted each moment, and at the same time nerving himself, with curses and taunts and broodings upon ashes and death, to shoot.

And the Indian, gazing upon Ottilie with folded arms, had now no soul, but only a mist instead, which was interfused in all its folds with an intense undeveloped lightning of pure worship.

And the air was full with floating May-balm of buds and young leaves and mountain-flowers, and every moment ten thousand May-germs thrilled into life, and emitted each an odorous sigh in salute to cool bulbous brethren and grave trees and leafy neighbors.

"And this, dear wife and daughter," continued John Sterling, " brings me to the practical application of my little sermon. Remember now all I have said; especially that the artist's business is to effect higher motions from lower ones. Now, Adam the first man, and Christ the second man, did grieve and grieve. It is to record this that the Bible comes to us. This is the one Fact of humanity. My dearies, let us shoot right up behind the lark, on the brightest morning, and see what we shall see! The hills and mountains first flatten and then vanish, in the common level of the plain; and, exactly so, those moral hills,—political distinctions, social inequalities, moral superiorities, ethnical disparities,—all vanish in the common level of humanity.

" As we go up, first die out the songs of birds and the murmur of brooks; then the roar of seas, the howl of great winds, the grind of polar ice-fields, the stound of earthquakes and volcanoes, faint away into silence; and, exactly so, the din of battles, the iron clangor of labor, the hum of commerce, the turmoil of life, all mingle, and we hear them not.

" Let us now leave our lark, whose wings refuse already to bear him in this thin air to which we are arrived, and let us ascend to where the atmosphere is rare enough—rare enough—well, rare enough, my girls, for the lungs of spirits to inhale.

" Here let us pause and look down.

" Upon the glimmering plain of human life we discern one huge pyramid which overglooms the whole desert.

" Up from this desert floats to our ears one single sound.

" This pyramid is a fact: it is suffering; and the sound is a moan!

" Brave Eye and Ear, therefore, withdrawing themselves to a convenient hearing and seeing point, inform us of suffering, of suffering, of suffering, alone.

" Now suffering being the result they bring to us, it is our duty, as good artists, to return forth a higher result, through eye and ear.

" How?

" Leaving aside Eye, for I have not time to talk of him, specially,—the great part of this suffering which comes to us is no better than mere physical suffering, mere sensual pain of appetites and disappointments, mere regret for a bad conscience whose principal disturbance is that it keeps us from sleeping well o' nights, mere dyspepticities and humors. All these base metals, music, a magic stone, transmutes into pure gold; into the strange sorrow *you* spoke of once, Felix. Know ye not the pain of music? It is composed of all other pains, fused and purified into a great, pure, unanalyzable yearning after God. This is what music does.

"Details?

"Well: to make a *home* out of a household (for instance), given the raw materials, to wit, wife, children, a friend or two, and a house—two other things are necessary. These are, a good fire, and good music. And inasmuch as we can do without the fire for half the year, I may say music is the one essential. After the evening spent round the piano, or the flute, or the violin, how warm and how chastened is the kiss with which the family all say good night! Ah, the music has taken all the day-cares and thrown them into its terrible alembic, and boiled them and racked them and cooled them, till they are crystallized into one care, which is a most sweet and rare desirable sorrow—the yearning for God. We all, from little toddler to father, go to bed with so much of heaven in our hearts, at least, as that we long for it unutterably, and believe it.

"My daughters, ye are both beautiful, and men will love you, and likely some strong hearts will halve a life with you. I wish you to show that the artist-life is not necessarily a Bohemian life, but that it may coincide with and *be* the home-life.

"And when ye play to your strong hearts, whether it be day-time music of wheels, needles, and household work, or night-music of pianos and voices, *play well*; that the listening folk beyond us may detect your note in the grand tone of the day, and may recognize it as a full, clear, round tone, well and featly and strongly struck from life, or from piano, or from voice.

"Amen!" said John Sterling; and fell instantly dead upon his wife's shoulder, who fell instantly dead upon his shoulder, both slowly sinking to the floor. For Gorm Smallin's bullet had passed through Sterling's right eye full into the forehead of his wife, which she had just laid lovingly against his temple. Terrified at his own act, Gorm's mind became almost a blank. There was but one definite idea in it—to keep still.

Cranston and the Indian, hearing the shot and seeing the

deaths, emerged into the light-lanes from the windows and simultaneously became aware of each other.

"O scoundrel, was it you?" hissed Cranston, and drew his pistol and fired at the Indian. Poor Chilhowee, believing in his turn that Cranston had committed the bloody deed, was in the act of raising his rifle as he received Cranston's ball in his shoulder. He dropped the gun, but continued running to the house, and he and Cranston rushed up the low steps and in at the open balcony window of the music-room together.

As Cranston, with the Indian just behind, dashed into the room, he stopped a moment to collect his thoughts. Felix had thrown herself upon the two corpses and was alternately pressing the yet-warm lips of her loved ones convulsively to her own. She raised her head a moment, and as she saw the haggard countenance and yet smoking pistol of Cranston, exclaimed, "O murderer! O my darlings!" and fell back upon the corpses, mute, with wild kisses.

Ottilie, involuntarily shrinking from the wild-eyed face which so suddenly appeared, had knelt near the bodies. She was praying, in a deep, husky voice. "*Liebe Gott, liebe Gott*," said she, "why dost thou not burn with lightning this fiend who ruins and murders, and then insults with his presence the living form of the ruined and the dead forms of the murdered?"

These words conveyed their meaning slowly to Cranston's mind. It was not till he had stooped by the bodies and placed his hand on the hearts and ascertained that no throb was in them, that the still-ringing words of the women flashed upon him the natural mistake into which they had fallen.

"I left here in disgrace," thought he rapidly; "they have not heard from me since; I reappear, at night, with pistol in hand,"—he dropped it in horror,—"just after the shot. Ha!" he said aloud in his bitterness, "just as I am on the verge of repentance, the merciful God bans me from my love with this hideous mistake, which every circumstance seems to justify, and which I cannot possibly disprove!" He staggered to a chair, and sat, and clinched his burning forehead in both hands. His reason began to strain and crack; brilliant sparkles commenced to shoot before his closed eyes,—sparkles known to the delirious. But the necessity for action warned him to dismiss the thoughts that were driving him towards madness.

A similar reflection had already brought Ottilie to her senses. She was half-aimlessly smoothing the dress and straightening the arms of the dead, when Cranston rose from his chair.

"Lend a hand," said the latter to Chilhowee. "It is done. Let's carry them where they can be cared for as the dead should be."

Up the broad stairs the bodies were borne, Ottilie leading the way and Felix following, mute, with stony eyes, blank-faced, broken-hearted, pathetic in her grief that had grown too scornfully great for demonstration.

Honest Gretchen, busy as any bee all day, had slept through it all, peacefully. Just as the bodies were being deposited in the apartment of John Sterling, loud screams were heard from the other side of the passage, and, a moment afterwards, Gretchen came running in, heedless of night-dress.

"Thalberg is a-fire!" she said, wringing her hands. "Thalberg is on fire!"

"Great God, is the whole house doomed? Show me where! Can it be put out?" exclaimed Cranston, dragging Gretchen back in the direction from which she came. A heavy volume of smoke was issuing from the open door of her room; a tongue of flame occasionally licked up through the smoke, and quickly the whole house roared with the angry murmur of the long-smothered fire.

"Down, all!" cried Cranston, darting back to the death-room. "Can you carry one body, Chilhowee?"

"Up with it then; follow!" With many a stagger and lurch, they got the dead out, and laid them upon the turf.

"Where is Felix?" Not doubting but she would follow, all had hastily descended.

But she had not seemed to hear the commotion. Seated, with hands patiently folded, she was gazing into vacancy, when Cranston returned to look for her.

"Come, Felix!"

She remained still as a statue.

There was no time to lose. The pine staircase was already blazing with frightful violence.

Cranston clasped the unheeding woman, and rushed, half-blinded with smoke, down the flaming stairway. His face was full of a fierce joy. He smiled, tossed back his long black hair, looked upward as he leapt along, and strained unconscious Felix to his bosom. One time, he thought, if never again!

On the way down, he passed Chilhowee, going up. Practical Gretchen! Just as Cranston had started back for Felix, Gretchen called Chilhowee.

"You know Ottilie's room?"

Did he not know it? It was his church. He had spent nights gazing at it.

"Yes!"

"Her jewels! She left them to-night on the bureau. Get them!"

The faithful Indian ran on his mission. As Cranston deposited Felix in Ottilie's arms, they saw him coming. As he neared the group, he staggered. Loss of blood from Cranston's bullet-hole had weakened him. He barely mustered strength to advance and hand the jewel-box to Gretchen, when he reeled and fell. Presently he opened his eyes, and fixed them upon Ottilie, and lay still. Long ago her woman's heart had divined his secret. She laid her hand upon his, and pressed it, in reverence for his long devotion. He smiled; and, ere long, death made rigid the smiling lips and glazed the smiling eyes. "Thou faithful heart!" murmured Ottilie, and leaned over and kissed the dark forehead.

Burning Thalberg did not long linger. A neighbor or two—neighbors were scarce in the Beautiful Valley—had arrived; but each stood in stupid bewilderment as he gazed at the dead on the ground and the fire leaping aloft.

The unsparing flames worked their will; and the mansion was gone.

So, upon the smoke of their home, floated up to heaven the souls of John Sterling and his wife.

So, in the ashes of this home, fell and was lost utterly, the Hope of John Cranston.

BOOK III

CHAPTER I

Chamberlain.— . . . As I live,
I'll lay ye all by the heels, and suddenly!

King Henry VIII

ONE DAY towards the last of March of 1865, Cain Smallin's appetite was immeasurably sharpened by untoward events. The scouts had been recalled from their operations on the Lower James. With Mrs. Parven and family in charge, the party had made their devious way to Petersburg and rejoined their regiment on the Petersburg lines, after parting with the wagons which contained the *Lares* of the Parvens, and which drove on to Richmond to deposit the said *Lares* in their city domicile.

Cain Smallin, provident man! was making biscuits. His culinary facilities consisted of a (technically so-called) skillet. *A bas* that upturned nose, thou French cook! A skillet? What could not one cook, or do, in or with a skillet? From a coffee-pot, to a Mambrino's helmet * to keep the infernal rain-strokes out of one's eyes o' nights, the offices of the skillet ranged.

The skillet was the soldier's *Lar.*

Around Cain's fire reclined in various attitudes peculiar to the old campaigner, Rübetsahl, Flemington, and Aubrey. Of whom Flemington, as he lay flat on his back, was singing with his whole soul a most pathetic ditty, beginning:—

Three foot one way, six foot t'other way,
Weighed three hundred pound! **

Aubrey was dreaming of fair Rebecca Parven, and Rübetsahl read a letter.

Now, by direction of the perverse fates, it had come about that, some days before the building of Cain Smallin's fire, a

* [Presumably the reference is to Ariosto, *Orlando Furioso,* or to Cervantes, *Don Quixote.*—ED.]

** [Current song, "Ole Massa Run Away."—ED.]

wandering shell had fallen upon the ground in that neighborhood, and had buried itself and smothered out the fuse. Moreover, the treacherous earth showed no sign of it, and Cain Smallin, being doubtless under ban of the sisters three, had selected the identical spot of the said burial for his culinary operations.

Rübetsahl's letter was a long one, and an old one. It bore date two or three months back. It was from Ottilie.

. . . .

"—So, I have told thee all. Friend, by that which hath been—and from *me* to *thee*, could there be holier oath of oaths than this?—I charge thee deal with me mercifully.

"But there are yet more things I must say. Art tired? Thou knowest we came here, to Richmond, with Cranston, from Tennessee. Wilt thou wonder that we came with one that seemed the murderer of our friends and the destroyer of our home? Well, *I* wonder, too; but what could we do? Despair had us; and I wished that Felix might be near her brother.

"So we came, at last. Some days after we had been at the American, Cranston came to our parlor.

"Ah, his countenance was so mournful, Rübetsahl!

"'I leave,' he said, 'to-day.'

"'Well?' I said, after some pause; and yet I pitied his sad, sad glance.

"'Ah,' he broke out, 'you still believe I did it. Think! Did I not save Felix from the flames?'

"'Yes.'

"'Did I not risk my life, defending yours, when we were attacked on the borders by the ruffians?'

"'Yes.'

"'Am I not in hourly danger that I be taken and hung for a spy? Have I even asked *you* not to betray me?'

"'Yes, and no!'

"'Have I discharged all your commissions? Have I found all your friends for you, and put you in communication with them?'

"'Yes.'

"'You still believe,' said he, with sinking voice, 'that—that I did it?'

"He spoke to me, but gazed all the time upon Felix, who sat near me.

"O Rübetsahl, was I wrong that I suffered my heart to be a little touched?

"Felix said nothing.

"'Felix,' said I, 'perhaps he is innocent.'

"Felix said nothing: would not even look towards him.

"'At any rate, sir,' said I boldly, 'we will give you the justice of the courts—the benefit of a doubt.'

"'I thank you,' he said with grave courtesy, 'for even so much. Farewell!'

"'Farewell,'—but I did not take his hand, and Felix still was dumb and vacantly gazing otherways. He descended the stairs, slowly, with downcast face. Shouldst thou meet him, be as I was to him: do not kill him, do not kill him, for the sake of the doubt!

"I must also tell thee that Felix is again alive; for she was surely dead, till three days since. The vacant calm of her grief was immeasurably pathetic. Ah, how I suffered!

"But, last Sunday, we went to church; for she would follow me like—*Du Himmel*—like a dumb spaniel! We arrived in time for the voluntary.

"Can it be that *thou* wast playing the organ that day? I could have sworn it. It was our Chopin that the organist played. As the first notes struck, Felix shuddered, and her eyes began to enlarge and to grow intelligent, and to gaze as if they *saw* something. Presently the rigid lips trembled, and trembled; and a tear, a blessed, blessed tear fell, and another, and then burst a storm of weeping so passionate that I led her from the church. Good friend, what a tempest was there when we were returned to the hotel! I was terrified; I feared her frame would go to pieces, like a vessel! But she 'rained her skies blue,' and was afterwards calmer, and slept; and she is now my own grave great-hearted Felix again. And she has thy letter;—thou seest, I can write it!

"And one more little corner to myself.

"God be praised! At length, I 'lean upon our fair Father, Christ!' How, and why, I know not, I care not; but I lean, and am strong. 'The wind bloweth whither it listeth, and thou canst not tell.' Perhaps it is because I am a necessity to Felix. To lavish upon her all tender cares and caresses,—this is my aim of life. And one lives not easily, nor long, thou knowest, without an aim of life.

" Rübetsahl, perhaps thy heart will be a little lighter for me, if I say again:

" God be praised!

" O—— "

Rübetsahl slowly folded his letter, and drew another, already well-worn, from his breast. Felix had learned to " thee " and " thou " from German Ottilie, till it was like mother-tongue to her.

" Thy letter is come," she wrote, " and mine shall meet it on the threshold like a hurrying kiss.

" And oh my king, my king, I do utterly love thee—and having written so, this pen shall never write another word, and I, this moment, cast it into the fire; whose yearning flames fly upward, as to thee flies thy

" Felix "

Cain Smallin sat, stiff-backed, upon the ground, sternly regarding his packed circle of biscuits in the skillet.

" How do they come on, Cain? Most done? " inquired Aubrey, from the other side of the fire, relapsing—how low, sweet Venus!—from his love-dream.

" Bully! brownin' a little, some of 'em. 'Bout ten minutes, yit," gloomily and sententiously replied the mountaineer.

. . . Six foot t'other way,
Weighed three hundred pound!

" And what the devil *are* the next words? " sang Flemington for the fortieth time.

The next words are lost to history, probably; inasmuch as Vesuvius *in petto* suddenly opened a crater immediately beneath Mr. Smallin's skillet; with consequences. The buried shell had exploded. Aubrey, being small, continued to gyrate for some time at varying distances from the centre. Flemington, a long man, rolled longitudinally to an amazing distance, and with dizzy rapidity.

Cain Smallin, receiving impetus from his feet upward, described six distinct and beautiful somersaults—six—and a half. The result of the half being that, at the immediate period of stoppage, Smallin's nose was penetrating the earth, and his eyes were sternly fixed upon the same, as if he were upon the point of detecting some agricultural secret of our ancient mother.

"Cain's perusing the 'volume of Nature!'" shouted Aubrey, who had risen first.

"'Sermons in stones;' he's reading one of 'em," echoed Flemington, holding his sides. Tweaking his own nose, to get the dirt off, Mr. Smallin arose with a dignity that struck awe into six admiring messes that had assembled.

"Boys," said he, in a broken voice of indignant but mournful inquiry, "have any of ye seed the skillet?"

CHAPTER II

Edgar.— . . . List a brief tale:
And when 'tis told, O that my heart would burst.
This bloody proclamation to escape
. . . .
. . . Taught me to shift into a madman's rags.

King Lear

LATE IN the afternoon of that day, Flemington got leave and strolled into town,—into poor, desolate Petersburg. He wandered aimlessly about through the upper part of the city. Flem was working off, as he was accustomed to say, his sentimentalities.

As the night comes on, one feels as if one approached the shore of life. Upon this shore, the receding wave of the day left phosphorescent sparkles. Lights began to glimmer in homes.

Occasionally, as a door opened to admit some late father or brother or other stay of a family, the laugh of children—for children did laugh, just as flowers bloomed, amid this desolation —escaped and saluted him like an unmeant caress. It was as if a bird sang while one hurried to a battle raging in the next woods.

Flemington wandered on, into the lower city. Here were no lights. The houses stood with doors open and windows up; and this, not by neglect of " careless tenants." There were no tenants. The whole quarter had been abandoned. Terrible Battery No. 5 had spoken a doom-word, and at its sound all these houses had been emptied of their souls. Like a cemetery of untenanted graves stood they, while hobgoblin shells screeched and chattered and made the emptiness hideous.

The night had come on gloomily, and the clouds were now black and threatening. The lines were quiet, and even Hoke's pickets were firing slowly and feebly. As Flemington turned, at the lower end of Bolingbroke Street, intending to go back to Jarratt's, the rain-storm broke upon him, and he ran up the steps of a brick house by which he was passing, to get shelter. He tried the door, found it unlocked, entered, and passed on into the parlor. The carpet was still on the floor. It had a soft "feel"; Flemington was tired of the pavements; he stretched himself out on the Brussels, and gave himself up to luxury.

He had listened to the rain but a few minutes when he heard the front door open. Almost immediately two persons entered the room in which he lay. "Somebody else got the sentimentals?" thought he, and peered curiously through the darkness. An inexplicable impulse forbade him to discover himself. As the figures passed him, a woman's dress brushed over his outstretched feet.

The strange visitors opened a door and went into an inner apartment.

"Jane," said a man's voice, "ye'll find some light'ood out thar in the passage. Git some an' kindle a fire, fur I'm wet an' cold. I'll strike a light in a minute."

Flemington saw that the light shone through, on one side the partition, into the room where he lay. He crept noiselessly that way, and found an alcove with a rack for flower-pots, on which were yet standing some rose-bushes. Glass-doors were between this alcove and the inner room. He leaned on the rack and peered through.

"A familiar tang is about that face," thought he; "where the devil *have* I seen it before?"

"If you'd 'a' had as much trouble as I have, gittin' out o' Norfolk, and 'd 'a' brought all these things strung about you, to boot, you might talk about bein' tired and cold!" said the woman, rising from the fire-place where she had been kneeling.

"Jane, don't git mad. Don't scold me, for God's sake! I'm a mizzable man. I'm gittin' skeery. I'm afeard to hide myself down hyur all day any longer. Forty shell, an' more, 's been a-whizzin' over my head to-day, an' hittin' the houses an' a-scatterin' the bricks down like it was rainin' brickbats fur good! Ef I wasn't afeerd o' meetin' some o' Sterlin's crowd I'd go back to the rigiment an' tell 'em some lie or other, 'bout bein' captured like, an' jes' got back, an' never deserted, an' all. But I can't do it. I'm mizzable, Jane!"

Gorm Smallin was lying on the floor with his feet to the fire, his head resting on a round stick of wood which he had rolled from a corner of the room. A black bottle stood on the floor, in arm's reach. He took a long pull and a strong pull at it. His spirits rose a little.

"Come, old gal!" said he, more cheerily. "Let's see what ye've got, this time, f'om Norfolk!"

The woman had already begun to disrobe, and having removed her outer cloak, was now unwinding a variety of scarfs, of all colors, from a waist capacious enough, naturally, to dispense with the assistance of smuggled goods. Carefully laying the scarfs upon an outspread cloth, she proceeded to divest herself of skirt and hoop, and presently produced, from beneath an inner skirt, a sort of half-hoop, from which dangled a miscellaneous array of vials and packages.

"Quinine, by the Rood!" said Flemington, enumerating to himself the articles, as she untied them and arranged them on the floor. "And—what *is* it?—sewing silk, I reckon, and three pair o' shoes, ladies' size, price one hundred and fifty a pair, so—needles, morphine, lunar caustic, lace—and—and a hundred other articles too numerous to mention! 'Gad, she must have sailed, overland, from Norfolk, with assorted cargo of dry goods and medicines!"

Whilst the vessel (weaker) was getting herself "light," Gorm Smallin had been taking on freight. Right whiskey in the real present, and good comfort in the near prospective, these had power upon the man. Up from the waves of sorrow, all dripping with the brine, arose the head of Smallin.

He became patronizing, grandiose, braggart.

"Jane," said he, surveying complacently the array of merchandise just landed, "thar ain't no manner of doubt but you're a sharp un an' a strong un! An' I *will* say, altho' I say it myself, 'at I don't know 'at I ever seed ary another 'oman besides yerself 'at could 'a' brought out a whole store, dry goods an' all, f'om Norfolk, right thu pickets an' gyards an' all, under her skyurts an' roun' her waist! I *will* say, Jane, ef I *do* say it myself, bully for you! I'm a deferent man to what I was afore I seed you, Jane"—

"A Janus-faced scoundrel!" quoth Flemington from the rose-bushes.

"I recomember when I was in the rigiment I used to say to myself, Gorm Smallin hit ain't no use to fight the military! 'Cause why? Why 'cause every time I run the block' to town, every single time, here cum extry roll-call, and drum beatin' long-roll away in the middle o' the night! and ' Smallin absent f'om roll-call ' next mornin', an' then, shore as shootin', dubble-de-dute! "

" An affectionate pet name for ' double duty,' ladies and gentlemen," whispered Flemington, gravely bowing to the roses.

" I did cum it on 'em awhile, tho', a-playing off sick on 'em! An' it *did* work elegint, *elegint*, Jane, untwell one Monday mornin', Jim Sunnypond, a mean sneak, swore 'at I was the only man 'at had the priv'lege of gittin' sick in the whole rigiment, an' said it was axin' *too* much of my comrades for me to want to be sick *all* the time, an' said fa'r play an' equal rights an' division o' labor! An' said Monday was *his* day to git sick; an' then every man in the whole rigiment got to havin' his sick-day, an' the military smelt a rat, an' so ' sick ' played out! "

" Or, as the Latins have it, *sic transit;* if my audience will pardon so much pedantry! " commented Flemington, with a deprecatory gesture which nearly betrayed him by overturning the most substantial of his audience from the rack.

" But, Jane, hit takes you an' me together, you an' *me* "—

" Oh that I had a stone-bow to hit him in the mouth! "* quoted Flemington.

—" To fool 'em, don't it? Mind what I tell you, no man don't fool with me, for nothin'! The military fooled with me; but you an' me has fooled *hit* to death, ain't we? An' ole man Sterlin' "—his voice sank involuntarily—" he mus' go an' try to fool with me! Jane, he better hadn't 'a' done it! "

Even in his drunken maundering, Gorm Smallin paused a moment.

" Jane, sometimes a fellow's brains seems to git actyve and peert, like, all of a suddent! I tell you what, I done that thing, that night, jest as well as ef I'd been to college all my life! Ye see, I tried, an' tried, an' studied, while I was gittin' to Thalberg "—

Flemington bent close and listened, almost without breathing.

—" To think how I could fix a slow-match 'at would burn untwell I had—untwell I had—had done the other thing. Fur

* [The line is from Shakespeare, *Twelfth Night.*—ED.]

I was afeared there'd be sich a stir an' rumpus about, a'ter that, 'at I couldn' git a chance to build the fire. At last, I cum to think about punk, as we used to call it when I was a boy, which it'll burn in a coal, 'ithout blazin', as slow as you please. And so I fixed it, 'ith powder an' punk an' some book-leaves an' laths; an' I even didn' forgit to dig two or three extry holes 'ith my knife in the plaster, for the air to git thu an' feed the fire, like!

"An' then I slipped aroun', Jane, roun' to t'other side the house, an' I seed a light shinin' out like "—Gorm Smallin arose unsteadily to his feet, grasped a piece of lightwood to represent his rifle (having risen into the high-tragic), and backed slowly towards the glass-door where Flemington stood; who, drawing his breath hard, had laid his hand on his pistol and was wildly debating which outweighed—the justice of killing this murderer of his friends, or the deadly sin of sending this inebriated soul to perdition.

—"Like this, Jane, an' I got me a tree an' stood thar, God A'mighty knows how long I stood thar, a year, may be, or two of 'em, an' at last in come Sterlin' an' his wife and the gals, an' then they played the pianner an' sung an' hullabalood another hour, an' then they all sot down together, 'ith Sterlin' in the middle, an' he talked an' talked; an' all the time I couldn' shoot somehow, my arms was weak, an' my eyes was dim, an' I thought onst or twiced 'at I was a-gwine blind. An' a'ter a while the ole 'oman laid her cheek agin *his'n*, an' somethin seems-to-me-like screeched in my ears like a car-whistle, 'Why ain't *you* settin' 'ith *your* wife, an', may be, child, in your house, enjoyin' yer comfort!' and afore I knowed it, Jane, God knows afore I knowed it, jest as ole Sterlin' was a-sayin' 'Amen!' I up gun an' shot an' seed 'em fall on "—

Suddenly a shell tore through the room where Flemington stood, into the next apartment, and exploded just over Gorm Smallin's head. Blinded and half-stifled by the thick sulphurous smoke, Flemington, with a great effort, conquered the stun of the concussion and staggered through the door, which had jarred open, into the fresh air of the street.

He revived, and listened. No sound came from the interior of the house save the occasional drop of plastering shaken loose by the explosion.

But the heavens had cleared, the stars were glittering through the humid air with a sort of rainy fire. The batteries on the lines had reopened, and the night was full of that unquiet strange thrill which runs through an army before a battle: for the long lines were like two strips of gold-foil, and always trembled and wavered with a certain unaccountable agitation, which prophesied victory, as the photometer light, afar off.

Time is a lens which should be clear. Gorm Smallin was a dust-speck upon it. God had blown him off. Who prays for dust-specks? and yet who will swear that he himself is aught more?

Serious of soul, questioning his heart, Flemington hurried to his camp.

Chapter III

Albany.—The weight of this sad time we must obey;
Speak what we feel, not what we ought to say.

King Lear

LATE IN the night of the first Sunday of April, 1865, passion and circumstance—those two accomplished wire-pullers—were not so busy in manœuvring hundreds of people away from doomed homes in Richmond but that they could also find time to arrange, in the centre of that devoted city, a most unexpected meeting between three parties not unknown to the readers of this chronicle.

Philip Sterling had escaped from prison, had lain in a fever some months at a country-house, had recovered, and late in the afternoon of this day had entered Richmond, emaciated to a skeleton, down-hearted for want of news from home, down-headed for weariness, tattered like an unsuccessful beggar, unnoticing the stir of life in the streets. As he made his slow way through the Capitol-grounds, the plash of a fountain met his ear; he dragged himself to the brink of the basin, lay down, and yielded himself to the caresses of that Sunday's balmy air. He fell asleep, and dreamed that he saw big wars standing up in ranks, like men, and fighting with thunders and wild-fires. On the flanks hovered airy pestilences skirmishing, and anon loud world-calamities exploded, jarring all space. Which dissolved; and he was walking upon an immeasurable plain where lay old dead universes, like skulls whitening on a deserted battle-field; but presently these faded out of sight, and the whole plain blossomed with vast odorous violets. He plucked a petal of one, wrapped himself in it, lay down, and fell into a dreamless sleep-within-a-sleep.

Later in the night, John Cranston, sitting in the Federal line north of the James, heard a loud explosion in Richmond, and saw a great glare shooting up from that direction. Love, which laughs not only at locksmiths but also at pickets and special orders, at this moment laughed and frowned at once, in Cranston's soul. The memory of a night when he had borne

Felix Sterling in his arms down a blazing stairs still flamed in his heart; and the anticipation of another such ecstasy was too much for duty.

John Cranston started for Richmond.

At an hour something earlier, also, Paul Rübetsahl displayed more excitement than had been visible in him during the war.

" Friends," said he to three, " Richmond will be sacked by infuriated men, inhabitants and soldiers. The women whom we all love are there, alone; the thought that they *are* there, at such a time, burns my heart. No battle will be fought *here*, and if I knew one *would* be fought, I still would risk the apparent dishonor of absence from it. I, for one, am going to Richmond, to bring out the beloved, or die. Who else? "

" I! " said Aubrey without an instant's hesitation.

" I, too! " cried Flemington.

Cain Smallin grasped Rübetsahl's hand, in silence.

How they strode, those four!

" By two to-night, men! " cried Rübetsahl, striding in the van.

Meantime Felix and Ottilie, hearing the news late in the day, had made great attempts to move, that they might get to Petersburg. But what chance stood two women in Richmond on the 2d of April, 1865? At last, after dark, they had sent Gretchen to Mrs. Parven's, beyond the Capitol, to beg her assistance. Gretchen had not returned; they feared she was killed at last. They sat still, pale with apprehension, and shuddering at the terrible cries that resounded from the streets.

Suddenly, a tap sounded on the door, and a voice said, " Come, come! " impatiently. Ottilie ran and opened the door.

" It is Rübetsahl, Felix! "

Without a word, they descended the steps. At the front door a wild figure rushed in and nearly overturned big Rübetsahl. Unnoticing, Paul kept on; but the other turned, with a quick cry, and then silently placed himself in the phalanx which the four had formed around the women.

Slowly, they marshalled the precious charge across the street. Front, flank, and rear, the phalanx struggled hard to keep the princesses in the centre from insult or blow of hurrying rascaldom, hurrying to or from the raging fires, laden with booty and seeking more.

At length they neared the Capitol gates. As Rübetsahl opened it, Gretchen, with a whine, like a faithful spaniel, grasped Ottilie and drew her on.

"Oh, I could not get back to you," she cried, "and I was about to die! Here are our friends—the Parvens—they came with me so far."

Cranston had stopped at the gate, and stood in the shadow, for the whole grounds were lit, as with daylight, by the fires that were consuming the city. He saw Felix, with a yearning smile as of a lost goddess finding heaven, twine her arms about Rübetsahl's neck. He grasped the iron pillar; it shook with his trembling a moment, then he folded his arms and remained still, in the Shadow.

"For God's sake," cried Flemington, "let us draw breath here a moment," and sank down exhausted, by the fountain.

Philip Sterling opened his eyes. He refused to believe them, at first; but quickly sprang upon Rübetsahl, the first he saw; then discovered Ottilie, and drew her to him.

She instantly released herself, and sank upon her knees.

"*Himmel!*" said Paul Rübetsahl.

The contagion grew. Aubrey caught Rebecca Parven by the hand, and whirled her to a bench that was in the shade of a tree.

"*Cospetto!*" exclaimed Paul Rübetsahl.

"Cain, they're all paired, and nobody left save you and me. But, Old Bony Fingers," continued Flemington, grasping Cain's extended hand, "you are more faithful than many a woman, and so I keep this hand by me, till I find one fairer and half as true!"

"*Cielo!*" Then, looking down into the deep gray eyes that yearned upward passionately into his own, "I, the wanderer among mountains, pray: May we build our nests upon the strongest bough of the great tree Ygdrasil, and may love line them soft and warm, and may the storms be kind to them! Amen, and Amen!" said Paul Rübetsahl.

THE END

SOUTHERN PROSE

FLAG PRESENTATION AT OGLETHORPE UNIVERSITY *

MR. EDITOR:—The idea of religious liberty was born in a scholastic brain; nor was Monk Luther's right arm wanting when, besides brain-work, sterner battle-work was to be done. Cola di Rienzi, in his youth, the Scaliger of a Roman Convent, was, in his manhood, the Washington of the old seven-hilled city. The students in German Universities have always led the struggles of that unhappy country for freedom; to them *Die Freiheit* (Liberty!) is a battle-cry no less thrilling than the religious enthusiasm of Rienzi's devout *Santo Spirito.* The fame of our own Ben. Franklin is founded equally upon his love for freedom and his devotion to philosophy. It has ever been, it will ever be, that those high spirits, whose flames, like holy tapers, burn before the shrine of knowledge, will burn with the same purity and steadiness and light in the Temple of Liberty. Nay, sir; those temples are the same, and the Goddesses are one, for "Knowledge is Freedom!"

So mused your correspondent while he witnessed, on the First of May last, the ceremony of a flag presentation to the "University Guards;" a company organized a few months ago, by the students of Oglethorpe University, E. Postelle Carter, of South Carolina, Captain. When I arrived on the grounds, I found the "Guards" attended by the cavalry of Milledgeville, and a detachment of the Troup Artillery, of the same place, drawn up before the Midway Female Academy, the front of which was "gaily dight" with flowers. *Par parenthese*, however, the windows of the building were thronged with the ladies who presented the flag, and where women vie with flowers for

* [First published in the Macon *Daily Telegraph*, May 15, 1861, from which the present text is taken; not subsequently reprinted. Several obvious typographical errors have been corrected. No MS has been found; but the article is identified as Lanier's by the use of the same pseudonym he employed in his College Notebook and by a letter from his father, R. S. Lanier, dated May 16, 1861. Apparently this was Lanier's first venture in print.—ED.]

a susceptible man's attention, one pities the flowers' chance, especially if, as some poets say, " they be jealous things."

After an impressive prayer by Dr. Talmage, which opened the ceremony, Dr. N. A. Pratt, Professor of Natural Science in Oglethorpe University, delivered the presentation speech in behalf of the ladies.—Dr. P., throwing off with wonderful facility that calm, impassionated style of oratory to which, doubtless, the cool reasoning of the scientific lecture accustoms men of his profession, proceeded briefly to portray the darkness of the dangers which surround us, relieved, however, by the brightness of a just cause. He deprecated over-weening contempt, undue hatred, and revengeful feeling on the part of Southern men, and bade the company be calm, that they might strike truly and heavily on the day of battle, insisting that the essential prerequisite to soldierly excellence was mainly virtue. He then, closing with a stirring appeal to them to guard well their flag, resigned it into the hands of the color-bearer; whereat, the cannon, in salute, made our old hills ring with " the music that warriors love to hear." Captain Carter followed in a short but beautiful speech of thanks. He painted a similar scene which had once occurred in his native State, and referred, eloquently, to the dangers and the death that brave men had suffered in the South Carolina Regiment in preserving their flag from the polluting hands of enemies. He pledged himself (if it should ever become necessary) with his company either to march to victory under a flag so hallowed as theirs, or to die wrapped in its folds; and closed with warm thanks and a compliment to the ladies. I marked the sparkling eyes and flushing cheeks of those young boys while he spoke, and, I doubt not, the consciousness of woman's sanctity, enveloping their flag, the emblem of liberty, would be a still but thrilling war-cry in the hearts that throbbed beneath it.

The Guards, having fired a salute and partly escorted home their Milledgeville guests, returned and went through a variety of light infantry evolutions, which your correspondent, who has often seen the best drilled companies of the State, pronounces hard to excel, and the knowing ones in the military line join in that opinion.

After the drill, the Guards proceeded to the house of General

Myrick, and partook of a feast, wherein the General seemed to have exceeded even his own well-known hospitality. And so, after firing various salutes, " the boys " marched back to the campus in remarkable order and with amazing vigor, considering the violence of the attack and the spirit of the engagement from which they had just withdrawn.

Honor to the brave youth, say I, and may liberty always have such defenders. Yours,

CACOETHES SCRIB

TIMEO DANAOS! *

A VOICE OF THE NIGHT

WHITE MAN WHAT PRINTS DE PAPAH!

IS BIN 'pinted by de niggahs ob dis plantation whah I is at prezent residin', to gib you de 'count ob a public meetin' ob de niggahs, dat wuz lately conwened at dis place.

I gib you de 'count.

All de niggahs what could cum, cum. Dey all met in Aunt Keziah's kitchen: but upon de 'count ob de unpleazunt oder, (de evenin' bein' wery warm,) de meetin' 'journied to de open air. A'ter we had all 'journied to de open air, de meetin' was opened by Unc' Fisher, who riz f'om de groun whah he was *rekibans sub tegminnows*,** and sed dis:

Cullud Childen ob Isril: You is cum, dis evenin', to considduh de condishin ob dese sebben million white people, who is suddenly flung upon your charities.

Dis riled ole Aunt Charity, (who, wid sebral other cullud females ob de very rankest rank, was prezent) an' she jumped up an' tole Unc' Fisher 'at she nuvver lowed nobody to fling at *her*: an' ole Unc' Tom riz an' shuk his fist tow'ds town an' sed he be dam ef he wouldn't like to see any white folks fling at Aunt Charity: but de speaker 'splained hisself, an' a'ter Aunt Charity had shouted glory hallelujah sebral times she settled down agin, an' de speaker driv on.

As I wuz sayin', my cullud frens, we is met to see what we kin do fur deșe poor white people, who is now beggin' at our dores: an' as we wishes light on de subject, we has inwited de distinguished gemplum (dat was me, hyah, hyah, I'se de distinguished gemplum f'om abroad, I resides 'bout fore miles f'om da on Mass Bloom's plantation) to 'dress us on dis mattah:

* [Previously unpublished; here printed from the MS, which survives in a rough pencil draft only (Clifford Lanier Collection, Johns Hopkins University); certain discrepancies in the dialect spelling have been corrected. The date of composition is indicated by mention of the article in a letter of Sept. 30, 1865. The title is from Virgil, *Æneid*.—ED.]

** [Virgil, *Eclogues*. The phrase is also quoted, correctly, in *Tiger-Lilies* (p. 19, above).—ED.]

an' dafore I has de pleasure ob presentin' my distinguished fren (dat was me, you recollec, hyah, hyah, hyah!) Jim Steveson, f'om abroad.

Wid dis all de niggahs hollered an' stawmped an' clapped deir hands, an' dat same unpleazunt oder filled de air, but I sorter liked it dis time: an' old Aunt Charity she cum round, as I riz, an' pattud me on de back an' sed blessed be de kingdum cum, preech to us, Jeems, preech to us, even az de Ass preeched unto Balaum.

I riz, ez I sed buffore.

My Cullud Frens, sez I, I is gwine to make you cry an' I is gwine to make you laff. I is gwine to make you cry fust. Git reddy to cry a good deal, 'mejiately.

When I sed dis, I seed big Isaac an' two more bring up de large wash-pot, and sebral leaned deir heads obah it.

I is gwine to gib you de 'count ob how de niggah cum to be black an' how his nose cum to be flat. I is gwine to do it brievously.

When Shem and Ham wuz in de plain ob Shinar, dey got mad one day, 'bout some vittles or suf'fen an' got to fitin'. At de fust round Shem got in a smasher wid his left on Ham's mug an' de claret flewd wery promiscu. A'ter dis Ham gib in: an' as he felt wery bad, de physickins adwised him to seek a warmer clime fur his health: and he cum an' settled down on Afric's burnin' soil, an' got soiled wery black: an' f'om dat day till dis tarr still is wisible, still is wisible an' his nose nuvver cum out agin.

At dis ole Aunt Charity, which wuz weepin' wery loud, sed, wery chokin', ef de poor cretur had only a-tried Sassiffrax poultusses, de Lord nose!

I driv on.

Niggahs, sez I, de nose is done cum straight, an' de skin is gittin' whiter ebery day, by de use ob a new Skin-powdah, which dey call Missegennit. De niggah was once trod wery heavy flat in de dus': he is now wery powuful. You kin git what you want. What does you all want? sez I.

Big Isaac hollered out, I wants a wagin-load o' water millions an' some papah collahs!

I wants ez much 'zerves ez I kin eat, sez little Dick, an' a pa' o' boots!

I wants to marry Mister Butlah, sez 'Viny, an' a white satin head-handkercher an' a pyanner!

I wants little Dick eadickated fo de gawspel, sez ole Aunt Charity, so he can preech unto de people eben as de Ass preeched unto Balaum!

I wants dis plantation, sez one big niggah whoze acquaintance I had not de honor: no, sah, I wants dat, sez big Isaac: no sah, sez Unc' Fisher I'm gwine to take dat: an' so in a few minnits dey all begin to fite about de plantation. An' ez I couldn' stand dat wery unpleazunt oder, which den ariz upon de air, an' ez I doesn't belong to de church-military, I widened f'om da wery rapid.

White man what prints de papah! dis happened sebral days ago. Since dat, I is bin to town. Sah, I is shocked—I is hurt—I is obfuscated, up to my knees. I is not de same niggah, which I was usen to be.

White man what prints de papah! I seed, in town, a free niggah, a-workin' ! ! ! ! I seed a large buck niggah, with a chain upon his free Angle-Saxwhen legs, an' a big bawl hitched to it, a-sweepin' up de street! ! ! ! ! !

I seed a niggah what wuz too lazy to swing his arms: an' de marshal (golly, I thought marshals wuz dead,—hung by Mr. Linkum) tied his hands up to a jice, to save him de trouble, so he sed!

I is bin considdahed a considuhble niggah, in dis neighborhood: an' de niggahs wuz gwine to make me de king of Bibb County, an' was gwine to gib me de run ob de county to pick out sebenteen wives for my pussonal self; but dat man da in town sez I is got to take care ob my prezunt wife, dough which ob de seben I is to support, de Lord knows!

While I was in de city I got wery hungry: an' I seed a ham a-layin' on de counter, an' 'cluded I'd take dat un: an' soon as I took a-holt ob it, a white fellah wid blue close on, struck me wery servere jes' about under de lef eye, an' den picked me up an' carried me to de guard-house, whah I rezided until dis mornin'; at which time, de guard tole me to go back home, an' go to work,—me, sah, go to work! ! ! ! ! ! Does you call dis freedom? I calls it free-*dam*! I wants suf'fen to eat.

White man what prints de papah! Ef you would like to hire a wery likely boy wery near my size, an' wery handy fur mos' any sort o' work, an' pay him in vittles an' your ole close, I knows a fellah (cullud) what tole me, he would be wery happy to lib wid you de res' ob his life—ef you ain't got no ole close, he'll stay (bein' it's *you*), jes fur de vittles!

An' wid dis I close de 'count ob de meetin'.

I is sorry dat I has to sign myself,

No longer yours

JIM STEVESON

BOMBS FROM BELOW: WANTED, ENGINEERS! *

SOME YEARS ago certain unsteady lights were detected upon the horizon of life which by some people were supposed to be stars, but which to more observant eyes did gleam like the wavering flash of a shell-fuse. These lights continued to grow at once more unsteady and more luminous until, between the years '61 and '65, a half-dozen of them flamed out with dazzling brilliancy, whereat the people who believed them stars shouted Paeans. But suddenly the lights exploded: and the observant-eyed, who had prophesied shells, did not exercise their right to triumph in turn but only wept and wept, the tears being not dry to this day.

For the explosions of these bombs had results.

To wit: some hundreds of thousands of men killed and hurt: some hundreds of thousands of widows and orphans: some billions of money destroyed by being created: some millions of characters male and female demoralized: some hundreds of thousands of boys doomed to ignorance by their inability to study on account of the noise of the shells: some billions of property burned by the intense heat: and a miscellaneous mass of poverty, starvation, disease and dirt precipitated upon the people: so suddenly that many were buried underneath these vast fragments beyond hope of extrication, save by that Good Samaritan—Death, who may pull some out.

Now the Six-thousand-years War is not yet concluded: some men absolutely refuse to sign the treaty with Lucifer: and he will bombard the earth again.

The sad foreboding that more of these bombs are to burst

* [Not previously published, except in part. There are two MSS (Henry W. Lanier Collection, Johns Hopkins University). MS A, obviously incomplete, occupies pp. 24-27 of Lanier's Ledger—a fact which suggests composition not long after the close of the war—under the title of "The Devil's Bombs: Wanted, Engineers!" A considerable portion of it was incorporated by Mims into his *Sidney Lanier,* pp. 45-47. MS B, from which the present text is taken because it is apparently more nearly finished and because it was presumably written later, fills fifteen and a fraction small sheets in Lanier's autograph. Mary Day Lanier has subjoined the note: "Between 1865 and 1870. Probably before 1867." In a few instances the punctuation and spelling have been brought in line with Lanier's practice in print.—ED.]

upon the country,—a foreboding which rises to the dignity of a prophecy in the light of fuses already sparkling—, is more than serious hearts can bear. This advertisement is therefore inserted to call the attention of Topographical Engineers to the matter. Fall to, Men! Let us have earth-works, in all senses, and bomb-proofs to protect us against the Bombs from Below!

Meantime, that the engineers may get some inkling of the necessities peculiar to barriers against these singular projectiles, a few historical facts as to their mode of construction and explosion may be useful.

They have one point in common: that, the longer their fuse the more terrible their explosion.

But they differ among themselves: and thereby hangs the description of

Bomb No. 1

The author thinks it was in the year 1857, at which time he was a college-student and had resided only about fifteen years upon this planet, that he became convinced of his ability to whip at least five Yankees, by his own personal puissance, in a fair fight.

The author does not know now, and did not then, by what course of reasoning he arrived at this conviction;—in the best of his present judgment, he did not reason it out at all, but absorbed it from the press of surrounding similar convictions, as one's body absorbs water when one takes the bath. For indeed, at this distance of time, the author cannot recall any circumstances which, if logically reasoned upon, would have justified the conviction to which he has alluded. The author had never excelled in athletic exercises. He was a spare-built boy, of average height, of under-weight, and constitutionally addicted to hard study, to long reveries, and to exhausting pulls at the German pipe. His knowledge of the Passado, the Stoccata, and the other mysteries of the rapier, besides being limited, was purely theoretical. He had fired few pistols except at dogs when he went to his secret club on Tuesday nights. He was unacquainted with the manual of musket or rifle: and, while he had killed his average share of partridges with the shot-gun, he yet confesses, with some shame, that he never much enjoyed the sport and would always let a poor bird go when he could decently do it. In short, by the broad-shouldered of the college-men the author was considered and usually classed among the "Feebs," a generic term for feeble men who read and who didn't squirm upon the ropes of the gymnasium.

And so, without malice prepense, without reasoning, nay in the face of all reason, the author had absorbed this idea.

He moreover was confident not only that he personally could whip five Yankees but that any Southern boy could do it. Indeed the whole South was confident it could whip five Norths of the same fighting-weight each. The newspapers said we could: the preachers pronounced anathemas against the man that didn't believe we could: our old men upon the street-corners said if they were young *they* could and By the Eternal they believed they could anyhow, whereat always applause and shouts of hurrah for old Smith: our young men said they be d——d if they couldn't: and our young ladies said they wouldn't marry a man that couldn't:—whip five Yankees.

This idea which possessed the whole section, which originated no one knows where, which grew no one knows how: this embodiment of a people's egotism: this perpetual arrogant invitation to draw and come on: this eternal posture of insult in which we walked about with our clenched fist thrust in the faces of all nations:—this was a Bomb from Below, whose fuse sparkled when Mr. Brooks struck Mr. Sumner over the head with his cane, and which at length exploded, with results already stated:*

Let calm people always remember that one bomb-shell does not make a war any more than one swallow makes a summer, and that the author does not by any means believe the late war to have originated in this popular vanity of ours. But the author does believe and contend that in as far as the war was con-

* [MS A proceeds as follows:

"Ridiculous?

"Of course we laugh at it, *now*: . . . Good God, do we laugh at the millions of white bones yonder, which we have not yet had time to bury beneath the washing up of any summer-rain?

". . . If these things are horrible, if groans and injustice and starvation and seduction and drunkenness and dishonesty and peculation and blasphemy and general abandonment-of-God-and-good men,—are terrible, infamous and worse than death and abominable in the sight of God,—then is national conceit abominable, then is 'I can whip five of you' as bad as blasphemy."—ED.]

ducted upon this popular idea, in so far the war was based upon a Weakness.

And, O Cadmus! —What a word is this word " weakness! " And how toothsome a word is it, when one does not wish to say " crime," or " vice "!

For is not modesty a manly virtue? And is not obtrusive egotism an unmanly vice?

And whereas good Society exacts individual modesty, ought not Civilization to exact National Modesty?

The big War that blazed out long ago in that strange place we call Heaven, has transferred its theatre of operations. In these days, we say, not: Michael contending with Lucifer, but: Man contending with his Self. Such a fearful Double was Adam! An Archangel and a Satan bound together, like two desperate duellists, face to face, so that the only salvation of one is the death of the other!

Now all wars, moral or physical, resolve themselves into this Ancient Feud: they are but petty skirmishes upon the outskirts of this infinite Battle between Love and Selfishness.

And so any war, led, in any measure, by national arrogance, is led, to that degree, by one of the Marshals and Winged Braves of Old Selfishness, and is like, on that flank, to meet disaster.

In the darkness of our life, come many stars above the black line of the sea: let us take none, not the brightest, on trust: they may be stars to lead us,—they may be mere sputtering fuses of Bombs from Below.

But that is not all. This particular bomb of our national arrogance is now exploded. Its fragments lie buried in the earth. Let us dig, a little, at the bottom beneath them. It is possible we may find gold.

For a long time there has been accorded, strangely enough if we look at it, the tacit consent of Christians, moralists and all, that nations should guide themselves by one set of moral criteria, individuals by another.

A nation, through its representatives, may diplomatize, may double-deal, may use strategy, may consult policy, may set up self-interest as its paramount good: an individual following his government's example is justly suspicioned and cautiously dealt with by his neighbors.

A nation may boast, may vapor and bluster, may call on the world to feel of its muscle, may praise its mountains, rivers and lightnings: an individual must use his " I " sparingly, else he is justly termed a bombastic fool.

Behold, here, the Antagonism of our time!

What is our theory of government? Do we not say, the rights and powers of governments are rights and powers delegated by individuals for the common good? If this be so, where has the government acquired rights and powers not possessed by any individual? Can ten million individuals delegate a quality possessed by no one of them? Can ten million zeros amount to more than just zero?

The stern Hebrew morality cut sheer down into vainglory, as the Sword of Richard Lion-Heart severed the Saladin's iron bar. But where is any distinction drawn in favor of nations as against individuals, legitimating national blustering and national self-assertion and national pomposity?

In these days, when religion is become fashionable and Meekness wears a silken trail of six feet, it is customary to say the world is Christian, and civilization follows Christ.

But, while individuals confess the obligation to be forgiving, to be charitable, to be straight-forward in dealing, to be truthful in word, to be modest in behavior, to be slow to anger,—are nations to be exempted from this obligation? Is a public man, as agent of a people, to be endued with authority to take liberties with the purity of morals, according as the passions of the national moment may urge him?

Ah, no. Let nations not forget that humility will cast a halo as well about a land as about one head. Let nations not forget that they, as well as each man have

> Stars o'erhead and graves below,

the one contemning, and the other rebuking, the proud. Let nations not forget that upon the plains of old life lie as many skeletons of bodies politic, as there are bleaching bones of men on the great desert, and that humanity is yet young, and that before it is old this today's-history of ours must become a mere melancholy sand-coast strewn with wrecks and fearful with warnings.

x x x x x x x x x

THE SHERMAN BILL *

Macon, Ga., March 15, 1867

AS THE train rolled me into the fine depot at this place t'other day, we thought the engineer did blow his whistle with a certain tremulousness of hand, whereby issued a rare weak and half-querulous tone therefrom—a tone which answered the description of the Welsh language—" something between a whistle and a spit." Moreover, the train did not rush in with a roar and a tremble as trains use; but with a certain subdued roll, as it were wishing to move on tiptoe. As the brakeman loosed his brakes, they did not rattle with a healthy, burly rattle; the slow wheels creaked, but thinly, a mere cricket's chirrup; the trucksmen and baggage-men cursed not with good, round " mouth-filling oaths," but swore feebly the demure objurgations of a comfit-maker's wife.

As I rose from my seat and shook me to unstiffen me, the unwonted toning-down of the usual depot-wises came dreamily upon me, and I issued meekly from the car into the crowd, which meekly received me.

Carefully avoiding to brush hastily against any man, I passed through the press, and entered the omnibus as if I entered a church.—I think I pulled off my hat. The driver moved his whip—he dare not crack it, and the horses made believe to trot to the hotel.—I registered my name upon the book, but was too sad to cut my favorite flourish at the end of it. With a funeral air, as if he bore a corpse, the waiter took my traps and marched me in slow time to No. 30.

The calm oppressed me, it became frightful, it grew cold and

* [First published in the Syracuse (N. Y.) *Courier and Union,* April 8, 1867, from which the present text is taken; not subsequently reprinted. Several obvious typographical errors have been corrected, and a few changes have been made in punctuation to conform with Lanier's usual practice. No MS has been found; but the article is identified as Lanier's by the use of the same pseudonym he used in his " Letters from Texas " (see VI, 187 n., of the present edition) and by the reference to it in a letter of Mar. 15, 1867, to Milton H. Northrup, a friend of Lanier's at Oglethorpe University in 1860-1861, who was connected with the staff of the Syracuse *Courier*, a journal friendly to the South. In place of the original heading, " Southern Correspondence," the present title has been substituted, since the article deals exclusively with the effects of the recently passed Reconstruction bill.—ED.]

deadly; I bethought me of a julep, as the becalmed boatswain remembers his whistle wherewith he does raise the wind.

"I would wet the whistle, waiter," said I, "take this quarter and bring me a julep." I washed my face, and, or ere I had half-finished my back-hair, the julep *was*.

I tasted, eagerly, as who should drown his sorrow, &c.

Kind Heaven!

There was no ice in the julep!! I turned fiercely upon the waiter. "Fiend!" said I, "O double-dyed traitor! Why didn't you have ice in my julep?"

"Ain't got no ice, sah," said the ward, and hung his head.

"Why the —— have you got no ice?"

"Can't 'ford it, sah."

"Why can't you afford it?"

"Travel done stopped, sah."

"Why," I thundered, "has the travel stopped?"

The poor ward burst into tears. He muttered something. I put my head close to hear what he said. I could not hear. "What," I agonized.

"De—de Sherman bill, sah!" between his sobs, and blew what nose he had. This blow was terrible.

"Good God!" I said to myself, (I had been traveling) "what is the Sherman Bill?"

I finished my back-hair, and sallied forth mournfully into the streets. I have many friends here.

I met my old constituent, Real S. Tate, Esq. I never shake hands with Real S. Tate, because his hands always have soil upon them, which, however sacred, is yet dirt. I however accosted him, cordially.

"How's trade in lands," said I.

"My dear sir," said he, "I have on my hands about one hundred and seventy-five plantations."

I looked at his hands in horror. "One hundred city lots, five hundred stores, and about seventy-five thousand millions of acres of land in Georgia and Alabama, for sale. My dear sir," (this is Real S. Tate's great oath) "I will take twenty-five cents, or a commutation thereof in Lager, for the whole of it!"

"Himmel;" said I, "what's the matter?"

Real S. Tate looked at me in amazement.—He led me into an alley, put his arms round my neck, inserted his mouth into my ear as into a sound tube, and whispered tragically, "The SHERMAN BILL!"

"What is it?" I said to myself, and walked into the Lager Beer saloon, of Schmutz & Co.

We all like Lager here, and Schmutz is an old friend of mine.

Nobody was behind the counter. I walked into the back-room, where the tables groan under the smell of the cheese. "Hello, Schmutz," I shouted.

Schmutz was asleep on a table. Mrs. Schmutz was also asleep on another table.—Eleven little Schmutzchens, progeny of those laid on the table, were struggling with a cheese, and the air (which, says Jean Paul, is the empire of the Germans) had to bear the brunt of the conflict. The brunt was an odor.

The spout, out of which the beer runs, was open, and the fluid was quietly streaming upon the table, yellow as Tiber.

As soon as I had recovered from my astonishment, I shouted to Schmutz again, shook him and woke him.

"Mein Gott, und Potz Tausend," said Schmutzig, "Vot ish dis? Vot you vant mit me?"

"Look at your beer, Schmutz!" said I. "It's all running away!"

"Ah, ah," groaned Schmutz, and fell back on his table in despair. "Let dis wrun, let dis wrun; it ish goot for nix: the beeples will nicht dwrink. I haf not sold ein pint lager dis great pig long time!"

"Why, Schmutz?" I tenderly inquired.

"Vy?" said Schmutz and sprang to his feet.

"Vy?" he shouted, and stood on a beer-barrel on his head.

"Vy?" he shrieked, and caught hold of little Schmutz No. 3, and caromed with him upon little Schmutzes Nos. 4 and 5.

"Vy?" he wailed like a cat, and squatted despairingly, and grinned ghastlily, and seized his pipe and ran his head into it, and covered his face therewith.

"Lizten," came a hollow voice from the pipe. "Lizten, Mein Freund. Py cot, cot tam, tam all over, tam up and tam down, tam in the mittle, and tam at bote ends, tam de paper it ish writ on, tam de ink it ish writ mit which, tam de double tam veller vich writ dis, tam de pr-rinter vich print dis, tam de beeples vich wote for dis, tam it all mixed up togedder, tam it, tam, t—t—t—t—am it!"

" Tam what, Schmutz? "

" Tam vot, tam vot, tam vot," said Schmutz, coming out of his pipe, and preparing to curse. But he saw that he could not do the subject justice. He rolled languidly upon the floor.—His muscles relaxed. His eyes closed. His lips moved. Wishing to convey his dying message to his weeping family, I leaned over him and placed my ear close to his lips.

" De Sch—Sch—Sch—erman Pill! " he sibillated.

He was dead. I rushed out of the store.—If there had been any crowd on the streets, it would have rushed in. There was no crowd. One man—he was a federal soldier—came in. " What is the matter with Schmutz? " said he.

" Died," I replied, " of the Sherman Bill! "

I rushed on. " Great God," I said, " What is the Sherman Bill? "

My Dear—: I am going up to see my friend, Keen Sabb, who knows about it. I will find out from him. When I have discovered what the Sherman bill, which has killed this country (alas, poor Schmutz!), is, I will write you.

OTFALL

THE THREE WATERFALLS *

Waterfall First

AN INDIVIDUAL of renown, in ancient days, was lowered into his grave by a raisin in his throat. My father met his death upon a similarly unfrequented road. My father once got off a pun, and immediately went on his death-bed.

As it was a custom in yore days for parents to die bequeathing nothing to their children but hatred of their enemies, so, in my day, my father left to me nothing by way of estates and hereditaments but an unconquerable aversion to puns. I can not help disliking puns; it is constitutional—and you know how hard it is to effect constitutional amendments!

With these premises, I beg you will not think that I trespass upon my own premises if any ambiguous words are found within this enclosure. They have no right there; they have been warned off; and if you should discover any of them secretly intruding to poach my reputation as if it were a hare, do me the favor to bring them to notice. I will administer to them the punishments administered to criminals by the Rajah of Punjaub.

I adore scenery. A mountain has always seemed to me an object of high regard; a valley is to me a fertile theme; a budding tree invariably brings a sense of releaf to my limbs; I find plenty of sermons in stones, especially in Blarney stones, in gravestones, and in the *Stones of Venice*; I have seen books in running brooks, having once thrown Tupper's Poems into a stream; and surely cataracts are noble, for they are always of high descent! In short, I have for a long time regarded the volume of Nature as at once a royal octavo and a diamond edition—a sort of crown jewel, as it were; and I would not like to see this volume bound in muslin, for I do not believe in

* [First published in *Scott's Monthly Magazine,* IV, 599-604, 679-83 (Aug. and Sept., 1867), from which the present text is taken; not subsequently reprinted. Several obvious typographical errors have been corrected, and the use of italics for foreign words has been standardized to conform with Lanier's usual practice. As in *Tiger-Lilies,* the conversation is sprinkled with literary echoes and allusions too numerous for footnotes: to Shakespeare's *As You Like It* and *King Henry IV,* Ruskin's *Stones of Venice*, Hugo's *Toilers of the Sea,* Bryant's "The Battle-Field," Fouqué's *Undine*, Hood's "Bridge of Sighs," and the Bible. No MS has been found.—Ed.]

muzzling the press—nor, indeed, in calf, for who would then reveal its secrets?

As an adorer of scenery, I have been particularly weak on waterfalls. How much sweet bread, full nourishing to the soul, has Ruskin cast into the waters of the Fall of Schaffhausen! I appreciate Ruskin.

I also appreciate the fate of Chattanooga, of the world at the time of the Deluge, of the pool at the foot of Niagara—in short, I sympathize with the emotions of any thing that has been spattered and ruined by a waterfall; for I have been entirely overwhelmed, knocked down, moistened, weakened, unstarched as to my knees, rendered utterly limp, washed out flaccidly, as it were, and drowned, by a—waterfall!

Good heavens! It is a thrilling story. I shudder even now, when it is over. Yet, I will relate it, impelled by a sense of duty to warn my fellow-men of certain pestilences that fly in the hair by day and night; and I will relate it to *you*—because then the women of Georgia will read it, and their hair henceforth shall curl with scathing regret—instead of hot tongs.

I live in a room upon the fifth floor of the hotel, and my experience leads me to disbelieve a certain French proverb. *It is the first step that costs,* quotha; but I find that the two hundred and seventeenth or eighteenth step (I go up four pair) is generally the one that ruins *me.* On the second story, beneath me, live some ladies—young ladies—an expression which, by an insulting insinuation, has come to mean exclusively *un*married ladies. Although these ladies occupy a position far, far beneath mine in society—being in the second story while I am in the fifth—yet, I do not scorn them. One of them, in particular, I do not scorn. Although, in harmony, the fifth is a dominant, and although I am a fifth while she is only a second—and although we all ought to live in harmony—yet, I do not dominate over her. In fact, she comes into dinner as if a star was hungry and sailed over heaven for some nectar. When I see her floating up stairs, I say to myself, Surely Venus has mistaken that stair-railing for the horizon of the world! When I meet her tripping down stairs, I attentively examine the steps where she trod, to see if the flowers of the stair-carpet have not sprung up and blossomed in her path.

I once breakfasted near her at the table. It was with difficulty that I refrained from knocking down the brutal waiter who, with satanic calmness, asked her if she would have some of the fried ham-and-eggs! Kind Heaven! This naiad—this silver star—this dainty foam on the wave of life—this sweet wavering blush-spot on the opal of time—this loveliest dew-drop hanging on the great tree Ygdrasil—that she should be supposed, even by a waiter, to eat, habitually, fried ham-and-eggs! That this lily-stalk with the petal face, this white summer-cloud with the lightning eyes — this exquisite war-of-loveliness, in which cheeks, nose, and eyes, fought ardently—this unapproachable north-west passage to happiness—this soul, white as a snow-flake and passionate as a rose—this glittering sun-lit point on the world's somber iceberg—this flashing diamond upon the bridal-ring of the year—this silken banner unsmoked by the world's battle—this fine flame-of-heaven, this star-child—that she should be constructed of fried ham-and-eggs! It is enough. I did not scorn her—not at all, I think.

On the 4th day of March, 1867, upon the thirteenth step of the stairs (you observe how my mind retains all the terrible particulars), as I was going up to arrange my back-hair (I part my hair behind), I met her father and mother coming down to dinner. I know that these were her parents, not because I am acquainted with them, but by pursuing the same argument upon which we predicate that the world belongs to the solar system: I had always seen her with them. Upon the twenty-second step of the same stairs I met her. It was as if the sun and moon went down together, and a star fluttered just behind them. Upon the twenty-third step the catastrophe occurred to which I alluded in the early part of this history. It lay there on the step. It was motionless. It was black. It was round. It had a look of flaccid horror, like Victor Hugo's devil-fish, and one of the antennae or suckers lay languidly extended along the step. It was enclosed in a sort of web or network of some dark material. A long, murderous-looking hair-pin was sticking in it. It was as if the thing had attacked some woman, and she had killed it with a hair-pin, and nailed it to the floor. It was dead. All of which observations I made afterwards. In the first shock, under the impression it was a rattle-snake, with his curling head protruding from the deadly coil, I recoiled in horror. But suddenly an idea flashed into my brain. I cautiously stooped and examined the—object. It was so. It was her waterfall! I clenched my forehead with my right hand, and sank down on the step. I knew that this was the gesture appropriate to the occasion, because I have often seen the diabolical villain use it when the Astounding Disclosure is made, in the theater. As soon as I had recovered from this revulsion of feeling, I meditated. *By'r lady!* said I to myself; *what a strong-headed woman, and come of what a stiff-necked generation must she be, who carried that thing, as I have seen her carry it, so lightly and so gracefully upon the back of her head!* Undoubtedly the waterfall was the invention of a person of mythological turn: Atlas, you know, bearing the world upon his shoulders. I discovered that this miniature world was as populous as its prototype. I am, in an amateur way, a minute philosopher. With some difficulty, I lifted this waterfall and bore it, staggering beneath its weight, to a window. I took out my magnifying glass —I drew it to a focus upon the waterfall.

Heavens! Earth!! H——!!! It was full of gregarines!!!! The left half of it contained, I doubt not, more inhabitants than the Western Hemisphere. The right half of it typified, in thronging barbarism, the crowded civilization of Europe. Now, gregarines are almost as bad as men. They have wars—they must eat—they will emigrate—and *Du Himmel!* suddenly thought I, while I am meditating she will enter the dining-room without her waterfall! What to do? How could I present it to her? And yet how could I endure the thought of her grief when she should see the men laughing at the absence of her waterfall? Picture to yourself such a dilemma.

At this moment there rushed upon me one of those magnificent inspirations which drew forth Leonidas—which nerved Mertius—which impelled Quintus Curtius. It brought fortitude —it instilled bravery—it conferred strength. I seized the *chignon*, and as it had been a feather, rushed madly with that ponderous thing in my arms down the stairs. I had determined to overtake her before she entered the dining-room. Regardless of gregarines, unheeding the stupendous obstacle that I had not been introduced to her (I would not save a man from drowning without an introduction)—forgetting my natural timidity, overcoming my want of physical strength—I bore the immense institution down the stairs. As I leaped along something fluttered out of the waterfall. I picked it up. It was a clipping from a newspaper. I read it. It was my last poem! Something else dropped. It was—I do not know what it was. I do not wear anything like it. And then a host of things fell from this waterfall. It was a cataract of rats, mice, coils, combs, curls, handkerchiefs, hairpins, two hug-me-tights, three newspapers, six powder-bags, two fans, a parasol, and a gaiter.

" *A chignon*," said I, hurriedly, to myself, " *is in the nature of a knapsack*," and strode on, with heavy heart and lightened burden. The Fates were on my side. The father and mother had just entered the side-door of the dining-room. The star-child was behind. Still bright she showed, though most like a comet that had lost its nebulous appendage. I called to her. She stopped. I fell on one knee.

" Maiden," said I, " your *chignon* has fallen. I have rescued it. Behold! "

" Ah," she said; " I am beholden. Where did you find it? "

" On the stair."

" You men," said she with dignity, " are always on the stare! "

" Thank you," said I.

" How will I fix it," said she, in a mournful voice.

" Allow me," I replied, and with astonishing muscular exertion I lifted it up. She turned the back of her head to me. It was as if day had suddenly become night. It was like the recent political revolution, in which white has become black.*

" How," said I, " do you hook it on? "

" To the hair," said she.

" Ah," exclaimed I, " it will never do. No wonder it snapped off from so brittle a support."

" Why," said she.

" Maiden," I said, with solemnity, " how could it hold to your hair when your hair is friz? "

She is a woman of strong constitution. She trembled, but stood it.

* [The Ledger, p. 31, offers a similar pun: " It is a levying of *black mails* with a vengeance when the Yanks enfranchise three hundred thousand black males in our midst! "—Ed.]

"Has it not made you," said I, "like Samson when he lost his hair—weak?"

"Oh, how?" said she. "It is but two minutes since I lost mine: and how can two minutes make one weak?"

I am also of strong constitution. Being crushed to earth, I rose again.

"Maiden," said I, "forty weeks, instead of forty days, the present waterfall has reigned, and—"

"Ah," she murmured, "if it had only been forty-two!"

"Why," I said, hoarsely.

"Because," she whispered, "I could then have endured this reign with forty-tude!"

"Thou," apostrophised I—"thou, deluged by this long reign of waterfall—I have an ark of—"

"No? ah!" she murmured.

"Not," I said, "of Noah, but my heart is an ark—"

"And an arc," she said, 'is but a piece of circle!"

"O, maiden," shouted I, "thou, deluged one! My heart *is* an ark—"

"Anarchy, you mean," suggested she.

"Heart is an ark," continued I.

"An Arcadian folly?" she said.

"Is," said I, "an ark—"

"Filled," she said, "like Noah's, with all manner of wild beast wickednesses—such as bulls, and bears, and tigers, to be fought, and elephants to be seen, and sparrers and ring-doves, like Morrissey and Heenan *—and United States eagles, and silver pheasants, and greenback ducks, and game, and all fowl chicanery, and panther-loons and coats, and deer doeskins, and rats and mice, and june-bugs, and humbugs, and blue-bottles (and black), and fiddlers, and army-worms, and rich ants, and Little Crickets!"

"An ark—" said I.

"Whose one gangway and window is a pocket," said she.

"Ark," said I.

"Yes, hark! said she, "for I seem to hear its timbers crushing in a monstrous wreck even now. Hark!"

* [John Morrissey, pugilistic champion, won an unpopular technical decision over John C. Heenan in 1858. Lanier also refers to Heenan in *Tiger-Lilies* (see above, p. 22).—ED.]

"O, Undine, of this waterfall—O, naiad, whose pool is a *chignon*—O, mermaid, in this sea of hair!" I cried; "thou art like to drown, and my heart is an empty ark—"

"That wants an ark-angel?" she said, blushing, and hung her head.

Indeed, this poor head of hers underwent the extreme punishment of law. It was hung, drawn, and quartered. It was hung by her, it was drawn toward me, it was quartered safely on my right coat lappel, where it lay motionless, waterfall and all.

Now, when a pugilist has gotten his opponent's head in chancery, as it is termed, he has a perfect right with his left to deal round blows squarely in the face. But I did not embrace this—right. I did not wish my wooing to begin where so many wooings end—in a Chancery Court. I looked around, as well as I could over her *chignon*, which obstructed my view, to see if we were alone. We were alone.

I do not think I kissed her. I do not think so, because I distinctly remember that three times when I was just about to do so she said, in a soft, appealing voice:

"No, don't!"

Of course I would not kiss her when she said, "No, don't." I am not a barbarian. I considered the situation a favorable one for assailing her with the torrent of bitter invectives which arose within me.

"Sweetest!"—I pronounced this stinging epithet in a tone of the most sarcastic softness—"Sweetest, the Carthaginian women cut off their hair to make bow-strings once: and your *chignon* must have come from the head of a Carthaginian woman!"

"Why?" said she.

"Has not your *chignon*," I hissed, "become a beau-string?"

She nestled closer to my coat lappel.

"Good beau," she said, "whom I have bent with a hair, shoot no more arrows at me, please! They 'arrow up my soul!"

"Arrah, no!" exclaimed I. "But O, my Silver-star, on every mist that arises from a waterfall there appears a bow, and—"

"You," she said, "are not missed; yet reign, beau!"

"O," breathed I fervently, "may I reign forty years—a second deluge of love!"

"Then would you not be," said she, "a bow of promise?"

"Promise," said I. "What shall I promise, O dainty pond-lily, under this waterfall?"

"Promise me," she murmured, upturning her blue eyes and making me feel as if some one had thrown two violets in my face; "promise me never to speak again of those dreadful gregar—"

At this moment the side door of the dining-room flew open and Mrs. Silver-star appeared, accompanied by Mr. S. S.

Women are always right. Women always jump at correct conclusions. Women have intuitions that amount to inspiration. There is nothing which I more reverently admire than the sagacity of women in detecting the truth at once, under any circumstances.

"Poor dear," exclaimed Mrs. Silver-star, "she has fainted!" and rushed toward us.

Never, to my dying day, will I be able to tell how it was that Mrs. Silver-star discovered so quickly that little Silver-star had fainted! I should not have thought of it if I had held her divine head on my coat lappel ten years.

"Yes, madame," said I mournfully, "she has feinted!"

I yielded her up to Mr. Silver-star.

"Thank God!" said he, "she is recovering!"

She had opened her eyes. They bore her away. I looked at her, and twisted my mouth, as near as possible, into the shape of an interrogation point. I was asking her, silently, if we should meet again. She turned her eyes upon me, full. Her eyes were affirmative. Her noes were silent. Her eyes were turned, for one moment, full upon me.

I will tell you, confidentially, what I saw in her eyes. I saw there a wavering form, which, one minute, wore the blonde countenance of joy — which the next minute exhibited the gentle paleness of melancholy, and then shaded into the brunette tint of deep regret—this glowing quickly into the joy-face again, and so completing the circle of sweetness. Then, like a naiad swimming up from the bottom of her spring, floated up in her eyes another divinity, who also had his Avatars. He came up slowly, in the likeness of a lily, and rested on the quiet eye, as on a quiet lake, one second—then, in a flash, he had become a spotted tiger, with tense muscles and still, gleaming eye, in the attitude of springing: and then the tiger wavered out of sight, and the lily reäppeared, quietly hovering, daintily undulating. Upon this lily my soul descended. O, love, thou tiger, I said to myself—O, love, thou lily, I love thee best in thy lily form: and so, upon this infinite petal of thee let me float over life forever! *

I proceeded to the dining-room and sat down in a dream—and a chair.

" Waiter," I said, " give me a tiger—I mean beef-steak, and some of the fried ham-and-lilies—when I say lilies I mean eggs."

I concluded, and blushed at the wondering gaze of the man that sat next to me.

The waiter did not heed my wild request, for I thought we were at breakfast instead of dinner. He brought me soup, as in duty bound. It was mock-turtle soup. Upon its surface floated a concave section of hard-boiled egg. The soup-plate extended itself before my dreaming eyes until its porcelain rim became the distant horizon of a calm sea, whose color was rich-brown, and whose islands breathed fragrances of lemon and spices. The egg section became a dainty shallop of milky pearl, and in it my unknown love and I voyaged the brown, stormless ocean, limited by no haven to be sought, for the whole shore of this sea was warm, and free, and hospitable, and tenanted by troops of big-hearted lovers.

But my soup-sea dream was rudely superseded. My attention was attracted by a commotion at the lower end of the dining-room. The proprietor, backed by a strong retinue, consisting of a policeman, two waiters, and some excited guests, rushed in the door, and came, with all his followers, up to my seat.

" This is the man," said he. " Take him, policeman! " and laid his hand on my coat lappel.

Kind Heaven! It was *the* coat lappel—it was the identical coat lappel upon which, a few moments before, little Silver-star had rested her divine head! I am not an auctioneer, but I deemed that the circumstances justified assail in public. The proprietor was the article up for assail. I knocked him down, for the highest bid was when he bade the policeman take me. Wiping his nose with his handkerchief, the proprietor im-

* [The paragraph has a reflected interest from the title of *Tiger-Lilies* (see Introduction, pp. xviii-xix).—Ed.]

mediately displayed the auctioneer's red flag over the policeman. Supposing, therefore, the policeman to be the article next offering, "Time valuable, gentlemen," cried I, "and sales positive!" and knocked the policeman down to old Bidwell, who sits at the end of our table, and who, although he had forbidden me, did not wish, I think, to purchase the article; at any rate, when it fell on his lap, he threw him off. Astonished at my activity in disposing of damaged goods (the proprietor's nose and the policeman's mouth being "not in good condition"), three waiters raised three chairs—and, as three cheers are never enthusiastic without a tiger, I jumped like one at the waiters. In view of the experience which waiters acquire as chairmen, three times a day, of public meetings, it was to be foreseen that, in a contest as to seats on the floor, I would be overruled. Strange to say, however, I secured my seat on the floor of the house; but, the first time I rose to address the chairman, who had decided in my favor, my measure (5 feet 11 inches and something) was laid on the table. Of course, the gravest consequences ensued; a famine raged at the table in consequence of the sudden scarcity of provisions brought on by the forcible rejection of the measure I had offered before the house. The stain of it will never be effaced—the whole floor being a gravy-swamp, with tussocks of beef and mutton interspersed.

As I lay upon the table, I took what may be termed a bird's-eye view of the civilized world: for England, represented by beef, Spain as mutton, and America *per* pork, lay about me; my right eye wept with the woes of Grease, and my left was angrily fixed upon Turkey; Italy, in the person of Maccaroni, lay crushed beneath me; and my right foot kicked at a Russian Charlotte, while my left one menaced China. At this moment a reinforcement of two policemen, regardless of danger, rushed in and secured me. I made no further resistance. "Gentlemen," said I tragically, "like all great conquerors, though I leave famine and desolation in my path, yet I must at last yield to Fate. Fate," continued I, patronizingly, as I walked along between two policemen, "Fate, gentlemen, has been successful as a policeman. Fate has probably arrested more delinquents than you two put together. Fate wears a star, and Death is his *quod*."

" 'N' you carn't bail out of it, neither," observed the policeman on my right side.

" No, sir," said I, warmly; " no, my philosophic friend; Fate is baleful—no more bail there."

We arrived at the place where policemen carry people.

" As a matter of mere idle curiosity," said I, before entering the door—an emotion which I blush to confess—" permit me to inquire what I've been arrested for? "

" Room broke open at the 'otel," said the sententious policeman; " articles abstracted while gen'leman and lady at dinner-table. Articles—watch and lady's garments. Gen'leman complained to p'rprietor. P'rprietor riccollected 'aving just seen you runnin' down the steps—somethin' in yer hands. Waiter picked up lady's comb and lady's garment. Same dropped by you, runnin' down steps. More'n all, resisted officer w'en officer went to nab you. Bad case, young 'un! "

With which cheerful peroration, the policeman closed the door of hope and of *quod*. For I was a stranger there; I had no friends; I was writing a poem or two; I lived by the same. Hang it! what made the scoundrel of a robber, whoever he was, choose the identical moment before I rushed down stairs with little Silver-star's *chignon* in my hands? What would little Silver-star—God bless her, God bless her!—what would she say when she heard the accusation?

They had put me in a cell alone, for knocking down an officer, I suppose. I fell down in a corner and groaned. I looked around me. I see no cheer, I said, in this cell. The situation, if I *could* sit, would be more chairful. Cheerless I lay till night. When night came I found a chair. It was Cassiopeia's. I could see this constellation through the window bars. My soul mounted in a dream of Silver-star, and sat in it.

Waterfall Second

I had therefore obtained my right ascension by a method hitherto unknown to astronomers: namely, by a dream, an instrument differing in some particulars from the sextants extant (confound it!) among the star-namers. In fact, this dream, regarded as an astronomical instrument, was far more powerful than Lord Ross's celebrated telescope, and I could have reveled in its revelations until reveille. I will record a scattered bundle of the sights I saw, as I sat in Cassiopeia's chair, and gazed through my dream at the stars.

Not far from me, I discovered a number of small shops and stands, over which hung the Zodiacal signs: I sat, as it were, upon a sort of *boulevard* of the universe, where, however, the shop-keepers were of great respectability, since they moved in the very highest and most brilliant circles. The zodiacal signs, each of which denoted a different shop, were peculiar, in that each sign was at once a sine of an arc—a co-sine, or sign of a company—a secant to the sign before it, and a *sine qua non* to the celestial traders. Imagine how learned were these zodiacal merchants, when I assure you that each one who owned a sign had taken thirty degrees in the highest and most difficult course known to mathematics!

The signs, however, were much like those which one might behold over the shops and buildings in any suburb. *Capricornus*, for instance, reared on his hind legs over a feminine kid glove shop; *Aquarius* was a jolly joke, on the *lucus a non* principle, for whereas the sign was a sign of a water-bearer, yet the shop was a wine shop; *Sagittarius* shot an arrow, in fanciful token, over the door of a pistol gallery; *Leo*, or the Red Lion, was an old-fashioned inn; at *Cancer*, they sold crabs, sauces for which could be obtained next door from one Pollux, who held a Castor in his hands under the sign *Gemini*, the Twins — *Gemini* being supposed to denote an exclamation, elicited by the strength of the pepper and mustard with which Pollux filled his Castor; at *Virgo*, was a little shrine of a vestal, which shone so beautifully that I could not but leave my chair and approach it. Kind heavens! There stood, in this shrine, my little Silver Star, my very own beloved Silver Star, smiling, smiling, dressed in a floating robe of white star-beams, to which a vivid blush on her cheek lent a pink glory. I rushed towards her. A loud scream broke upon my ear.

How could a man seem to dream a scream (hang the—but no matter) so vividly? It must be a real scream, I said, and rubbed my eyes.

By Night and Somnus! As I opened my eyes, I beheld the living form of little Silver Star, standing bodily there in my cell, with a turnkey, holding a lantern just behind her.

"Good gracious! How you frightened me when you jumped up off the floor and ran at me so!" said little Silver Star, half reproachfully.

"O, my Vestal," said I, "I was just dreaming I had caught you on the *boulevards* of the universe!"

"Are you awake?" said little Silver Star, smiling.

"Yes. Pinch me. Oh!" cried I, as little Silver Star fillipped the back of my hand with her dainty fingers—so lightly that she wouldn't have brushed the down off a butterfly's wing; no, it wouldn't have discolored a magnolia petal. By George! it wouldn't have made a sensitive plant shrink.

"I just come," said little Silver Star, blushing and looking down, "to tell you that—that—that *I* didn't believe you took the watch!" and in an instant she was gone and the turnkey had locked the door.

I was bewildered. I slapped my own face. I tweaked my own nose, to see if I was really awake. I *was* really awake. Little Silver Star *had* actually stood there, a moment ago. She *had* actually come down, at midnight, risking slander and all, and gained admission to my cell, to save me the agony which her loving heart prophesied in mine, at the thought of her contempt for me in my disgrace!

Wasn't it just too exquisitely sweet for a man to bear? I knelt at the place where her feet had consecrated the floor, and kissed it. What in the name of all oddities do you think my lips encountered as they approached the floor? Silver Star's waterfall! I lifted it up. It was heavy. Something jingled inside of it. I turned it over and shook it. Out fell two skeleton keys, a rat-tail file, and a piece of cord!

It all rushed upon me in a moment.

Little Silver Star had fooled the turnkey on his own ground! She had brought me the means of escape in her *chignon*, had dropped it at her feet, had surprised the turnkey out of a search and me out of my senses! Little Silver Star had evidently read romances.

Have you ever been in such an agony of tenderness, aroused by some sweet act of one that loved you, that you have grown temporarily insane for want of expression, and have desired, as the greatest boon to man, that you might (for instance) stand on your head and make a speech to the stars and the antipodes, including the Hottentots and the Patagonians, upon the subject of paper collars, aesthetically regarded from the point of view of a mackerel? Guess how I come to think of mackerel in such a connection?

Mackerel was suggested by salt; salt, by brine; brine, by a tear, which, with a hundred more, fell from my eyes as I knelt and wept and passionately kissed little Silver Star's *chignon,* and held my breath to keep my heart from swelling so painfully.

This night, otherwise so dark, sparkled brilliantly with this little woman's love; it was a black diamond of nights—a glittering jet ornament of my whole life, and I will wear it forever.

But it wore away. I dreamed it through, with open eyes.

Ten o'clock—the fateful hour of derelicts—came, accompanied by a policeman. The star on the policeman's coat had a bodeful gleam about it, like a star of evil destiny.

Surely my nativity must have been under the house of Saturn, so saturnine, grim has been my life!

"Good morrow," said I, "thou deputy Fate, thou clerk of Destiny, thou bum-bailiff of Time; how's your eye, where I hit it yesterday?"

"Only tolluble," said the man of *quod,* regarding me with some attention. "I wouldn't 'athought a man o' your size could 'adone it, knockin' me into old Bidwell's lap, that way!"

"Ha! 'twas well said," exclaimed I, "'*a man* o' my size,' indeed! For I *am* a man of sighs, great sighs, deep sighs; and I would I knew where is this Bridge of Sighs, renowned in verse, and in reverse; I would cross upon it to the other side of grief. And as for old Bidwell's lap, be comforted my dear Pandarus of Justice's lust; you fell into Bidwell's lap; Bidwell is a man of age; in the lapse of ages, all must fall—it is written."

My solemn manner unmanned the policeman. He wiped off a tear with one arm, and inserted the other in mine. So, armed to meet my fate, I marched from my headquarters towards the enemy.

In the breast of my coat lay Silver Star's *chignon.* Of course I didn't use the skeleton keys and the rat-tail file, knowing that disgrace is like a dog, and catches you if you try to run, but runs if you try to catch it. We walked into court. "A 'earty younker as ever I see," remarked Police, as he relinquished my arm, " and I hope he'll get off, spite o' the black eye I owes him! "

It was my first presentation at court, and I realized the propriety of the kneeling posture before sovereigns, for, at this moment, I found that my knees, which shook like a leaf in the wind, had as lief make a shake-down on the floor as not. The wars of the white and red roses were hotly waged in my face; I was, as to the eyes thereof, most sheepishly downcast, and my wits were gathering the wool of these sheep, but were only getting worsted.

At length my case was called.

" Has the prisoner any counsel? " tenderly inquired his Honor.

" Please your Honor," said I, " e'en from my boyish days I wrote it in the copy books, 'Keep your own counsel,' with a capital *K*, and the teacher always added, 'Mind, now, it's *sel* and not *cil* for counsel': which it to say, counsel is a sell that undermines a man and not a sill that supports him. I will plead my own case. I am ready. Not guilty! "

Like to a surgeon smilingly about to operate upon a " lovely tumor," the prosecuting attorney called old Silver Star to stand and deliver some light upon the case. The mashed nose of the hotel proprietor had acted like an editorical notice of my trial—all his friends, and many of his boarders, were present. There, in the crowd, like a star just seen behind a cloud, appeared little Silver Star blushing by old Mrs. Silver Star.

Old man Silver Star, as he rose, looked as if he would much rather set; his face was already set, as it were, with roses.

" By Jove! " began the old gentleman, " I—that is— "

" If it is possible," observed his Honor blandly, " the witness will simply tell what he knows of the case, without objurgatory epithets or other the like exclamations."

" I'll do it, please your Honor," observed old man Silver Star, with a face redder than Bardolph's, " but by the Eternal, if I'd known I'd have to get up here and make a speech about it this way, hang me (excuse me, your Honor) if I'd have arrested the young fellow; looks like a decent young man, too," continued the old gentleman, putting on his spectacles, and regarding me over the top of the same; then, suddenly recollecting himself, dashed on: " Please your Honor, I was on the —let me see—see—on the—wife, what day of the month was it yesterday? Have to be particular about these things, you know. Dear!—Ha!—so, yes, on the 17th day of March,* 1867, I left my room with my wife and daughter to go down to dinner at the ——Hotel, in the city of ——; —don't suppose you want to know what I had for dinner, do you, Tompkins? " (to the counsel). " Ah; yes; don't want to know—very well. I—as I way saying, please your Honor, I—where was I, wife? Umph! humph! —get on very well in a moment—warm day, please your Honor—inclined to perspire always—family tendency to obesity. Father weighed—let's see—weighed—wife, how much did father weigh? God rest his soul."

" You must keep to the watch, dear," mildly suggested Mrs. S. S.

" Ah! yes. Keep watch. Keep watch, good—Bible says so. Wife knows Bible devilish well, your Honor—and so, as I was saying, humph! — was going to dinner with my wife and daughter at the —— Hotel, —— city, 17th May, year of our Lord 1867—and counsel don't want to know what we had for dinner—and—humph!—daughter was walking behind self and wife a little distance, and went into the dining room and sat down, and both self and wife supposed daughter would be in in a moment after, and presently daughter didn't come, and I made the remark to wife, 'Wife,' said I, 'isn't it time for daughter to come in?' and wife thought it was time, and the idea occurred to look at my watch, for I was under the impression that daughter had been absent full five minutes, and was alarmed about her; and upon looking for my watch, found that it was not in my left vest pocket—I always keep it in my left vest pocket, please your Honor, and have done so, man and boy, these forty years past, and value the watch very highly as an old family watch, and have always kept it, as I was saying, in my——. Hold on?"—putting his hand to his head. " Stop! By the ——! Wife, didn't I change my —hold on just five minutes, Judge! " shouted old man Silver Star, and rushed from the witness stand, dexterously eluding the clutches of a half-

* [The date previously given (p. 215) is 4th March. Another inconsistency in date (perhaps merely typographical) appears in the second paragraph below. (Note the date on p. 230.)—Ed.]

dozen people who supposed him temporarily insane; the fat old gentleman plunged through the crowd, seized little Silver Star, carried her to his carriage, fairly pitched her and himself into it, and drove off furiously towards the hotel.

As soon as the Judge had recovered from the comatose stupor into which, as into a slough of despond, his astonishment had thrown him, "Arrest that witness immediately!" shouted he, fuming, "and bring him to answer for flagrant contempt of court."

Meantime the officials endeavored to restore order in the court room; but, as in most restorations, had to fight for it. The greatest difficulty was experienced in quelling a furious discussion between several gentlemen as to the cause of old man Silver Star's sudden lunacy.

Before quiet was fairly obtained, a new commotion was observed outside the court room, and an irresistible rush was made for the windows. Down the street came old Silver Star's carriage, the driving of which was like the driving of Jehu. Upon the box, with the driver, stood old Silver Star, flourishing a huge garment, which showed most like the swaddling clothes of some sick elephant.

"Don't condemn him! don't hang him! A-a-ll right!" shouted the old gentleman, with his hands closed over his mouth to make his voice like a trumpet. In a moment more he rushed into the room holding the watch in one hand, and his colossal waistcoat in the other. "Please your Honor," puffed old Silver Star, "I ch-changed my vest before dinner—and le-left my watch in the other—pocket!"

There is (or is said to be) a time to laugh and a time to weep. At this moment old Silver Star's watch indicated both these times, for everybody in the House laughed except little Silver Star, who wept. The minutes of the court were of but secondary importance, for the day was hours!

Old Silver Star wound up his watch, and the court wound up his watch-case.

The old gentleman could not bear to look at me. As we left the court room, he stole sheepishly to my side. It is my belief that old Mrs. Silver Star pushed him towards me.

"What can I—I—do to repair this wrong I have unintentionally done you, sir?" said Mr. Silver Star.

"Sir," said I, sternly, "prepare to repair by pairing!"

"Ha!" said old Silver Star, vacantly.

"Sir," continued I, "I had meditated a bloody revenge for this. But—I am needy. I will compromise—for a consideration!"

"Humph! Needy?"

"Yes, sir," said I solemnly, "my heart is a pauper, and is like to die of a love-starvation. I——" I whispered a word in old Silver Star's ear.

"Ho!" observed he.

Waterfall Third

Of course I didn't marry little Silver Star—I am not a barbarian.

But I will relate to you a little incident which occurred under my personal observation on the 17th of April, 1867.

At the foot of the great waterfall of Niagara stood seven people. One was a clergyman, and had just finished a marriage ceremony.

As Mr. and Mrs. Silver Star and the two witnesses said "Amen," little Silver Star was strained to the bosom of a man who stood at her side.

Her blue eyes yearned upward to his black eyes. It was as if he looked down, instead of up, into heaven.

Unable to endure these blue eyes, which swam with too-exquisite love, "Dear little Silver Star," said he, pointing to a glittering bow that arched the high mist, "dear, honored wife, forever and forever may there hover and bend tenderly over thy waterfall, as over that one yonder, a Beau of Promise!"

JOHN LOCKWOOD'S MILL *

A NOVEL

CHAPTER I. INTRODUCTORY

THE CLOSE of the War of 1861-'65, amid many dissolutions, wrought one transformation especially magical.

A land of leisure became suddenly a land of labor. A people which had dreamed away half a life, instantly began to work away the other half. Idleness became the one crime, in a country where, for years, Leisure had been the popular pride.

It would have been natural enough, if this sudden plunge into a harder life had produced, in minds not seasoned by labor, some tendency to plume themselves upon their alacrity in embracing hardships, and some unpleasant disposition to brag of the heartiness with which they had obeyed the sudden call to labor.

But the departing war, having swept away all else, left us as a solitary residuum of property, a hundred thousand graves. Out of these arose a nameless sweet influence which interpenetrated all the toiling and the trading, and tranquillized them into a calm activity which seemed very beautiful and very resolute and very promising.

"What, ho!" cried all the kitchens in the land, "what a glory is this which is come upon us!"

For there suddenly shone, about all the cooking-stoves and

* [This uncompleted novel is here first published. Internal evidence indicates the Spring of 1868 as the time of composition. The MS (Charles D. Lanier Collection, Johns Hopkins University) originally comprised forty pages, of which the last bears the mere heading "Chap. V"; but p. 16 has disappeared, and p. 39 is mutilated.

Besides the four chapters of narrative, an unfinished summary of the plot is extant, occupying pp. 676-77 of Lanier's Ledger (Henry W. Lanier Collection, Johns Hopkins University). In this volume it is reproduced at the end of the narrative text. The MS, apparently a hasty first draft, is filled with inconsistencies in mechanical matters: punctuation, capitalization, and devices for indicating paragraph divisions; those which do not reflect special meaning or emphasis have been standardized to conform with Lanier's practice in print. Also, in a few instances a word or mark which Lanier obviously meant to strike out has been cancelled silently. The variant spellings of the hero's name (Royston, Roylston) have been left unaltered, since Lanier's final choice is not indicated. —ED.]

dingy fire-places, a fair halo of bright eyes and dimples and white arms. People were poor, black cooks were expensive, daughters could work, *voila*! a Hegira of the negro cooks, an Occupation of the fairer daughters of the family,—a departure of the night, an advent of the dawn!

It was as if all the Nymphs and all the Naiads had gone together to see Proserpine, after she was Pluto's Wife.

What a reddening of once lily arms, what a floury besmirching of slim fingers, what a trim tucking of dresses about the waist, what a strange clatter of pans and clang of swung pots about dainty ears, was here!

Happy calamity, (said the men among us) which, like a Scandinavian death, has transported us through the pains of the grave into a Valhalla where sweeter maidens than the Valkyrie minister to our daily need.

Nor was the field, the workshop, the counting-room, the counter, behind-hand in receiving honor.

For, in this energetic Spring of '66, where was he who had led the brilliant charge at Petersburg?

Behold, his steed was become a stool of three legs, he was bending over a monstrous ledger; he was no longer heading the charge of a column, he was footing a column of charges.

And where was the slashing buck of the *ante bellum*, with the marvellous full shirt-front, with the supernatural pump-boots, with the filmy-wheeled trotting-wagon, with the clever soul, the careless air, the free laugh; he, whom each of our towns knew in the olden time, he, whom all the waiters at the Virginia Springs grinned to see in the old summers, he, whom each little home-world had apotheosized for itself: where was he?

He might have been seen, any day of this Spring of '66, tilting a burly barrel of sugar upon the round edge thereof, and wheeling the same featly as any porter, from sidewalk to store: and the wondering friends of his old days would discover flour upon his pantaloons, and would bear away odors of bacon and salt from the gripping of his hand.

But, in this Spring of '68, who can discern aught of this happy resoluteness, this cheerful energy which gave such promise? It is gone, the land is again idle, this time from necessity, and while there are a million *workers,* there is no stitch of *work.*

The towns are full of clerks who vainly offer their services for their food: of operatives, discharged upon a day's warning: of factories that have ceased to run: of empty workshops, of overstocked stores, of mortgaged dwellings, of gloomy markets.

"The laborer," said God, "is worthy of his hire." This was a marriage-service in which God pronounced the divine union of Labor with the Reward of Labor. Some men in the land have put asunder what God joined together: they have dissevered Labor from its Reward; and the consequences are as stated.

For at the close of the war, our one hope for the Future, our one forgetfulness of the Past, our one refuge from the starving Present, was Labor. And, today, we cannot labor, for there is here neither reward nor demand for labor. Our hope, our forgetfulness, our solace, has been drowned in some vile muddle or other of politics in which we had no part and no interest: our life is filled with the intolerable gloom of idleness, in order that some vile party or other may retain or acquire its offices and its patronages.

To give some picture of this two-years' revolution from work to enforced idleness:—a picture so sternly realistic that no figure shall appear in it which can not be exhibited in the flesh, and no transaction be recorded which does not stand upon the books of some officer of that Law which has called itself higher than justice and better than wisdom: This book is written.

CHAPTER II

On the twelfth day of July 1866, at sunset, a cloud flew into the sun like a moth into a candle: the west became straightway full of red cinders: which presently ceased to glow, and it was night.

On the same day a precisely analogous series of events happened, in the household of Richard Royston.

For on that day Richard Royston died: his two children followed him to his grave, where their hearts grew as full of grief as was the west with cloud-cinders: and when they returned to the masterless and motherless house, there was upon them at once the night of earth and of life, a double darkness.

Richard Royston, son of the dead Richard, oppressed by this two-fold shadow over eye and heart, could not sleep that night. After vain attempts, he gave up in despair, arose, dressed, and descended the steps, for a walk.

As he left the house, a gleam of light from the window of his sister's apartment met his eye. He retraced his steps, and knocked at her door.

"Is it you, Richard?" came from within.

"Yes."

"Come in."

"You're up late, Anne."

"I cannot sleep. I do not feel now as if I would ever be able to sleep again. And yet,—I'm *so* tired!"

Richard Royston spread his arms on the table and bent his head on them. In the stillness of the night, the rush of his own blood through the veins was like that of a far distant tornado. His nature was not unlike a storm, which *must* continue to grow until it has broken, and has spent its fury. A multitude of thoughts, bitter, sorrowful, angry, proud, hard upon the dead, harsh to the living, crowded upon him. To such impatient souls, at such times, it is necessary to speak out the plain thoughts which torture: it is only in the rain of words that such stormy hearts as Richard Royston's may relieve themselves.

Anne Royston knew this. She prepared herself to hear bitter things. She remained silent.

"It is hard:" presently said Richard Royston, without lifting his head, "—it is very hard. He was — I'll die, Anne, unless I say it out — he was drunk — when he died! It's my father, do you understand, Anne: it's my father that I'm talking about. I passed a knot of people on the street this afternoon, as I was coming back from the grave. One of them was saying, —— 'brought home from a dinner-party, drunk. Died soon after, very suddenly and,' — thank God, I didn't hear the rest. The man was talking about —— about my father, Anne: — my father. And I can tell, as well as if I had heard it, what the rest said." Richard Royston Jr. was silent for a few moments. "'Royston did a heavy thing in sugar, during the war, didn't he?' says Mr. A. 'Yes,' says Mr. B, 'but owed heavy debts

North before the war.' 'I'm told he's been drinking terribly, of late,' says Mr. C. 'Yes,' chimes in Mr. D, 'and worse things than that are whispered.' So: they make us a name. And, Good God, it's true: it's all true."

"Richard!"

"Doesn't your religion say the sin's in the thought and not in the deed? I think these things. I brood on them until my heart is afire. Why should I not say them? The sin's done.— Why is it that I regret his death? I could have borne it ten times as well if I had loved him! The shadow has been between him and me a long time. The grave does not lessen it: it thickens the cloud. It is appalling. Do you know what is the legacy of him who was our father? It is distrust, nameless suspicion, plain disgrace. What right had he to lay this burden on us?—None. It was criminal to do it. His life has been a weakness, mayhap worse: his death has been a palpable crime. A weakness—!—Where is my mother, she whom I loved? He broke her heart,—with his weakness! He killed her,—with his weakness! If I am at this moment in my soul a wretched parricide,—*he* made me so,—with his weakness! If"—

"O, my brother!—If you will not spare *him*, who is dead,— spare *me*," sobbed Anne Roylston, and threw her arms about the neck of the excited man, who had half risen and had extended his right arm in a menacing gesture upward. Her piteous tone, her white face, her pleading eyes, brought Richard Royston's thought away from himself. He drew her to his breast, and kissed her passionately. He felt her tears upon his hot cheek. His anger sunk deeper into his breast.

"I *was* a beast to wound you with these things. How good you are! Put your hand on my forehead. So! Let me kneel here, a little, by you. Let us be still."

Love did a good part, in this moment, for Richard Roylston. Love for his sister drove out of him the demon that began to possess him.

He remained, a long time, in silence. He then arose, without a word, kissed the girl who had been bending over him, and softly left the room.

Capricious sleep will come to soft thoughts, as a humming-bird flies to flowers. Roylston went to sleep, in a tender, brotherly dream.

Whilst Anne, the sister, whose grief was at once deeper and less violent, sat through the night, with folded hands, and still face. The filial disrespect which she could not crush out of her heart, and which rankled there as a crime committed without her will, yet as criminal as if it were voluntary, stung her sorrow in a thousand places and poisoned it. This strange combination of involuntary yet responsible crime, with a grief which could not account for itself, all night wrought upon the woman. What dark philosophies, of those domestic systems which women in the silent hours construct for themselves, might be born of such moments? Attacked on one side by a shadow which was impalpable, and on the other by a sin which was inevitable,—what weapons had Anne Royston against these? If, for one moment, she drove the Shadow back, then the Sin redoubled his sting. If, for one moment, she crushed the Sin in the dust, then the Shadow drew stealthily on, and overwhelmed her, and in the dark the Sin writhed out again, and stung.

Towards morning, she threw up one hand in a strange, pathetic *

x x x x x x x x x

Chapter III

John Lockwood's home stands upon the ridge of a high white-sand hill which slopes on one side to the sea, and on the other, with more abrupt descent, to the town. Its imposing front is towards town: a more modest doorway is judged good enough for the sea, on his side. And so the house stands, as it were, with one eye on man, and one on Nature: it gazes, one way, upon the to-and-fro of trade; another way, upon the majesty of the sea.

John Lockwood loves to sit upon the somewhat stately balcony on the town-side of his house: but his daughter, Meta Lockwood, frequents the small vine-covered porch that looks toward the sea. The father has a range of stores over yonder, which he can see from this porch; and the mass of his mill-buildings shows very fair, off yonder to the right, where the

* [Here a page (No. 16) of the MS is missing.—Ed.]

stream must leave off kissing the foot of the hill—and all love-talk to the sedges and grasses, and is set to work, to turn the wheels of John Lockwood's prosperity.

The daughter, on the other hand, has but one possession. It is the Sea. He lies out there, at her feet. He is her Pet. He crouches, like a tamed lion; or he arises and lashes his sides and roars through the air as a man-eater through the woods: or he foams in desperate fight with those untamed beasts, the winds and the clouds: or he capers in a burly frolic with friendly breezes: or he lies in profound reverence and allows the glittering Sun, as king of the beasts, to walk over his prostrate form. In all these moods of her huge play-fellow Meta Lockwood shares. The caprice of the Sea has gone into her soul. She has her Torrid, her Frigid Zone. In her heart are hot islands, full of passionate-odored flowers: but there are also cold snow-countries, which no man may fathom.

Once Meta Lockwood saw her lion open jaws and crunch a ship, like a bone. The ship held seventy men. This horrid bite revealed to Meta a bloodthirsty propensity in her Sea, which had inspired in her an undefined fear of him. The mystery of the Sea was penetrated with this fear, and it continually over-gloomed Meta, like a cloud with undeveloped lightning in it.

At ten o'clock, in the summer mornings, the lion's breath is cool, and comes gratefully floating shoreward, over the glittering white sand, over the strange wee oaks that cover the smaller hills, in through Meta's vine and lattice. This ten o'clock sea-breeze generally brings John Lockwood out of his business-room, which is on the town-side of the house, for a few minutes. He likes to get the first refreshing breath of it on the hot mornings, and to feel it swell and blow steadily, as if a dying man suddenly drew back his life with a longer gasp and breathed vigorously again.—Not that John Lockwood thinks of a dying man, or of regained breath, or of anything of the sort. It is only his habit to sit here a few minutes: then to return to his papers, his letters, his business visits from the foreman, his ride down into the town, or other such occupation.

Today, however,—which is a day somewhat past the middle of July, '66,—Lockwood has not been out on the sea-balcony, to get his breath of the sea-breeze. Since nine o'clock, he has been closeted with a stranger. When this stranger entered, Meta, from her balcony at the other end of the wide passage-way, noticed that he wore side-whiskers, that his nether limbs seemed ridiculously small compared with the bag-pantaloons which at that time prevailed in Southern sections, and that his shoes were of great length, thick-soled, pointed and turned up at the end. This costume, which was in every respect the direct antipodes of the mode which Meta was accustomed to see, had attracted her attention to the stranger as he entered, and he had responded to her unconsciously prolonged gaze by a half-bow which somehow gave Meta a certain sense of impudence attaching to the side-whiskers.

The door of John Lockwood's business-room had been closed for an hour and a half. Suddenly he appeared, and drew the stranger by the arm towards the balcony where Meta was sitting.

"See here, Mr. Melton!" said he, in an unwonted enthusiasm at which Meta lifted her brows. "Look yonder: at that wretched looking little dock, there are thirty feet of water! The *Great Eastern* could steam right up alongside, and land freight on it! There's not such another round the bend of the Gulf. "There's" —here John Lockwood became aware of Meta—" My daughter; Mr. Melton:—there's room enough for the sea-trade of ten States, down yonder. And think of what must come here, to be sent away, in a year or two! Think of the range of climate from here to the North line of the State! Up yonder "—Lockwood pointed to the northward—" we make thick ice in the winter: down there "—he pointed to the slope of his own hill —" I make oranges as fine as ever grew. From ice to oranges, Mr. Melton: that is the range. And see, what's between! Iron, in unlimited quantities: and coal, lying in bed with it like a brother; and kaoline and gypsum and marl: and, to round off the whole thing with a kingly finish, gold, Mr. Melton, in untold quantities. Don't the world need gold, Mr. Melton: don't it need iron, and coal, and kaoline? Nature has gifted this young State, as the old Fairy Godmother gifted a good child."

"I wish, Mr. Melton," said Meta, "you could enjoy the exquisite revenge which fills *me* with its sweetness, at witnessing my father's enthusiasm. Whenever a bit of nature insinuates itself into the doings of trade, one is forced to speak of trade somewhat poetically. My father has just yielded to this necessity. 'Ice to oranges': and the brotherhood of iron and coal: and the 'kingly finish': and the Fairy Godmother: and 'a good child':—*voila*, the poetry! This is fine.—My father hates poetry, Mr. Melton: and I, —— don't."

"Perhaps, Miss Lockwood, your tastes are not so irreconcileable as you may at first imagine. One could easily forgive your father for hating the poetry which is in books, when he is forever surrounded by the poetry which is out yonder"—Melton waved a graceful gesture towards the sea—"and which he has saved himself from the imputation of hating, by locating his house here, in command of it."

"A bad job, Mr. Melton—to reconcile Meta and me. We've been at loggerheads ever since she got hold of Tupper's po — "

"Father!"

"Well: Tennyson's, then: a fig for the difference."

"Of course," said Melton, deprecatingly, "it's my patriotic duty to stand up for Tennyson"—

"Tupper, too, Mr. Melton,—if patriotism's the word! You're all three countrymen!" said Meta.

"O, Tupper has won so much more fame among you Americans, Miss Lockwood, than he has among his own countrymen, that we consider him denationalized."

"You preserve your neutrality well, Mr. Melton! as between Father and me. I hate neutrality! What *has* changed you Englishmen so completely, of late days? You used to have a finger in all the war-pies that were cooked in the whole world. Nowadays, you're as peaceable as Quakers!"

"My dear Miss Lockwood," said Melton, in a cool, charity-school-teacher manner which provoked Meta almost beyond endurance, "there was once a youthful and highly fortunate individual, who had been gifted, by some good person, with—you will pardon me for running your own illustration farther—a plum pie. It is related that this imprudent youth, upon a certain occasion, inserted his thumb into the aforementioned pie, and extracted therefrom a plum. So far, his conduct was highly decorous: but his elation overcame him, and at the moment when the juices of the plum had overcome his equanimity, he cried out 'O, what a brave boy am I!' The printed narration of this thrilling event ends here: but it should not have done so: for the highly-pleasing affair very quickly transforms itself into a tragedy of the reddest hue. The vaunting remark of the young plum-holder attracted the attention of a plumless and ragged youth, *round* the corner: upon whose nature envy and cupidity and hunger and the natural aversion to taking-a-dare which is displayed by some races of beings, so worked that he fell upon the unhappy braggart of the pie, tooth and claw: and although this last did his manly devoir in the battle, and so struggled that, in the final clinch, *both* combatants fell to the ground; yet, alas, the end was a tragic one, since they descended pell-mell into the midst of the pie, and neither the conqueror nor the conquered got more of it than what was smeared upon their jackets,—a worse than worthless possession since the said smearing procured for each of them a sound thrashing from domestic hands at home. Now your America here has a fine pie; but we English have long ago found out that it isn't by any means a good way to keep our pie, to shake our fists in everybody's faces and shout our own bravery forth. We therefore eat in silence: or at least with peaceful talk: which helps our digestion of our plums amazingly. We consumed a long time, and lost many excellent pies, in finding this out:—pardon me, but I am afraid your United States, here, is going to lose all its time, and all its chance of pie, unless it profits by the experience of men that have been Jacky Horners and know what it is!"

John Lockwood's eyes twinkled.

"Well,—Meta! What d'ye say?"

"That it's good philosophy for those prudent youths whose ambition in life is a plum pie, and nothing else: but very poor philosophy for a — a — Man!"

"She says 'Man' as if she said 'Your Majesty,' or 'O King!'" said Lockwood, coming to rescue Melton. "My dear daughter, forty years of trade, in which I've been thrown with many people, have not fostered in me this reverence for my sex which you display, and"—

"Let me keep mine, then, Father, as long as it will last," interposed Meta.

"You'll be compelled to put it in water, like a flower, and not expose it to the cold air, Dear," said John Lockwood.

" In the scarcity of such flowers, Sir, we perhaps value them all the more for taking a little trouble to keep them fresh," sturdily replied Meta.

" All of which shows, Mr. Melton," said Lockwood turning to that gentleman, who had been silent for some time, " what a poor argument a metaphor is! For it always has two edges and two handles! And don't care which side wields it.—But, let's go back to business. I hope we shall have you here often to take the breeze with us."

Meta remained seated on the balcony. As John Lockwood and Henry Melton seated themselves in the business-room, the former sent a keen glance from under his bushy eyebrows at his companion's face, as if he were endeavoring to divine his intentions. Both were silent for some moments.

" I see," said Lockwood, " that you are not as enthusiastic as to the prosperity of the Town, here, as I am."

" The thing looks well, Mr. Lockwood, it looks well, Sir. But your country here isn't settled, yet. I confess I feel considerable hesitation in investing so largely in lots, whose appreciation depends upon so fickle a thing as the political future of this country. When trade and commercial prosperity come to hang upon the actions of so whimsical a body of politicians as seem to rule in your Congress, yonder,—the wisest may consider well what he does. Give me a little time. Let me look about. I have the money which you need. If I don't go shares with you in the purchase you propose,—why, perhaps some way of securing me in an advance of the money to you will present itself."

" Well," said Lockwood, after some moments, with a slight shade of disappointment in his tone. " You will, at any rate, permit me to request that your decision will be as prompt as possible. Every moment of delay loses me so much money: since the lots are even now appreciating daily: and if the present holder should get any means of carrying out my idea,—that of inducing the two Railroad Companies to buy some of the lots, for a depot when the Roads are completed,—there'll be no chance of getting them at any price whatever."

Again the two men were silent. In this silence, there floated up into John Lockwood's consciousness the memory that he had been called a man of unflinching business-nerve, by business men. Why, in this moment, when in all human probability, an honest fortune (highly honest, according to the rules of trade) lay in his grasp? And then his mind's eye saw the town grown into a city. He say a stately depot rise on his lot: he saw men flocking to his business-room here on the hill to purchase a few square feet of his other lots near so busy a centre: he went through the negotiations: he saw the checks signed: he gathered them into his hand: he was a millionaire.

John Lockwood arose quickly from his chair, unlocked a drawer in his Secretary, and came back to his seat at the centre table, with a bundle of papers in his hand.

"Pshaw!" said he. "Why should I delay what is certain? I'm not afraid of it. Here's a valuation of my mills, my plantation, and my dwelling-house. They're worth a hundred thousand dollars. I can buy those lots yonder for fifty thousand. Let me have the money for eighteen months. Take a mortgage on my whole property, to secure yourself. A year and a half from tonight, I shall laugh at you, and shake a half million in your eyes.—Will you do it?"

In spite of John Lockwood's off-hand talk, his teeth were clenched, and he spoke in a hurried manner as if he were not insensible that his step, regarded from the prudent point of view, was a somewhat desperate one.

"I will do that, Mr. Lockwood."

"Will you do me the favor to meet me here, tomorrow at ten, for the purpose of arranging the papers?"

"With pleasure."

Henry Melton and John Lockwood sate for a few moments in silence.

"Perhaps I shouldn't have risked it *all*," Lockwood was saying to himself.

CHAPTER IV

Meta had remained seated on the porch, looking seaward. "Good Heaven!" she thought. "Is this man, this smooth-mannered, side-whiskered trader,—is *he* come from the old sea-kings?"

Over the rim of the sea, to Meta's day-dreaming eye, sailed a ship of the old sea-king times. She could see the great thews and sinews of the swart sailors, as they lay on the deck, while the sturdy prow plunged forward, on the landward tack. She could see, as the vessel approached, those glittering eyes to which the world was new, and out of which shone those intense souls that used to rush over life vigorously and fearlessly as the salt breeze bounds over the sea. How the sails strain, how the ropes tighten, how the mast curves, how the stout hull sways, how the spray glitters in momentary consecration and baptism of the long locks that blow backward from bare heads, how the eager eyes strain, how the young waves leap, how the young wave-rider bounds! Ha! That magnificent and indescribable *send* of the sea bounded in Meta's soul, and she involuntarily rose upright.

"Pardon me!"

The speaker was on the lower step. He stood still a moment, with one foot on the step above. "I fear I startled you. I have mistaken the entrance, I believe. You will do me the favor to lay my error to the charge of your winding walks around the hill here, which misled me, amongst the shrubbery. Perhaps you are the lady to whom I have the honor to bring an introduction."

The stranger advanced, and handed Meta a letter.

"Ah:—from my dear Anne Roylston," said Meta, glancing at the address: "'introducing her Brother Richard.' I'm glad to see you, Mr. Roylston:" Meta offered her hand, with a genuine cordiality which made Richard Royston smile with gratification.

"It is long," continued Meta, "since I have heard from her. We were intimate friends at school, in New York. Be kind enough to sit down, Mr. Royston, while I read Anne's letter."

A good sea-king! thought Meta as she opened her letter: only, his beard's very black.

The letter ran:

" My Dear Meta:

" Death and Poverty have come to see us, together. Death is gone back to his grave. He took my father: and has left us his friend Poverty instead—Richard wishes to work. He has turned over the whole estate to some New York creditors of my father. It leaves him and me utterly penniless. He has seen an advertisement, signed by your father as President of the Board of Trustees, for a Principal of the Academy at your place. He wishes to make application for the position. Can you help him, by introducing him to your father? You know, Richard took the Honors at College.

" —Dear, when I read this over, I see that the sentences are short and sharp. They have taken the form of the aches which throb in my heart. I'll write you no more of them, now. Wait till I am better. You know,—you *know*, Meta,—that I'm

" Your Friend

" ANNE ROYSTON "

Meta had scarcely yet recovered from the confusion into which Royston's sudden appearance, as if in answer to her reverie, had thrown her.

" Allow me to carry you to my father, Mr. Royston," she said, and led the way to the business-room.

She knocked on the door, and opened it without waiting for reply. Just as she entered, Melton was coming out. He stepped aside, and allowed her to enter. As she passed him, followed by her black-bearded companion, Melton elevated his eyebrows, and glanced curiously at the pair. Somehow Richard Royston, with his soul already in a whirl at this meek way in which he was allowing a woman to help him forward in life, saw an immense degr[ee] of impertinence in this glance of [Mel]ton's. He returned it with a s[tern and q]uite unmistakable defianc[e to interr]upt.

So begin [antipathies.]

Melton pass[ed on.] John Lockwood had not noti[ced th]is

by-play. Meta introduced Roysto[n], and left him alone with her father.*

x x x x x x x x x

Plot

John Lockwood's Mill

Richard Roylston Sr. dies, reported much involved. He had been, during the war, engaged privately with an Englishman named Melton, (a Captain of a blockading Steamer) in running out a quantity of cotton to England, in the purchase of which cotton he had exhausted means which he should have retained for the payment of his Northern debts. He eventually succeeds in getting his cotton to England: but Wilmington is taken, no communication, except that very uncertain one by Galveston, exists between Roylston and his factors, and shortly the grand crisis comes on, the Confederate scheme bursts through. Roylston makes ineffectual attempts to hear from Melton, and, one day, dies suddenly. He leaves no evidence of his ownership of the cotton sent out, among his papers: and has said nothing of it to his children. In fact, the sale of the cotton has been made in Melton's name, Roylston fearing that his creditors might get wind of the transaction and mulct him of the proceeds.

On the trip in which Melton carries out the cotton, his pilot, Billy Beaseley, who has been running the blockade for two years and has made a large amount of money, carries out his daughter, Caroline, a beautiful girl of sixteen, whom he wishes to send on a visit to relatives in England, and there to perfect her education. After they arrive at Bermuda, they hear of the capture of Wilmington. Pilot Beaseley determines to come back by way of Galveston, but sends his daughter along with Melton, who concludes to visit Liverpool. He hears nothing

* [A hole is torn near the bottom of p. 39 of the MS; the restorations in square brackets are conjectural; p. 40 contains merely the caption: "Chap. V," and here the MS ends. The partial summary of the plot which follows (from Lanier's Ledger, pp. 676-677) is all the evidence that survives as to the probable contents of this unfinished novel.—Ed.]

more from the daughter until after the war when a letter reaches him from Melton stating that Miss Beaseley had been lost overboard, on the voyage to England. Broken-hearted, Beaseley returns to the house, built on a low island in the bay, a short distance from the mainland, near John Lockwood's house. This house is a favorite resort of Meta Lockwood's, whom the old pilot, in the days of peace, had liked because she liked his daughter and had taught to navigate a small sail-boat, an art in which, from constant practice, she had come to be very proficient.

FURLOW COLLEGE ADDRESS *

I AM HERE, to-day, to address you upon certain features in the present condition and future prospect of some great departments of life in that peculiar portion of the United States which we inhabit.

I choose this theme: because, if you are sad—and I see full many a melancholy countenance upturned towards mine—I know that the glittering spectacle of that future which I hope to unveil before you within this hour could not fail to fascinate the most mournful soul among you; because, if you are merry—and I behold on all sides the hilarious sparkle of young world-enchanted eyes—I know that the ghostly dangers which I hope to call up within this hour from the deep of our seething present, might well startle the merriest among you with salutary fears, and cool your most wayward wit into that wholesome sobriety with which the prudent man contemplates a fearful and imminent peril.

If you are timid, this theme gives me the cheerful anticipation of placing before you such just grounds of hope as may cause you cry courage! to yourselves. If you are overbold, this theme will develope such apprehensions as may give you prudent pause.

If you are bitter in soul, with hatred of them that have cruelly and foully maltreated you, perhaps here you will find some divine inward stirring of the soul toward forgiveness. If the repeated blows of sorrow upon some self-same spot in your hearts have made you—as, alas! they have made many of my countrymen—utterly callous to all grief and all pleasure, perhaps here you will find that the new struggle of our life is in desperate need of you, and that the new pathos of our laboring hunger and thirst is irresistible in its appeal to you, so that you

* [First published in the *Catalogue of the Trustees, Faculty, Alumnae and Students of Furlow Masonic Female College, Americus, Ga., 1868-1869,* from which the present text is taken; there it bore the title "Annual Address Before the Furlow Masonic Female College, Delivered June 30th, 1869," of which the present title is a condensation. Reprinted by Jay B. Hubbell in *American Literature,* II, 385-404 (Jan., 1931), under the title "A Commencement Address by Sidney Lanier." Acknowledgment is hereby made to Professor Hubbell for various courtesies, including permission to make use of the information in several of his notes. No MS has been found.—ED.]

can not possibly be longer indifferent to the progress and the vicissitudes of things about you.

If you are amazed and confused by the hideous clamor of corruption, of extravagant rascality and of loud-mouthed irreligion which now fills the land, perhaps here, you will grow more tranquil as you discover that powerful elements of faith, of honor, and of purity, still exist among us whose exquisite symbols may even now be detected, floating, like silken banners in a battle, through the dreadful turmoil.

If the rude encounter of hunger with the stolid forces of nature has overtrampled the softer amenities of your social life: if the stern opposition of your difficult soils, of your expansive fields, of your tenacious tree-roots, of your capricious cotton-plant, has tended to develope your muscles at the expense of your æsthetic faculties: perhaps, in this closer view we are now to take of our times, you may discover some faint but glorious presage of a more fortunate and swiftly advancing era, when down from the generous bosoms of our mineral mountains shall sweep a kingly stream of wealth that will fertilize our prolific fortunes until our homes will blossom with all social loves and friendly hospitalities; an era when all this robust manhood, which you drop into the ground along with each cotton seed, shall have sprouted and flourished vigorously, until it shall defy those hostile combinations of European capital which have been straining the ponderous powers of self-interest in the effort to stifle out our vital agricultural industry; an era when our fields shall present not only the gleaming white of opening cotton bolls, but shall nod and wave and glow and swell with all manner of bountiful grains and grapes, and of profitable leafage and fruitage; when the swaying sail of our commerce shall wander forth softly and silently as any dove, and bring back to us friendly olive branches and tokens of legitimate profit and of hospitable assurance, from all the islands of the oceans and all the nations of the continents; when our laws shall lead us by the reason in our brains, and not by the chains on our wrists; when our rulers shall rule our respect rather than our pity; when our conquerors shall discover that insults are not peace-makers, that taunting arrogance blisters the unhealed wound of the conquered, and that magnanimity is infinitely more powerful and less expensive than standing armies;

when our Art shall enchant our tired souls with lute and picture and statue and poem; and when our Religion, pallid from her long struggle with those devils of unrestraint which the war engendered, yet serenely smiling in her unarmed victorious majesty, shall stand in the centre of the land and win the unresisting people to all the benignant pulpits and sacred shrines of her expanding catholic temples.

My countrymen, I am not here to-day to flatter you. I beg you to remember that this era of which I speak is yet to come. It stands yonder, ahead. In the ancient days, when on national anniversaries and on commencement occasions the orator painted before his audience those splendid pictures of national prosperity of which we were all so proud, and pleasantly titillated that national vanity of which we were all so naively conscious, he but answered the pardonable expectation of his hearers, and everybody understood the harmless exaggerations of his oratory. But those ancient days are not, now, forevermore. We have scarcely time, now, for more than the unvarnished truth. Often, indeed, the rush and hurry of our modern life leave us no time for *that*.

To-day you have stepped aside from the onward press of the toilers, to see your daughters, your sisters, your sweethearts, take their last farewell of college life. Here we draw breath a moment. It is a good hour. Let us use it well. Let us gaze, with stern and uncompromising eye, through that outer shell of circumstance which encrusts our epoch. Let us see where we stand and whither we go. Let us note some figures, at least, in the long retinue of subsidiary facts left in our midst by that most striking fact in our history, the war of Southern Independence. For four years this haggard witch of battle lifted her skinny fingers over the great caldron of our society and flung into it handful after handful of weird and incongruous elements.

Double, double toil and trouble,
Fire, burn, and caldron, bubble;
Eye of newt and toe of frog,
Wool of bat and tongue of dog,
Adder's fork and blindworm's sting,
Lizard's leg and owlet's wing,
For a charm of powerful trouble
Like a hell-broth boil and bubble.*

* [The lines are, of course, from the witch-scene in *Macbeth*.—Ed.]

These elements have mingled themselves inextricably with our social condition, with our agriculture, with our politics, with our art, with our religion. Let us briefly contemplate the result of this admixture, as exhibiting itself in the present and the future of these departments of our Southern life.

And as I commence, in pursuance of this outline, to speak to you of our present social condition, I will confess to you that my heart is filled with the strangest conflict of tremulous fears and exhilarating hopes. For, to-day, when we speak of social questions, we can scarcely speak of aught else than questions which directly concern themselves with the education of women, with the rights and privileges of women, with the welfare of women, with the marriage of women, always with *women.* Young ladies, matrons, maids, wives and widows, do you hear? The acute intellect of the modern world cannot discuss the world's welfare without paying you this compliment, magnificent in itself, and exquisite because unconscious. When we discuss society, we discuss *you.* You, then, control society. You, then, are the heart, the one-flower, the sole passion, the only beloved, of society. To you society cries, as Othello cried to Desdemona:

> . . . Perdition catch my soul
> But I do love thee, and when I love thee not
> Chaos is come again.

And therefore, as I said, while I hope, I am afraid. I am afraid, because certain suggestions float about in the air that a time may come when you will no longer be loveable, when we *can not* love you, and when, by consequence, chaos *will* come again. I am afraid, because yonder in Europe, yonder in the North, I hear certain deluded sisters of yours crying aloud that women must vote, that women must hold political office, that women must be lawyers and physicians and ministers. *Female suffrage; female office-holders; female professional people; there are more women than men in the world; we own the larger half of the round earth; give it us, if not we will take it.* Such is the clamor that fills the time. These women have their shrill treble supported, so men say, by the bass of Mr. Gladstone, a great power in politics; of Mr. Mill, a great power in philosophy; and of Mr. Greely,* a great power in humbug. These women have elegant suites of rooms in the greatest city of our continent; they have newspapers, ably edited and profitably supported; they have conventions; they have lecturers; they have organizations; they have increasing memberships; they have money; they have prestige. Their affairs prosper. Their cause grows and looms apace.

But listen. On the instant, when this cause shall have attained its accursed object, on that instant the prophetic agony of Othello's tortured soul will consummate itself in a million manly bosoms, on that instant we will love you not, on that instant chaos will come again. As voters, we could not love you, for you would be no whit different from men, and men do not love men. As lawyers, as ministers, as physicians, we can not possibly love you; we ourselves are all these, and we want something *beside* ourselves; we want two in one, and not one in two.

It would be easy enough, if one were so minded, to raise your laughter over the absurdities of these misguided persons; but this, to me, would be like that mournful joke which Lessing perpetrated on the death of his only son; ** it would be horrible wit. I, for one, have in my heart no ridicule for the advocates of female suffrage; I have only pity and fear and horror. Let us not delude ourselves with the fragile hope that this storm will pass by and leave our Southern waters quiet. The time draws rapidly nigh, when these questions, of female suffrage and the like, will sweep down upon us and demand to be answered. Lightly as you may now smile at the mention of these things, presently the brunt of this tempest will whirl about; you will find yourselves in the midst of it; you will be compelled to determine promptly.

In whatever way you decide, in that way will run the fate of our society. The question is simple: will you rule our votes, or rule our voters? At the ballot-box, you can control the votes; at home, you can control the voters.

Women of my country, in a vision which is no dream, I see

* [*Sic*. On the ground that most women would never care to vote, Horace Greeley actually opposed woman suffrage, though he favored a widening of the range of woman's employments.—Ed.]

** [The story may be found in James Sime, *Lessing* (London, 1877), II, 175-176.—Ed.]

society kneeling at your feet, supplicating, with mournful voice, with imploring eyes, with clasped hands, for its one divine necessity. Hear it! *Give me, O woman, that which you only can give, a Home; that society which keeps its homes pure is invulnerable to all those serpents, physical, moral, political, social, religious, that creep and crawl about the world and leave their slime upon what they can not poison: in this sacrosanct shrine of home their entrance is difficult and their fangs are harmless. By the cradles in which your virgin virtues were nurtured, by all the heavenly overwatchings of the serious eyes of motherhood, by all the brotherhoods and sisterhoods of clinging infancy, by all the social loves that make life tolerable, by all the germs of honor that remain in the world, by all the purities and sincerities and generosities that must live if I live, I implore you preserve for me this genuine Holy of Holies, whose soft name falls on the ear as a rose-petal falls on the water, this true Heaven on Earth, which men call Home!*

Ah, if we ask you for a home, will you give us only a hustings? If we invite you to be queen of our souls, will you abdicate this magnificent sovereignty, to seat yourselves upon the hard and vulgar throne of the ballot-box? Now, may God forbid it!

Nay, I think *you* will forbid it. For, as I said, whilst I am afraid when I think of the possible chaos that might blot out the present promise of our society, there yet come certain hopes which struggle with these boding apprehensions and give me courage.

Ah, I do not forget, that I speak to the mothers of the heroes of the Southern Confederacy!

I do not forget, that I speak to the sisters whose cheerful alacrity in hurrying brothers forward to the field of battle, has ennobled and sanctified all sisterhood forever.

I do not forget, that I speak to the sweethearts whose contempt for cowardice and admiration for bravery were at once the most dreadful punishment of the coward and the most thrilling inspiration of the brave.

I do not forget, that I speak to the wives whose kisses, lingering on the lips of husbands, did, in the day of battle, burn them onward right into the blazing hell of hostile batteries.

I do not forget, that when the heats of summer suns would

have debilitated our frames, your anxious forethought had provided remedies; that, when the winter nights of inhospitable climates would have frozen the picket's fingers stiff about his musket, your busy needles had anticipated protection; that when we were hungry, you fed us; when we were thirsty, you gave us drink; when we were sick, you visited us; when we were in prison, you comforted us; when we were naked, you clothed us; that always, in whatever necessity of our natures, whether we craved the light of brilliant eyes, or the animation of smiling lips, or the tendance of dainty fingers on wounds, or the solemn comforts of religion at death-beds, or the tributary fragrance of flowers on graves, always you were ready, always you responded, gazing, smiling, tending, comforting, scattering flowers.

I do not forget, that this tribute of soldier's gratitude has been paid you before, and that some cold soul might carp at the twice-told tale; but, so long as the Heavens are friendly to me, I will never forget that that day will be black when the orator on any rostrum in this land shall omit to devote his most glowing periods and his most earnest rhetoric to those faithful women who have so loved, who have so lost, but who, thanks to Almighty God, have so survived the Southern Confederacy!

Shall we not, then, have good hope that in the day when the legion of female suffrage move down upon us and agitate their unnatural propositions, our women, in one unanimous outbreak of womanly scorn and contempt, will spurn the absurd and pitiful privileges which these pseudo-benefactors propose to confer?

Let it never be dreamed that in rejecting female suffrage, you reject female influence in politics. So far from that, you can not, if you would, abandon that responsible attitude which in all ages and in all nations women have maintained towards the State. Consciously or unconsciously, directly or indirectly, silently or loudly, you *must* be a political power. Whether you crowd our hustings or preside over our households, whether casting your ballots or dusting your parlors, you are compelled to exercise commanding influences over all departments of the State. I pledge you the faith of all history and all philosophy, if you keep the private house pure, then the State-house will never become hopelessly corrupt; if you exhibit to us lofty ideas of womanly dignity at home, then the national Senate will not go, as it has gone, mumming and capering in clownish follies, utterly unrebuked; if you deal with daily cares in candor and sincerity, then all the sooner will the nation abandon its shuffling diplomacies, to substitute the broad and winning integrities of honest statesmanship.

Now, because I thought that you, young ladies, would have already seen how your woman's life, though apparently bounding itself within the four walls of domestic matters, does nevertheless stretch out unseen and powerful arms into all affairs of social and of national importance; because I thought that you would never consider yourselves intelligent women until you had thoroughly informed yourselves as to the conditions and prospects of the great institutions of your country; and because I thought you would appreciate the compliment of being addressed upon subjects which men too often arrogate to themselves, as if men only were intelligent, as if men only were patriotic; it was for these reasons, that I proposed to speak to you next of those elements, either good or evil, which the departing war left in our agricultural system.

The substitution of free labor for slave labor came upon us so suddenly and so mournfully, that it threatened for a time to paralyze all our industrial energies. In truth, this spectre of free labor marched down upon us in such bad company, that it might well have excited the most alarming apprehensions.

Under its feet, lay the dead body of our political independence. Trooping behind its back, came a fearful retinue. Poverty, lawlessness, marital demoralization, political incapacity, physical indolence, domestic improvidence, agricultural ignorance, moral profligacy in awful twinhood with religious fanaticism; all these stalked along in the train of free labor, as they had been the supple courtiers of this seemingly dreadful king.

We theorized upon it.

Do you not all remember the multitudes of dismal communications which filled our public journals with predictions of death to all our planting interests in the South? Do you not all remember how many of our farmers declared that the planter would never again be able to earn his living on Southern soil, and how they sold out houses and lands, and hurried away to

Brazil, to Cuba, to Central America, to California? Do you not all remember how, in the public prints, one writer reiterated vehemently that the freedmen would never, never work; another, that even if we should be able to raise cotton, its price would always be too low to pay expenses, by reason of Egyptian and East Indian competition; another, that the war had in some mysterious way engendered perennial hosts of boll-worms, of army-worms, of caterpillars, of droughts, of freshets, of fevers, of agues, which would forever render our farming impracticable and our country uninhabitable; how, in short, there was a universal reign of dismal fancy and of whimsical foreboding?

But what has been the real result?

It is now four years, almost to a day, since the last tired soldier of the Southern armies laid down his useless musket and wearily travelled back to his desolate fields, with the dust of recent battle scarcely yet shaken from his garments. Without implements, without stock, without labor, without money, without credit, without anything but scarred hands and scarred hearts, we started to work. The worm came, the drought, the freshet, the ague came, repeated failure came. Nevertheless we worked on.

How is it, now?

We have new-equipped scores of old railroads, and we are building scores of new ones; we have been sending our children to schools and colleges; we now fill our newspapers no longer with prophecies of agricultural failure, but with practical discussions of new projects in fencing, in fertilizers, in improved seeds and varieties, and in experimental systems of culture; we revive our agricultural fairs and present ponderous lists of prizes to competitors; we begin to import breeding-stock; we begin to inquire about immigration; we pay off multitudes of old obligations; in short, and in entire explanation of all these marvels, we sell two hundred and fifty million dollars' worth of cotton in one year!

We discover that the dreaded competing fields of the East Indies must abandon cotton and grow some grain, in order to save hundreds of thousands of natives from death by starvation; that the narrow lands on the banks of the Nile, besides commanding fabulous prices per acre, must also supply the population with food as well as cotton; that the Brazilian thousands of bales are not so formidable after all, since they only weigh about one hundred and fifty pounds to the bale; that however other countries may compete with us as to the *quantity* of cotton raised, nevertheless the superior quality of our uplands and sea-islands leaves us always in easy command of markets; that shortly the Pacific Railroad will bring us multitudes of laborers, whose competition will forever check any absurd demands of our present farm-hands; nay, if you will listen closely, you will actually hear certain persons beginning to whisper among themselves, *perhaps after all, Cotton* IS *King.*

These are cheering results: but as we felicitate ourselves upon them, let us not forget to accept and digest the lessons which they learn us.

Let us not forget, for instance, to accept and digest the unpalatable truth that we, here in the South, are among the crudest theorizers in the world. We put together too many unsubstantial hypotheses. Day after day our public journals are filled with letters whose conclusions rest neither on logic nor on fact. I fear we are inordinately fond of predicting, of supposing, of prophesying, in agricultural matters. Let us learn to delay our conclusions until we have gathered together many facts, until we have taken all large and many-sided views, and above all, until we have actually tried them by material weights and measures. Let us distrust every hypothesis concerning our planting interests which has not been subjected to that greatest of all strains, the test of time. Experiment as much as you can. Try this and that fertilizer; plant an acre in this grain, an acre in that cotton, an acre in the other vine, but *keep back your conclusions.* Wait till all the facts are in; wait till time has mellowed them together; wait till reason has measured and weighed their relative proportions. Do not announce your projects before they are born: do not bury them before they are dead. Think, labor, *wait.*

My country women and countrymen, this last word which I have spoken—this word "wait"—is a wonderful word. Unquestionably it should be the watch-word of our agricultural system at present; not less unquestionably should it embody the principle of all our political behavior under the exceedingly trying and delicate circumstances which surround us.

Day by day we feel the smart of some new and ingeniously-devised lash on shoulders which are sore enough, God knows, with the galling burdens of the past.

Abroad, unblushing slander has usurped sole charge of our reputations. At home, pitiful dissensions over the public monies waste the time and distract the energies of our statal rulers. The manufacturers of ready-made outrages ply their busy pens like shuttles in some dirty loom, to supply the demand of trading politicians for this new and popular article of party commerce. A monstrous distortion of Justice pleases its idle whim with punishing intelligence by subjecting it to ignorance. O, with the small malignities of our conquerors, as with multitudes of irritating javelins, our souls are stuck full.

What shall we do?

Shall we appeal to arms?

Not so! I have infinite and unconquerable faith in the benignities of the slow process of time. Millions of men—if we had them!—with arms and batteries—if we had them!—*might* conquer; but time, time, only time, can permanently convince. Let us wait.

Or, shall we go about peaceably to change the Republic into an Empire?

Here, indeed, one discovers the most extraordinary spectacle in all the history of those political vagaries which arise out of wars and their consequent perplexities. It is reported, and I doubt not truly, that many of the worthiest men in our land deliberately entertain the hope that our republican government may speedily crystallize into a monarchy. It is reported, and I doubt not truly, that "The Imperialist," * a journal whose name explains its import, boasts a large and rapidly increasing subscription list at the South. I personally know that many good men among us do ardently desire that we should have a king, fancying therein some refuge from the present ills of the country.

Surely, surely, these gentlemen have been driven into wild unreason by the intolerable misfortunes of the hour! Ten years ago the United States Government fell into the uncon-

* [A New York weekly, established in 1869, which advocated the establishment of an "Imperial central executive" on the theory that the majority of American people were incapable of self-government.—ED.]

trolled hands of a party whose avowed object was to overturn the wise polities of our forefathers, to sweep away the autonomy of the States, and to centralize the vast powers of the republic in its federal head. With marvelous dexterity, with adroit applications of party cries and focalizings of party resources, this faction has succeeded beyond its wildest expectations. Look, if you please, along the multitudinous range of governments, from the iron autocracies of Asia to the rude tyrannies of Ethiopia, and find me, if you can, a single individual who wields more unlimited sovereignty than the present President of the United States! In the name of Heaven, have we not centralization enough—have we not consolidation enough? If we could change the government into an empire to-day, would we have more? Is not this a new sort of political homeopathy, to cure the ills of consolidation by administering an infinitesimal dose of consolidation? Nay, if the Imperialists will pardon me a too obvious joke, is not this precisely the policy of that unfortunate individual with whose comical troubles we were familiar in our childhood?

There was a man in our town,
  And he was wond'rous wise;
He jumped into a bramble-bush,
  And scratched out both his eyes.
And when he found his eyes were out,
  With all his might and main,
He jumped into the bramble-bush,
  And scratched them in again!

Having scratched out our eyes with jumping into this infernal bramble-bush of consolidation, think you that by jumping into the identical bush, which we now call an empire, we will scratch them in again?

Ah, no. What we want, believe me, is not the empire, which we already have! but the republic, which we have not. After a time, sure as Heaven, we will get it; and paradoxical as it may seem, nothing will bring it to us more speedily than patience. A certain acute Frenchman * has declared that patience is genius. A celebrated American has embodied all

* [Buffon. The reference in the following sentence is to Longfellow, "A Psalm of Life."—Ed.]

our political economy of to-day in the admonition: Learn to labor and to wait. Our public men tell us that we are shortly to see a multitudinous immigration of Chinamen into our section. For more than agricultural reasons, I rejoice that this is so. The Chinaman is patient as time, he is patient as nature, he is patient as the steady-wheeling, unfaltering earth. From the minute diligences and slow assiduities of his tedious, yet successful, system of culture, let us catch the enduring, the marvel-working, the God-like virtue of patience. Already, upon the far horizon, a patient and observant eye can discover certain early scintillations that flash up from the advancing sun of our political regeneration. Presently, those obscure mists that arose from the reeking fen of the war, and that have so long obscured the reason of our rulers, will begin to tremble beneath the hot energies of his far-reaching fires; they will burst asunder; they will float away, utterly away, from off the face of the land; they will become mere clouds in the distance, and the magic of the morning will silver them into glittering palaces, with manifold spire and pinnacle of warning to the nations. Presently, the very chains of ice that now bind our energies will themselves dissolve, under this fervid sun-rising, into cool and refreshing drops that will fall upon our dusty past and fertilize it with fruitful admonitions. Presently, I verily believe, the glory of the fresh hopes of a new daylight will outspread itself, fair and warm, about the peaceful homes of this contented people.

But, in the midst of our hot attack upon the impurities and poverties of our new life, let us have an unremitting care lest our ears be so deafened that we cannot hear the noble voices of Poetry and of Music, singing to us through the battle; and lest our eyes be so blinded that we cannot see the fingers of Painting, of Sculpture, and of Architecture, beckoning upward through the dusty smoke.

Be warned in time; do not allow yourselves to be run away with by those perverse exaggerations of the dignity of labor which are so likely to catch the unwary spirit of a people suddenly condemned to unwonted manual work. Truly, all labor is dignified; to plow the field with one's own hand, to sweep the house with one's own hand, this, at the time of necessity, is indisputably a high and sacred duty, and we rightly despise him or her who could shrink from it. But manual labor is not the *only* labor; there are other high and sacred works; and among these none are higher, none are more sacred, than those which we call, by a happy terminology, Works of Art.

Unable to fulfill the hope which I had indulged of addressing you with some detail upon this inviting topic, I yet cannot leave this subject without referring, in sorrowful fashion, to a certain insidious evil, which, especially since the war, has been the very bane and poison of all our humble artistic endeavor here in the South. I mean the habit of inviting purchasers to buy artists' works, *simply* because they happen to be Southern artists. I mean the habit of regarding our literature as *Southern* literature, our poetry as *Southern poetry*, our pictures as Southern pictures. I mean the habit of glossing over the intrinsic defects of artistic productions by appealing to the Southern sympathies of the artist's countrymen.* I mean the constant invocation, which one finds in all the public journals, "to patronize *Southern* talent." Patronize? Patronize? Despicable word! How ignoble must be the ambition of that artist, whether he be poet, painter, musician, sculptor, or architect, who could consent to palm off the crudities of his indolence upon the patronizing good-nature of his countrymen! The basis of all this is unsound, and if we erect any superstructure of Art upon it, the whole building will inevitably topple into disgraceful ruin. For, the basis of it is hate, and Art will have nothing to do with hate. Young ladies, you who some day may give us worthy poems, worthy pictures, worthy music, burn into your souls these principles: First, Art is a genuine creation. Second, God is the first Creator, and therefore the first Artist. Third, God is Love, and Love only is creative, while Satan is Hate, and Hate only is destructive. Therefore, Fourth, every artist must be like God, that is, must be full of love, which is creative, and empty of hate, which is destructive. This love, of which I speak, is not a sentimentality; it is that grand overmastering passion for all that is noble in human life, and for all that is beautiful in

* [Lanier could apply his principle to his own artistic work and standing. Though pleased when Southerners praised him, he did not wish them to do so on sectional grounds. See his letter of April 27, 1876, to Peacock and his prose article "The Centennial Cantata" (II, 267, of the present edition).—Ed.]

natural organism, which each man and woman of us brings, in more or less vivid brightness, out of childhood into later life. Never yet saw I a child that would not gaze with serious eye upon a flower; never yet saw I a child that would not listen, with serious ear, to a song; never yet saw I a child that would not give his serious soul to a fairy tale; and if these things be so, then, surely, never yet saw I man or woman that had not, in the deep of the heart, some germ of love for beauty in nature, in music, in poetry.

If then we would be genuine artists, let us love true Love, let us hate false Hate. If we sing, let us sing for the ear of the whole world; if we write, let us write for all the nations of all the ages; if we paint, let us paint for the eye of time; if we build, let us build for the cosmopolitan taste of the myriad diverse peoples whom destiny will speedily pour into the length and breadth of our land.

In this early morning of our national day, let our Art circle, and circle, and circle upward, like any lark, and from some immeasurable elevation in the heavens, high over all the fret of men and jar of nations, let it carol some tender and *many-voiced* melody, that will draw the heart of the whole world upward to that adorable God of Love in whom Art must live, and move, and have its being.

And when our Art, as all Art tends to do, shall have installed itself in the sweet voluntary service of Religion, then we shall know, more unquestionably than some of us now begin to feel, that that wild element of religious distrust which came upon us with the departing war, is beginning to disappear before the manifold bounties of our inscrutable Master. How many of you, on some rainy night during the four dreary years of our war, prostrated yourselves before the Heavens, and prayed with agonizing ardor that son or husband or brother might be spared in the day of battle—and heard next day that son and husband and brother had been stricken down, even while your prayer was going up?

How many of you, day by day of those bitter years, wrestled with the great God for the prosperity of our cause, and received no answer but crushing defeat? How many of you, wounded by these sharp responses to your supplications, were ready to cry out that you no longer had faith in the sublime promises of our religion?

Undoubtedly, this element of religious distrust remained with us when the war was gone, and crept about in heart and home, hissing and rejoicing over the wretchedness it wrought. Nay, there arose a cry in the land from certain sensational people, that Protestantism was a failure; that religion itself was a failure. But where is the failure, to-day?

Has nature failed you?

Yonder, the ripening wealth of your plenteous fields, the billowy foliage of your forests, the dainty flowers of your wild-wood answer eloquent, No!

Has life failed you?

Everywhere arise your schools, your villages, your cities, your factories, and the heaven-pointing spires of your religious temples!

Has God failed you?

The dawn that broke in glory upon us this morning denies it: yonder sun that hangs upon His right hand in heaven denies it; and to-night, the faithful stars, with a myriad silver voices, will deny it.

When these fail you, religion will fail you. Until then, you have naught to do but smile at those absurd birds of evil, who, having found some decaying carcase of a sensation, straightway begin to flap wing boisterously through the air, and to screech out that the world is dead.

Such, young ladies, is a meagre outline of hopes and fears in the Society, the Agriculture, the Politics, the Art, the Religion, of our Southern life. Whatever be these hopes, whatever be these fears, I charge you, young women of my country, remember that for their realization they are mainly in your hands. If we wish for purity in our social morality, if we wish for industrious patience in our agriculture, if we wish for dignity, integrity and calm obedience in our politics, if we wish for world-broad love in our art, if we wish for undying faith in our religion, you, you, in the tranquil privacies and virgin sanctities of home, must furnish and mature and send forth these inestimable virtues.

Permit me to ask, what is it you commence, on this day, which you call Commencement Day?

You commence your education. Hitherto, you have toiled, you have obeyed, you have studied, under the guidance of your teachers, not by any means to finish your education, but solely to enable you to begin it rightly. Henceforth, however, you study *without* a master. Henceforth you toil for love's sake. Henceforth you obey the solemn disciplinary commands of life. Do not forget, as you commence this arduous curriculum, that Holy Writ has declared, not lightly, that man was made in the image of his God. Now, God is a Trinity, and we, too, are all little trinities. We consist of body, intellect and heart. Take heed to educate these three symmetrically, that you may harmonize with yourselves physically, intellectually and emotionally. Fichte has declared, "I can live in harmony with any one who lives in harmony with himself." Live, then, in harmony with yourselves. Educate your powers evenly and in admirable balance. A noble generalizer writes * that there is in every civilization a certain element which may be called the feminine element, and that the true beneficial course of modern civilization lies in the development of this feminine element. Advance, then, the type, multiply the potentialities, intensify the spiritual beauties, of this feminine element.

Educate your physical powers. Let us see again in the world those tall, lithe, graceful, redlipped, brilliant-eyed, violet-breath'd, lissome-limbed queen-women, who sometimes sate on the early thrones of Germany and France and England.

Educate your intellectual powers. Question unceasingly, question audaciously, all history, all science, all philosophy. Be content with no half answers. Be bold enough to accept any truth. Be wise enough to preserve from improper distortion, and to classify, in proper relation, every fact. Beware how the quick intuitions of the woman hurry you on to erect isolated instances into general principles. Life and art and knowledge will cast upon you the necessity of drawing many grand conclusions. Let these conclusions be from large inductions, be slowly drawn, be carefully weighed, be rigidly outlined. Cut your clear way through the sky of womanly work, like Goethe's star, unhasting, yet unresting.

And lastly, exercise your emotional powers. Many people

* [Presumably the reference is to the passage in Tennyson, *The Princess*, which Lanier often cites elsewhere.—ED.]

forget that we educate our *loving* energies, as well as our thinking and acting energies. Never forget that marvellous epitome of all the Law and the Prophets, which the Master left with us before he departed. That was, Love God: love thy neighbor as thyself. There is more in this than meets the shallow thought. To love God is to love the higher; to love one's neighbor is to love the lower. Love for the higher—this is what we call Faith. Love for the lower—this is what we call Charity. Between these two, out of that chastened regard which we are expressly allowed to entertain for our own feelings, is born Hope. Faith, Hope and Charity, these three, are enough for all life and for all the world. Be never satisfied, then, until you have educated yourselves to love adequately—mark the word, *adequately*—everything that is above the earth, within the earth, beneath the earth.

As I part from you to-day, permit me to hope that you have not been wearied by these last words into which I have endeavored to condense many conclusions of history, many utterances of aged experience, many intuitions of spell-bound genius, many crystalizations of divine precepts. Permit me to hope that you commence your new life with many pure, earnest, steadfast enthusiasms burning in your souls. Yonder, on the swift car of by-passing existence, I see coming another Commencement Day that shall be greater than this. On that Day the multitudes of the life-pupils of the ages shall assemble themselves together before the world's Master for final examination. Amid the thunderous terror of the tumult of that day; amid the lightning revelations of its piercing question and startling answer; amid the tender glories of Him who shall conduct its investigations; amid the melancholy scowls of him who shall receive its unsuccessful candidates; amid the exquisite confusions of its long-delayed meetings, its long-growing fruitions, and its long-pursued satisfactions; amid all the sights and sounds of that Commencement Day of Eternity, permit me to hope that you, serenely wrapt in the near contemplation of those lovely ideals which on earth you could only pursue afar off, may be lifted into that upper Heaven, where the Master shall stand, directing the jubilations of the harpers over the women who have taught themselves the secret of life, and who have penetrated the mystery of death.

CONFEDERATE MEMORIAL ADDRESS *

IN THE unbroken silence of the dead soldierly forms that lie beneath our feet; in the winding processions of these stately trees; in the large tranquillity of this vast and benignant heaven that overspans us; in the quiet ripple of yonder patient river, flowing down to his death in the sea; in the manifold melodies drawn from these green leaves by wandering airs that go, like Troubadours, singing in all the lands; in the many-voiced memories that flock into this day, and fill it, as swallows fill the summer; in all these, there is to me so voluble an eloquence to-day that I cannot but shrink from the harsher sound of my own human voice; and, if I might but follow where these silver tongues lead me, far rather would I invite your thoughts to their spiritual guidance and keep mine still. Indeed, I will pursue this preferable course, and so combine my duty as orator and my inclination as man; for if I have rightly interpreted the sentiment which supports your memorial organization; if I have accurately comprehended the enduring idea about which your society has grown and wound itself, as a vine about some firm pillar of white marble; then, in giving utterance to this most musical converse of Death and Nature and Memory, which goes on in this place by night and by day, so will I best utter those emotions which animate your Association, and which call for some mouth-piece to-day. I take it, the very words which I have employed in describing the elements and circumstances of this scene, do most accurately symbolize and embody the precise virtues which it is the direct tendency of your Association to perpetuate and keep alive in our midst.

Believe then, that in the few words I have to say, I shall but translate to you that formless and soundless rhetoric of which

* [First published in the Macon (Ga.) *Telegraph and Messenger,* April 27, 1870—under the title "An Address. Delivered Before the Ladies' Memorial Association at Rose Hill Cemetery, April 26th, 1870"—from which the present text is taken. Exactly seventeen years later it was reprinted in the same newspaper; it was reprinted in *Retrospects and Prospects* (New York, 1899), pp. 94-103, with several verbal and mechanical variants, under the shorter title here adopted. A few obvious typographical errors and mechanical irregularities incident to newspaper printing have been corrected. No MS has been found. —ED.]

I spoke in the outset, aye, that majestic oratory of death's silence, of the forests' stateliness, of the Heaven's tranquillity, of the river's patience, of the music of winds and leaves, and of the strange commingling of grief and glory and joy that lies in our memories of the days when these men died for liberty.

I spoke first of the *silence of death.* My countrywomen and countrymen, I know few wants that press upon our modern life with more immediate necessity than the want of this same silence. In this culmination of the nineteenth century, which our generation is witnessing, I tell you the world is far too full of noise. The nineteenth century worships trade; and Trade is the most boisterous god of all the false gods under Heaven. Hear how his railways do thrill the land with interwoven roaring and yellings! Hear the clatter of his factories, the clank of his mills, the groaning of his forges, the sputtering and laboring of his water power! And that is not half. Listen how he brags, in newspaper and pamphlet and huge placard and poster and advertisement! Are not your ears fatigued with his loud braggadocio, with his braggart pretensions, with his stertorous vaunting of himself and his wares? Nay, in this age of noise, the very noise itself, which is usually but the wretched accompaniment of trade, has positively come to have an intrinsic commercial value of its own. It is a fact that some trades succeed by mere force of noise, by mere auctioneer's strength of voice, by mere loudness of stentorian advertisement, without possessing a single other element of recommendation or success.

Now, far be it from me to condemn the sounds of hammer and saw and anvil; far be it from me to censure advertisements, which form the legitimate appliances of success in trade. I am not here for that, to-day. This is not the place or the time to draw the distinction between the legitimate and the illegitimate rush of commerce—between what is vile brag and what is proper self-assertion in the merchant's advertisement. But I know that there is an evil in all this noise. Out of this universal hubbub there is born a great wrong. A certain old homely phrase expresses this evil in vivid terms: In these days, there is *so much noise that we cannot hear ourselves think.*

What time have I to enumerate the signs and evidences of this evil, of not hearing ourselves think? They are on every hand. Crudity, immaturity, unripeness, acidity, instability—

these things characterize our laws, our literature, all our thoughts, our politics, our social life, our loves and hates, our self-development.

Permit me, then, to felicitate your Memorial Association, because, among many other reasons, one of its immediate consequences is to counteract these evils of noise which I have depicted. You, my countrywomen, invite us once in the year to escape out of the turbulencies of trade, and to come here among these silent resting-places of our dead soldiers. You lay a tender finger on the blatant lips of trade, and bid him be still in the august presence of the dead who speak not. You help us to hear ourselves think, for a moment. This is well done. If there be in this company one broken heart; if there be here one who has her dead lying in this Cemetery; if there be here one who has learned from silence the divine secret whereby a man may harmonize the awful discordant noises of life, I invoke its witness that my words are true, that silence is the mother of a thousand radiant graces and rare virtues, and that if one will lean for one hour over these graves of our dead Confederate heroes, there will well up into his soul more

Large, divine, and comfortable words

than ever fell from living human orator.

Ah, old comrades who lie sleeping about this yard beneath tomb and hillock and sculptured pillar, you fought for us in your lives, you died for us in your love, and now—if our human voice might float over the dark river to where you are gone on the other side—we would cry across to you that still, after death, your unselfish ministrations to us continue; still, after death, your graves send up benignant blessings to our souls; still, after death, your dumb lips answer the tributary flowers that we bring you, with responses and strengthening benedictions that rain sweet influence on our distracted life.

For this, my countrywomen who compose this Memorial Association—that you enable us to appropriate this after-death beneficence of our silent dead—for this, in the name of an age half insane with uproar, I thank you.

I spoke, next, of the stateliness of the trees. In these days, stateliness is an antique virtue. This age is not grand; it is, rather, active. We have substituted adroitness, in the modern, for the massive strength of the old times. Where the antique man was strong, the modern man in supple; where the antique man was large, the modern man is keen. In such an age as ours, how extraordinary was the stately grandeur of those noble figures that arose and moved in splendid procession across the theatre of our Confederate war! Look with me down the long temple of history, and I will single you out two figures, wherewith I am willing that my beloved land shall front the world, and front all time, as bright, magnificent exemplars of stateliness. Mark them! Whether their swords gleamed in the hottest smoke of the front of battle, or their peaceful hands waved from the professor's chair, stately always: stately in victory, stately in defeat: stately among the cannons, stately among the books: stately in solitude, stately in society: stately in form, in soul, in character, and in action; aye, each of them,

> From spur to plume, a star of tournament.*

Do you not know them? One is still stately in life; the other lies stately in death. Their two colossal statues are already set up in fame's glittering gallery of the stately souls of time. The convulsive tempests of the war-ocean have lashed and lashed at them, and they have not moved. Multitudinous arrows, shot by the ingenious malignities of a thousand enemies, have fallen blunted from their mighty sides. The insulting fulminations of tyranny have lightened about their tranquil heads in vain. There they stand, high-reaching, eternal sculptured images of stateliness, in sight of all the nations. Glory has set but a simple inscription upon them.

It is the same inscription which love has written on every heart in this land. On one, ROBERT E. LEE: and on the other, STONEWALL JACKSON.

For this, my countrywomen who compose this Memorial Association, that you bring us to contemplate the stateliness of the chiefs, and the stateliness of the unswerving private soldier, who fought or fell in the Confederate war—for this, in the name of an age when stateliness is rare, I thank you.

I spoke next of the *tranquillity* of the overspanning heavens. This, too, is a noble quality which your Association tends to

* [Tennyson, "The Passing of Arthur."—ED.]

keep alive. Who in all the world needs tranquillity more than we? I know not a deeper question in our Southern life at this present time, than how we shall bear out our load of wrong and insult and injury with the calmness and tranquil dignity that becomes men and women who would be great in misfortune; and, believe me, I know not where we will draw deeper inspirations of calm strength for this great emergency than in this place where we now stand, in the midst of departed heroes who fought against these things to the death. Why, yonder lies my brave, brilliant friend, Lamar; * and yonder, genial Robert Smith; and yonder, generous Tracy—gallant men, all; good knights and stainless gentlemen. How calmly *they* sleep in the midst of it! Unto this calmness shall *we* come, at last. If so, why should we disquiet our souls for the petty stings of our conquerors? There comes a time when conqueror and conquered shall alike descend into the grave. In that time, O my countrymen, in that time the conqueror shall be ashamed of his lash, and the conquered shall be proud of his calm endurance: in that time the conqueror shall hide his face, and the conquered shall lift his head with an exultation in his tranquil fortitude which God shall surely pardon! O happy Lamar, O happy Smith and Tracy, O happy heroes all! Ye who died whilst liberty was yet a hope in our bosoms, and whilst tyranny was yet only a possible speck on our future! If we may not envy you your death, we may at least solace ourselves in the tranquillity of your graves until we, too, shall join you in those regions

Where beyond these voices there is peace! **

For the contemplation of this tranquillity, my friends of this Association, in the name of a land stung half to madness, I thank you.

I spoke next of the patient river. See there how it draws on steadily to where it shall mingle with the salt sea and be lost in it through fair or foul weather, by night and by day, under snow or sunshine, by rugged hill or alluring valley, reckless of obstacle, patient of opposition, unhasting yet unresting, it

* [Presumably John Hill Lamar, an intimate of Lanier's, killed in the battle of Monocacy, July, 1864.—Ed.]

** [Tennyson, " Guinevere."—Ed.]

moves onward to destruction. Was it not like this, that these soldiers walked their life of battle, patient through heat and cold, through rain and drought, through bullets and diseases, through hunger and nakedness, through rigor of discipline and laxity of morals, aye through the very shards and pits of hell, down to the almost inevitable death that awaited them?

For this, that you bring us to contemplate this vast patience, I commend you.

And I spoke of the music of winds and leaves. I like to figure every event as a tone, and all events as one many-toned harmony that arises to the great music-master and composer, up yonder. That the tone of this day may be round and melodious, we come here without resentment, without scorn or hate or any vengeful feeling to mar our love for these dead. That we can do this—that we can contemplate these dead faces without unseemly revenges burning in our souls, is to me a most marvellous triumph of divine Christianity. I have had occasion once or twice to speak of certain antique virtues in which the ancients excelled us. Here now, we rise immeasurably above the classic people, on our new wings of divine faith in yonder great Forgiver and great Avenger. Listen to Mark Antony, when he looks upon dead Cæsar's face, *his* murdered friend!

O pardon me, thou piece of bleeding earth,
That I am meek and gentle with these butchers!
Woe to the hand that shed this costly blood!
Over thy wounds now do I prophesy,
Which like dumb mouths do ope their ruby lips
To beg the voice and utterance of my tongue!
A curse shall light upon the limbs of men;
Domestic fury and fierce civil strife
Shall cumber all the parts of Italy;
Blood and destruction shall be so in use,
And dreadful objects so familiar
That mothers shall but smile, when they behold
Their infants quartered with the hand of war;
All pity choked with custom of fell deeds;
And Cæsar's spirit, ranging for revenge,
With Ate by his side come hot from hell,
Shall in these confines with a monarch's voice
Cry *havoc*, and let slip the dogs of war.

So, Mark Antony; but not so gaze we upon our dead. To-day we are here for love and not for hate. To-day we are here for harmony and not for discord. To-day we are risen immeasurably above all vengeance. To-day, standing upon the serene heights of Forgiveness, our souls choir together the enchanting music of harmonious Christian civilization. To-day we will not disturb the peaceful slumbers of these sleepers with music less sweet than the serenade of loving remembrances, breathing upon our hearts as the winds of Heaven breathe upon these swaying leaves above us.

Lastly, I spoke of the memories that throng this day and this place. Here, my heart and my tongue fail me. In the presence of these mighty remembrances of those strange, sad, glorious moments when the land was full of war, I falter. Who is here that needs help to recall the glory of those days when young Liberty sailed in front of our arms, and her radiant eyes beamed upon our victorious armies, as a maiden's upon her lover in the first blush of love? Who is here that needs help to recall the suffering that followed those early victories, the stern endurance of defeat, the sickness of long apprehension, the weariness of prolonged expectancy, the hardships of straitened circumstance, the broodings of love over beloved ones absent in battle, the hope, the fear, the prayer, the tear, the frequent agony? Who is here that needs help to recall the dreadful thrill of that last blow, when the land, like a strong man stricken, bowed head and shrouded face in mantle and wept, knowing beyond doubt that it could not be free?

To these memories I commend you, as you proceed to your reverent employment. They exhale from these graves to meet and greet the fragrance of your flowers.

Before I leave you to your most loving task, I have one word which these departed soldiers, if they were in life, would certainly wish to be spoken. I know that I am here to-day as your representative, to honor my dead comrades: but now I take heart of grace, and I become for this brief moment, the representative of my dead comrades to honor you. My countrywomen, these men who have gone into the silent land; these men also have their memories of the war, which they have carried with them. I speak for them when I thank you that for every wound, and by every sick-bed, in camp and hospital and home, there came the white hand of woman, soothing and tending and comforting. I speak for them, when I thank you that there was no brave man in battle who did not receive the liberal glory of your woman's smile for his reward, and that there was no coward in battle whom your woman's soul did not frown into merited contempt. I speak for them, when I thank you for a myriad graces that beamed from you in a time of darkness—for a myriad tendernesses in a time of cruelty—for a myriad kindnesses in a time wild with revenge. I speak for them, when I thank you for this annual tribute of the early glories of the spring which you bring to lay upon their graves. O ye bright companies of the martyrs of liberty! O ye glittering battalions of the dead that died in glory! O ye stately chieftains that lead in Heaven as ye led on earth! One day ye shall witness for yourselves, in burning acclamations of gratitude, how ye remember, and how ye shall eternally remember, the uncorrupted souls, the gracious hearts, the brave characters, the stainless eyes, the radiant smiles, and the tender fingers, of the women who glorified and sanctified the Southern Confederacy!

ROBERT E. LEE: IN MEMORIAM *

MR. CHAIRMAN: In the antique times, it was a fair custom at the beginning of a feast, to pour out generous libations of purple wine, calling at the same time upon the name of some strong God, so that the divinity might descend, out of heaven, and hover above the circling cup, vouchsafing prosperity to the wit, dignity to the mirth, and glory to the festivity.

Sir, my heart throbbed quicker and certain unseen impulses stirred my blood, when I heard you pronounce that name, first of all names, as if he were to be the tutelar god of this banquet. Fortunate, fortunate, thrice fortunate that feast whose inaugural invocation is unto the mighty, matchless spirit of Robert Lee! For, Sir, he indeed is a greater than any antique deity. All the Gods of Greece are dead; but Lee has only now begun to live. The Gods of Greece at this moment have not a lover left in all the lands of all the world: but Lee,—ah, there is not a heart beating about this board, wherein he does not sit, shining with immortal radiance and encompassed with the purest loyalties that human hearts can offer. The Gods of Greece were shadows; they were myths, no man ever saw them: but our godlike Lee, old comrades, have we not beheld, with our own eyes, the majesty of his incarnate manhood, glorious amid the red pomps of battle, glorious amid the simple fashions of peace?

Sir, the last time that I saw with mortal eyes—for, with spiritual eyes, many, many times have I contemplated him since,—the scene was so beautiful, the surroundings were so rare, nay, time and circumstance did so fitly frame him as it were, that I think the picture should not be lost. There was nothing melodramatic in the circumstances, nothing startling, nothing sensational: which was all the more particularly in

* [First printed entire at Greenwich, Conn., 1928, in a pamphlet issued by the William Alexander, Jr. Chapter of the United Daughters of the Confederacy, entitled *Stratford on the Potomac.* The passage describing Lee at religious services, when Lanier last saw him in the summer of 1864, is quoted by Mims (pp. 50-52) and by Starke (pp. 59-60). The address was delivered at the memorial services in Macon, Ga., soon after Lee's death, Oct. 12, 1870. The MS, from which the present text is taken, is preserved at Stratford Hall, Lee's birthplace and the headquarters of the Robert E. Lee Memorial Foundation, of which Mrs. Charles D. Lanier was the first president. A few mechanical irregularities have been here altered to conform with Lanier's practice in print.—ED.]

accord with his character, for this was one of those grand but modest, sweet souls that love simplicity and shrink from all that is loud and vulgar. It was at fateful Petersburg on one glorious Sunday morning, whilst the armies of Grant and Butler were investing our last stronghold there. It had been announced, to those who happened to be stationed in the neighborhood of General Lee's headquarters that religious services would be conducted on that morning, by Major General Pendleton, of the artillery. At the appointed time I strolled over to Dunn's Hill, where General Lee's tent was pitched, and found General Pendleton ensconced under a magnificent tree, and a small party of soldiers with a few ladies from the dwellings near by, collected about him. In a few moments, General Lee appeared, with his camp chair, and sat down. The services began. That terrible battery number five, was firing, very slowly, each report of the great guns making the otherwise profound silence still more profound. Even Hoke's line was quiet. I sat down on the grass, and gazed, with such reverence as I had never given to mortal man before, upon the grand face of General Lee. He had been greatly fatigued by loss of sleep. As the sermon progressed, and the immortal words of Christian doctrine came to our hearts and comforted us, sweet influences born of the liberal sunlight that lay warm upon the grass, of the waving leaves and trembling flowers, seemed to steal over the General's soul. Presently his eyelids gradually closed, and he fell gently asleep. Not a muscle of him stirred, not a nerve of his grand countenance twitched, there was no drooping of the head, nor bowing of the figure, and I could not have been sure that he really slept had I not observed that a venturesome fly crawled unheeded upon his brow. As he slumbered so, sitting erect with arms folded upon his chest in an attitude of majestic repose such as I never saw assumed by mortal man before: as the large and comfortable words fell from the preacher's lips; as the lazy cannon of the enemy anon hurled a screaming shell to within a few hundred yards of where we sat, as finally a bird flew into the tree overhead and sat and piped small blissful notes in unearthly contrast with the roar of the war engines; it seemed to me as if the present earth floated off through the sunlight, and the antique earth returned out of the past, and some majestic god sat on a hill, sculptured in stone, presiding over a terrible yet sublime contest of human passions.

Ah Sir, it was not very long after that pleasant slumber, that we heard he had passed into the pleasanter and sublimer slumber of death. So easily did he glide from one to the other that one might fancy he had prayed, in those beautiful words of Paul Hayne's *Ode to Sleep.*

Then woo me here, etc.

and that his prayer had been granted.

So, O magnificent Spirit, we invoke thee now; descend out of heaven, that hast presided over unimaginable feasts of death where the wine was blood and the wit was a death shriek; preside now over the splendid hilarities of these old comrades, who have fought together, who have toiled together, and who would now rejoice together: as thou wert in life our Commander, still, still, over the river of death send thy voice to our hearts, still let us be inwardly thrilling to know that in life and after life and forever, thou art our own hero, our foremost one, our well-beloved General Robert Lee.

Whereas, The souls of departing heroes are fitly accompanied to their last repose by the solemn aspirations of living peoples, grateful for their lives and mournful for their deaths: and

Whereas, General Robert Edward * Lee, in the fullness of fruitful life, in the consummation of heroic patriotism, in the majesty of silent fortitude, in the glory of splendid manhood, in the security of an entire people's faithful and enthusiastic regard, is gone unto that brilliant reward which Almighty Providence will assign to a Christian Soldier whose heart was as humble as his deeds were illustrious:

Be It Therefore *Resolved,* That we, the assembled citizens of Macon, do with sincere devotion lend our common voice to those mournful utterances evoked by the death of Robert Lee not only from our countrymen but from all the manly spirits of our time:—calling upon the world to respect the grief of a people who in one moment have lost a vigilant soldier, a humane victor, a beloved leader, a stately man, an admirable citizen, an undoubting Christian, a brilliant son of that Virginia which always teemed with illustrious progeny, and a lineal descendant of long and honored ancestry.

* [The MS reading is "Edmund."—ED.]

Resolved, That we invite our countrymen to unite in some enduring testimonial to the stainless life and glorious services of our departed general, and that, in the judgment of this meeting, such monument would assume its best propriety in the form of a great Hall of Fame to be built by such voluntary contributions as shall be within the compass of the humblest citizen who loved him and who desires the grateful privilege of laying some tribute on his tomb.

Resolved, That we respectfully tender our sympathies to the family of the illustrious deceased, pointing them to the noble consolations which present themselves in the spectacle of a nation which earnestly shares their grief, while it proudly extols their kinsman.

MEMORIAL REMARKS ON JUDGE E. A. NISBET *

MAY IT PLEASE YOUR HONOR:—

I COUNT IT certainly not the least among the unfortunate incidents of our human imperfection, that often when the heart moves most freely, the tongue will balk most sorely.

It would seem that emotion, on the one hand, and expression, on the other, must needs be at vile cross-purposes; and I, at least, have frequent occasion to deplore that when the former is at full tide, the latter will be at ebb.

This consideration would have kept me silent today; but I am drawn to my feet by a sentiment which I know not well how either to define or to resist. The sentiment to which I refer is gratitude.

It is not the first time that such a feeling has been alluded to, in the course of these proceedings; but the gratitude hitherto meant was one, in which all members of the Georgia Bar have a common share, for Judge Nisbet's judicial interpretations of the law.

It was my lot, however, in the days that were, to be befriended, no little, by that generous spirit whose name has been so often pronounced on this floor this morning. Debtor to him, as I am, for so many and so unexpected acts of kindly interest, and eager to pay the debt,—yet separated from my good creditor by that impregnable blank wall of death which has so suddenly built itself up between us; unburdened, it is true, by my obligation, yet ardently desirous that he himself might know how sensible of it I ever was:—in this melancholy strait there is to

* [Title supplied by the editor. First published in the Macon *Daily Telegraph,* Feb. 2, 1927 under the title: "Memorial Address (Extemporaneously Delivered and Later Reduced to Writing) at the Georgia Bar Association's Memorial Exercises for Judge Eugenius Nisbet, a Member of the Supreme Court of Georgia"; previously uncollected. The only surviving MS—from which the present text is taken—is entitled "Remarks of Sidney Lanier at the meeting of the Macon Bar to receive the resolutions of the Committee upon the death of Judge E. A. Nisbet." This document, in the autograph of Robert S. Lanier and carrying the explanation "(Copied from the original manuscript in handwriting of Mr. Lanier in possession of Mr. Wingfield Nisbet)," is preserved in the Washington Memorial Library, Macon, Ga. Judge Nisbet died on March 18, 1871; the meeting of the bar took place in April (Starke, p. 142).—ED.]

me but one recourse, and that is, publicly to acknowledge the debt.

What other purpose, indeed, could have induced me to claim your ear, at this time? Certainly, there is no lack of flowers on this grave; nor lack of tears to water them!

His partners, his colleagues, his brethren of the bar, his admirers, his friends, all these, in your hearing this morning, one by one, have approached his tomb, and glorified it with armsfull, and heartsfull, of tribute.

If now, behind them, one steals in modestly and quietly, and as it were in secret lets fall his humble violet from the woods upon the glorious pile of homage, dropping thereon his unobtrusive tear;—believe, I beg you, that it is in no hope of swelling the sweet mound of these funeral flowers, but only in the sincere and heartfelt desire to speak in some poor fashion, after death, the gratitude which he had no opportunity to manifest before.

It would be little becoming in me, speaking to you and to these gentlemen, to eulogize him who is gone. If you stood in the full sunshine, could it interest you if one should inform you that the sun was bright? If you had spent half your life in contemplating some rare picture, would it interest you if one should inform you that it was beautiful? If you had lived many years in daily hearing of noble music, would it interest you if one should inform you that the music was fine?

And, now, when the light of this genial soul has vanished, here, to shine in other lands; now, when the wellnigh faultless picture of this Christian's life has uprisen to beautify forever yonder glittering palace walls; now, when the music of this man's work on earth has been translated into some far more enchanting melody of the life that is lived beyond the blue; how should I waste your time, to repeat to you who knew it so well, that his soul was a brilliant light, that his life was a perfect picture, that his work was a good harmony in God's creation.

I remember, full vividly, a certain afternoon in my boyhood, when, chancing to pass his office, he invited me in, specially. It was late, of a summer's day, and he seemed to be at leisure. He closed the door, sat down, and commenced to talk with me, in the kindest manner, in reference to my future course in life.

As his wise and gentle words flowed from his lips with that singular fluency for which he was always so remarkable; as his slight and graceful figure swayed easily to and fro, with his gestures, as, finally, one large ray from the setting sun slanted through the pane and wrought a golden glory upon his earnest and animated countenance;—it seemed to my boyish imagination as if I had been suddenly transported back into that sweet primal age of the world, when the tender and eloquent spirits of Heaven were accustomed to descend and instruct the sons of men in the mysteries of life and time.

I have never forgot, I will never forget, the beauty, nor the counsel of that hour. Ah, this tender and eloquent spirit has been already transported into the ravishing companionship of those self-same angels, of whom he then reminded me.

Yet, I cannot dream that he has gone, far.—It is not far, indeed, from here, over across death, to the other world. I am confident that waving wings of spirits fan us often, when we know it not; and it may be that the spiritual being of our departed friend, at this very moment, sits here among his brethren of old, smiling kindly at these stammering voices, wherewith we endeavor to solace ourselves for his loss. I would it might be so. For then he would hear, in whatever struggling utterance—these my sincere and grateful acknowledgements of his kindness, which otherwise could never have been made, to him this side of Heaven.

RETROSPECTS AND PROSPECTS *

I

THERE IS an old problem of early school-days, which, if it had been intended for an allegory, would make one think of fine John Bunyan. It was doubtless concocted by some steady-going pedagogue, of mathematico-religious proclivities, who little dreamed how he was therein symbolizing the strange question which, in wonderfully different shapes and guises, may now be considered the one question of history, of current politics, of current socialism, of current science, of current poetry, of current religion:—

A boy, quotha, *starts to church: every minute he steps three feet forward, but is blown by the wind two feet backward; the church being* (given) *miles distant,—to find the time in which he will reach it.*

Now Humanity is a boy (as yet), and he has started to church; but the time is windy, and the wind is against him, insomuch that his heart, which is naturally devout, is fain to cry out, "How long, O ye heavens that rule the winds,—how long?"

Doubtless, in spite of its distinct appearance, the Church of All-Workers is yet a long way off; doubtless, young Hopeful will pass many a lonely quagmire where warlocks and jack-o'-lanterns will confuse him; doubtless, he will often, in the school-boy way, make long *détours* in order to avoid those graveyards of history in which his hot fancy has beheld ghostly calamities

* [First published in the *Southern Magazine,* VIII, 283-290, 446-456 (March and April, 1871); reprinted with minor variants as the title essay in *Retrospects and Prospects* (New York, 1899), pp. 1-33. Two MSS exist (Charles D. Lanier Collection, Johns Hopkins University). MS A, entitled "The New Time," was written before Mar. 22, 1867 (see letter of that date to Clifford Lanier); it is the shortest version, consisting of only 28 small pages, and obviously the earliest, lacking as it does the opening allegory and the passage on the disbanding of the Confederate armies. MS B, consisting now of 91 small pages (a few pages at the end being lost), approximates the print version, but clearly precedes it; this MS was written before the end of May, 1867 (see letter from Mary Day Lanier, Mar. 15, 1891, MS Charles Scribner's Sons). The text adopted is that of the *Southern Magazine,* slightly modified in punctuation, spelling, and paragraphing (through reference to MS B) to conform with Lanier's more usual practice. Several passages from the MSS, previously unknown, are summarized in the footnotes.—ED.]

stalking among the dead and menacing the living; doubtless, he will often have to regret taking those side-paths to right or left which began so charmingly and ended so dismally in gloomy forest or trackless moor; and perhaps he will meet by the way one or two wise-hearted, white-headed folk who will cry, "Courage, little man! The church is far, but a brave heart will take thee to it." And so, after rare adventures, he will get there—if the head-wind will let him.

Will it? A parlous question! For some men, when they hear it, droop their heads and whisper that the two opposing forces of leg-muscle and wind are precisely equal; that while Humanity has been sturdily stepping out for six or more thousand years, he has been as sturdily thrust back for six or more thousand years, and that he is now exactly where he started; though truly time has changed the looks of things about him in the interval. Humanity is foolish, say these men, to suppose that he is marching forward: he is only marking time, and he will die in his original foot-tracks, for the Devil is in the wind.

It cannot be questioned (to abandon the allegory) that man's work, whose result we call civilization, has two powerful tendencies, one of which is forward and the other backward; and recent events have caused many worthy people to fear that at present these two tendencies are *in equilibrio,* or even that the backward tendency is beginning to exceed the forward. They observe that at each new upstarting of man's energy—and what age has seen so many as this?—the resulting invention or discovery, be it in material or in spiritual matters, immediately inures to the benefit of *both* the tendencies of civilization. These two tendencies, they conclude, are like two expert duellists, who by the constant attrition of mutual parry and thrust are continually sharpening each other's swords, and continually finding occasion to bewail advantage gained at the expense of advantage conferred.

For instance, "Look at the sea-cable," cries Progress; "how beautiful were the greetings of the East and West!"

"Aye," reply the Equilibrium men; "but the sea-telegraph brings nearly as much war-news as peace-news, and it talks as rapidly in the service of wealthy falsehood as of needy truth!"

"Well, but what say you to the multitude of the type-foundries?" again inquiries confident Progress: "see how the heathen are lit with Bibles every year!"

"So," rejoins Equilibrium sturdily, "and observe also how the breakfast-tables of the enlightened are darkened every morning with seduction-cases and crim.-con. reports, and chaffings and vile abuse and blasphemies, well and legibly printed in the newspapers!"

"How about steam, then?" shouts Progress, getting red in the face. "Shortly, steam will take you from New York to the Rocky Mountains in half a week!"

"True," whispers Equilibrium, in stage-tragic voice, "true; and steam already runs whiskey distilleries enough to throw the whole world into *delirium tremens;* and three thieves to one honest man will make time by your railroad."

In view of the respectability of these parties and the consequent weight of their opinions, it is surely worth the while of earnest people to look more closely into the age, to note the two opposing forces in our civilization, and to see which one of these is really availing itself of the new resources offered by exhaustless invention. With more force now than ever before, it may be said that to comprehend his epoch is at once the most difficult and the most pressing emergency of the thinker, of the sober citizen, or of the selfish demagogue. For he who today says "Let us look into the time," speaks a thrilling word. Into *what* time does he invite us? Into the twentieth century! That old road we called the nineteenth century is ended; we stand at the mile-post with beating hearts and gaze up the unfamiliar avenue of a new era.

And the emergency is difficult. In this era-dawn, it is as if we rubbed our eyes at daybreak. We are amazed at the singular dawn-noises and dawn-sights which present themselves on all sides in wild contrasts. Yonder are the dim forms of the night-animals slinking away into the forest, and growling in bloody fights for lairs and refuges; about us is the stertorous upstarting of day-animals, hungry for prey; above all the blood and the snarling bends the morning-sky; and the morning-star, that love-light in the misty blue eye overhead, gleams upon the serene dew. Who at such a moment is so calm of soul that he can scrutinize the low clouds yonder, and prophesy sunshine or foul weather for the day?

Yes, that central idea which has for a considerable period been controlling with centripetal force the vast revolving circle of circumstance, and which we have been denominating the nineteenth century, has abdicated its position; and a new idea, which we will doubtless call the twentieth century, is but now settling itself in the central seat of power.

What is this new idea, and in what direction will it whirl the old passionate energies of men? Which of the two prime opposing forces in man will succeed in leaguing with it? This is the problem which demands solution in some sort alike at the hands of the public and the private citizen, of the honest and the villainous, of the benefactor and the robber.

Of course, he who exaggerates the difficulty of a problem and then proceeds to solve it in sight of the people may be justly accused of charlatanry. To disarm such accusation, this present writer declares that his aim is not to solve but only to clear the way for solution; and if in so modest emprise his success be to lighten by one stroke the labor of stronger and wiser men, then his most soaring hope will alight and fold contented wing.

A soul and a sense linked together in order to fight each other more conveniently, compose a man. A fearful double is he; and these two combatants, when all is said, are simply the two duellists that sharpen each other's swords, and are the two confronting powers of the boy struggling forward and the wind pressing backward.

This conflict of soul and sense is precisely the old conflict of Roman Patrician and Plebeian. Sense is luxurious; luxury is called sensuality: sense is brutal because it knows only itself; sense is fastidiously nice in small matters; sense measures precisely with dainty rule and square, and calls its measurements conventionalities—all of which are Patrician characteristics. Soul, on the other hand, is essentially Plebeian. Soul loves and hates, and grasps and flings away, and laughs and weeps in a thoroughly loud, vulgar way—vulgar at least from the Patrician view of the proprieties.

Now the Plebs won in Rome; and soul must win in life. The Patrician is always old, the Plebeian is always young. The old luxurious patrician East is full of "Hindoo life-weariness"; * but the young plebeian West is

* [The phrase is attributed to Novalis in Lanier's Ledger, p. 17, and in "Paul H. Hayne's Poetry" (see p. 325, below).—Ed.]

. . . young
As Eve with Nature's daybreak on her brow.

Sense drops his languid hands and sighs for a new titillation, which, when he has got it, can elicit from him only some gentle trituration of gloved hands in the way of applause; soul offers him a fresh dewy enthusiasm of love, a brave morning-energy of life. Now if, in spite of this conflict and contrast, the Patrician sense should awake to the nobleness of the Third Estate, should voluntarily abandon his own pseudo-nobility and fall into the wild ranks of the Plebeians, like the old Roman Tribune of history, like the Romney Leigh of fiction,* considering his apparent disgrace a true promotion,— then would the rightful progress of man go on.

It is hoped to prove that this is not only the right progress of humanity, but that it is and has been the actual historic progress of men and things and events. For as time flows on, man and nature steadily etherealize. As time flows on, the sense-kingdom continually decreases and the soul-kingdom continually increases, *and this not by the destruction of sense's subjects, but by a system of promotions in which sensuous things, constantly etherealizing, constantly acquire the dignity of spiritual things, and so diminish their own number and increase the other.* This paradoxical ennobling-by-disgrace of the material into the spiritual expresses the historic development of the world. Over this route Nature and Art, like a bird's shadow and a bird, have flown up to to-day. By this course politics and religion, which are respectively the body and the soul of life, have acquired their present features.

And first with the first.

Nature, in that fine ramble of hers along the shore of the great deep (a ramble which we call Time), has been good enough to write and strew along the sand at intervals short monographs of autobiography which remain for our reading. These quaint epistles of Nature, like all women's letters, full of blots, of erasures, of false syntax, of queer spelling, of ejaculations, of double underscorings, of marvellous punctuations, of confidential disclosures, of tiger-hates, of lily-loves; ** these

* [E. B. Browning, *Aurora Leigh*.—ED.]

** [For the possible clue in these phrases to the meaning of the title *Tiger-Lilies* see Introduction, pp. xviii-xix.—ED.]

rare incoherent letters, in one line repeating starry compliments, in another retailing muddy scandals of old convulsions and hideousnesses,—a scripture complex with crossings and re-crossings of the page, a composition intricate with breaks and clauses and parentheses; these violet-stained letters, I say, of our sweetheart Nature, all breathe one tone in respect of the constant etherealizing process which she has been undergoing. He who collates her earliest letters with her latest will discover that whereas she *was* a stormy virago of sixty, she has now been magically rejuvenated and is become marvellously like to a gentle and dainty-fingered maiden of sixteen.

What Frederic von Hardenberg has called the "old Titanic times" of Nature, "in which all objects lay strewn about the earth like the remains of a terrific repast"; times in which volcanoes flamed and earthquakes cracked, and glaciers crawled and avalanches fell, and oceans overbrimmed, and islands rose above or sank beneath the sea; times in which land, air, and water were horrible with megatherium and pterodactyl and ichthyosaurus; these times are gone, things are less hideous and behave more gently. To-day we have from Nature rather dews than avalanches; to-day she gives us more of the fruitful mould and less of the barren rock; to-day sees petroleum-wells and healing-springs instead of volcanoes; to-day the woods emerge from the gloom of giant ferns, and revel in the lights and odors of tiny flowers; to-day we pluck fruit from off rocks that once starved a fir.

But more than this. Nature has in these days really caught the spirit of man. In the Greek times, Nature rose half-way to the dignity of man with her oreads and nymphs and fauns; in our times she has risen *all* the way. If Tennyson stroll into a glen, the *genius loci* is now not a hamadryad but a veritable human soul; and to Tennyson (and through him to us) the tree laughs and loves and hates, and is jealous and generous and selfish, like any man. The sea should not mourn for his lost Triton; for the sea should now have done playing like a sea-god, and should rage passionately and repose grandly like a man. The modern poets have flown out and put a star on the forehead of each rock and tree and cloud and wave: it is the star of love and grief which is worn by purified men.

For, listen! Yonder in England grows a *Talking Oak* that

talks as well as Tennyson! Verily we have heard nothing like it since on yon Midsummer's Night the wall held forth of Pyramus and Thisbe, and good Demetrius swore it was the wittiest partition that ever he heard discourse. A very English oak, a right gnarled fellow with root, trunk, and branches, watching the world revolve about him as if he had a man's eye; swearing "By summers!" plumping an acorn with fatherly pride into the bosom of a maiden sleeping therebeneath, and returning thanks for this honor which had befallen his progeny; and lastly, weeping and sighing, which was most human of all.

In this fine forest of Master Tennyson is another tree that thrills with an inward agony; and down upon it gazes the sun, which is become a human eye, with fringed storms for eyelashes; and the by-passed tempests moan and call out of other lands. And Coleridge's mountain-top struggles all the night with troops of stars; and Swinburne has overheard some sea-conversation which he has translated into good English; and angelic Shelley, and sweet Christina Rossetti, and deep-thoughted Elizabeth Browning, and quaint Jean Ingelow, and over-brimming Ruskin, and sad Maurice de Guérin, and that tempest Victor Hugo, and dainty John Keats, and all-mingling Jean Paul, and priestly Novalis, and a thousand more poets in verse and prose, have proven to us how human physical nature has become by translating Nature's maiden-fantasies for the general ear.* So that now-a-days not only may the geniuses of the world—those ministers plenipotentiary at the court of Nature—hold diplomatic interviews and discourse high topics with her, but so well have they made her language known and so gracious has she proven, that all the commonest domestic folk may run out and chit-chat with her, whenever they will, a million at a time.

Nature, therefore (to return to the soberer philosophic method), does really spiritualize herself, as time rolls on, into a genuine companion and friend of man.** She does really come under the influence of that great central idea of the ages which

* [MS B amplifies the idea by quoting, with facetious comment, a line from Browning's "Old Pictures in Florence" (which appears in *Tiger-Lilies*, p. 89, above) and by declaring the stone church "not only a man, but a modern man." —Ed.]

** [MS A adds the idea: "Humanity [in its turn] begins to conquer Time and Space, its natural enemies. . . . [In contrast to St. Paul] Mr. Beecher may fly over land or sea, and may converse rapidly with the brethren in Asia."—Ed.]

presides over the conclave of special ideas controlling special epochs—the idea of etherealization. A most provoking word! For it so nearly expresses and yet does *not* express that process which combines the two ideas of an old woman become beautiful by rejuvenation and of a young woman becoming wise and gentle and pure by age.

Now if Nature be the glancing shadow, and Art the living singing-bird above it, surely the motions of the shadow will be but copies of the flutterings of the bird; and we shall expect to find that Art, too, has been spiritualizing itself, has been forsaking its Titanic days and chastening its frolic awkwardness, has been learning to rely more on soul and less on sense, has been divesting itself of unsightly material props and supports; has been, in short, etherealizing and floating in the thin air of the spiritual.

An exhaustive treatise on this department of the question would have to contain separate volumes devoted to each of these following subjects, namely, a searching analysis of the past and present conditions and characteristics of architecture, sculpture, painting, music, poetry, and prose, together with various discourses under the head of the useful arts. But this present paper must content itself to etch, by single and therefore necessarily inexact outline-strokes, the contrasting portraits of these arts as existing heretofore and now.

As for architecture, one scarcely knows in this day whether it has not voluntarily abandoned its old tendencies towards preaching, and gone into business with the conviction that commerce pays better than piety. What time has architecture to spend on churches, when here are thousands of railroad-depots and newspaper-buildings and dry-goods stores thronging around him, jingling their pocketsful of money and offering heavy prices for airiness, lightness, and rapidity of construction? Yet in spite of the fact that architecture has become rather one of the useful than of the fine arts, in those very words " airiness, lightness, and rapidity " has been indicated the veritable etherealizing change which it has undergone. Trinity Church compared with an Egyptian temple is as Tennyson compared with Milton; the massive force of the former has been refined into the spiritual power of the latter, a power full as strong and greatly less unwieldy. And so when architecture builds now-a-days a place for the wealthy who die, there arises, not a pyramid to lie like a dead-weight on the breast of the dead, but some airy and light mausoleum whose taper proportions direct our thought rather to the soul that is risen out of the grave than to the inert bones that decay within it.

And what of sculpture? Well—and let no one cry out until he has read to the end—here is Webster's statue in marble, or Washington's equestrian *eidōlon* in bronze. What? Webster, with white eyes, with white hair, with white draperies? Or Washington, with bronze eyes, bronze hair, and bronze horse? We approach these statues, then, with a preliminary chilling sense of unreality; and we crush back this sense: all felt and done half unconsciously. But we observe that the statues are well executed, that they indicate faithful study, that the pose is good; and we say to our friend:—" It is a fine imitation: how natural is the hand! how perfect that nail! " Why, this is precisely the criticism of Gellert's Fool; only, here, wisdom and folly agree, and the judgment is a true one. For imagine a Greek led in to see the Phidian Jove. There sits the majesty of Olympus, amid thunderbolts and winged Victories; the Greek's eye is misty, and looks at the statue through a rosy dream; a divine breath from the god's lip penetrates to the man's soul, which grows tense therewith, as a cloud is tense with lightning. Will the Greek step close and pick at the great toe-nail to see if it be well chiselled? Imagine it! He rather walks slowly out and dreams, through the streets, of heaven and of immortality, and the like. Now the power, factitious or otherwise, of Jove had informed his statue, and made it *quoad* the Greek, transparent, so that the Greek looked *through* the statue, and not *at* it. Sculpture, *per* Phidias' genius, wielded this power of Jove, and so cast an unearthly glamor over the incongruities of its work. But, unfortunately (for sculpture at least), sculpture has lost this power. Webster and Washington were great men, but not gods; we approach their statues with reverential but not with frenzied souls; we are calm enough to judge in the matter of nails and eyes; and we are, unwittingly, at once true enough and cruel enough to stab poor sculpture to the heart, when we walk away smiling and saying: — " How fine the nail!" For Art does not imitate: it creates; and if the artist has only imitated Webster in stone, and has not veritably re-created Webster in our soul,—then Webster, the artist, and we, all three, are to be commiserated. So that sculpture, like architecture, has grown at once more rich and less exalted by abandoning religion to take up trade; and though in this lower capacity it still in all respects bears out the theory which has been enunciated, yet as a useful art it is not to be now treated of. The truth of the whole matter seems to be that Art, striving in these modern times for that most rare combination, *truth and reality*, has come to regard sculpture as a glaring unreality embodied, and has purified herself of it; has knocked it away as a mere material prop, weak in itself and unnecessary for support.

It is impossible, however, to speak of modern sculpture without referring to what is perhaps the brightest example of genius in that art yet afforded by our country. I mean the small groups of Rogers,* some of which are still to be seen in the public show-room of Schaus, on Broadway. Little mention has been made of these groups; but surely genius had a hand on the chisel there. And one cites them with all the more pleasure since they in all respects bear out the theory which it has been partially attempted to enunciate—the theory of etherealization, of spiritualization. They are genuine creations: the black man, there, for all his turned-up toes and his patched knee, will start some high thoughts in the minds of the meditative; and the little cottage-porch, whose vines are thrilling with the lingering kiss of the departing soldier on his trim lassie's lips, sends a man's soul wandering away amid a multitude of sweet and sad things. These groups afford perhaps the only field now left to sculpture. They engage themselves with the *domesticities of* our life; and by as much as home-life is tenderer than camp-life, by as much as an idyll is more heavenly than an epic, by so much are these groups more ethereal than the groups of ancient sculpture.

Signs exist that painting, *as such*, will follow its brethren of the compass and chisel. If, however, this word be considered as the general name of that art which depicts upon flat surfaces by means of perspective and light and shade, then better things

* [John Rogers, American sculptor, 1829-1904.—Ed.]

must be said of it. As photography, as engraving upon wood, stone and metals, painting has suffered a rare sea-change on this long voyage of man. It has abandoned the purple and gold in which it long ruled over men; it has come down upon us in a rare new avatar of the colorless photograph and engraving. These two, besides having copied most of the beautiful old pictures, give us daily a thousand new things full as beautiful. How grand is painting, then, as simple shade and light! The dark, the bright; night, day; death, life; how all these ideas couple and symbolize each other! And how impartially, like death, has painting knocked at the doors of all palaces and huts in the land since it became only colorless; and how radiantly, like life, has painting lit up the humble as well as the pretentious homes in the land since it became photography and engraving! Like two new worlds, each half-lit and half-shaded at once, and each bearing a whole worldful of rare and strange beauties upon its surface, float forth these two newly-discovered planets, and glitter in a free heaven for all to see. No man may have a home now-a-days that is all unlovely. The poorest may have a picture that the richest would prize; and the richest can scarcely buy a picture whose faithful *eidōlon* is not attainable by the poorest.

See, then, how this art, painting, has arisen and floated away free as air and sunshine into all homes and all wastes, simply by having lightened itself of the purely material load of color! So that painting, also, like nature, like architecture, like sculpture, etherealizes; and we get from it now rather tender home-scenes than barbarous battle-scenes; rather little ones saying prayers at mothers' knees than bloody-heeled conquerors soiling the plain.

II

For himself personally, this present writer is right glad that he is now come to speak of music. This is the art of to-day; this is the art into whose hands has fallen the unfinished work of the bygone arts. Music, Music:—one repeats this word a thousand times to oneself, as a boy murmurs his sweetheart's name in solitude.

And here one must beg indulgence for some brief time. For does the student of physiology run to his beloved and calmly strip off the pearly skin and dissect the dainty limbs, in order to improve his science? And if not, how can this writer, in the presence of this divinity whom he is scarce bold enough to love, prate of her food-assimilations and stomachic-actions, and progress, and the like? No! By her dawn-gray eyes, and by the red lips of the Nine, and by all the holy oaths of art, he will for this once sink the philosopher in the man; he will for this little while refuse to be music's surgeon: he will leave this to some one who is called a Doctor of Music. He will only remain kneeling, and swear to all knights of the age that this Music is the fairest of all God's creatures, that her heart is a harp and her voice is a flute; the which he will maintain with sword, lance, and battle-axe against all comers, Paynim or Christian! And having so discharged his challenge-obligation, let him now, for some few blissful moments, breathe in whatever extravagant tropes the passion of his love will lend him, his knightly duty and reverence and loyal love to music.

A silver horn represents the dead mineral kingdom, a wooden flute represents the half-animate vegetable kingdom, and a sinew-strung violin represents the living animal kingdom; so have the three kingdoms of nature sent each a minister to the court of King Man, and music is their diplomacy. The horn is, therefore, the controlled and firm voice of the enduring metals; the flute is the pure yet passionate voice of the trees, which live and yet are sinless; and the violin is the strange, mournful-joyful voice of blood happily bounding in veins or painfully shooting from wounds, and of breath peacefully working in life or laboringly departing in death.

The new-born child hears before he sees; the dying man hears after his eyes are forever dimmed: and so hearing is, as Richter says, " the first sense of the living " and " the last sense of the dying." This sense therefore clasps in its arms more of life than any other. Upon the musical air-waves float to and fro invisible ships freighted with strange freight, trading between souls and finding wharfage on the shore of the ear: to which ships, full cargoes, both ways, forever and forever! is the earnest wish of all true hearts.

Melody is as if one loved without reciprocation: harmony is the satisfaction of mutual love. Perhaps for this reason melody fascinates disappointed humanity, and harmony pleases the satisfied angels. When the young lusty earth leapt out of the night like a white doe out of the woods, and sprang into the open heaven-road to make a race for life, then the morning-stars sang and charmed it into a circular path which it has never left: such is the power of music over animals! As the blue sky, at the horizon-line, adjusts itself precisely to all the unevennesses of the land, so music, our other sky, adapts itself to all the inequalities of life, and has a tune to suit the lowest or the highest in society and the most barbarous or the most enlightened in civilization. From Ashango-land to America; from Poor Tom, the singing idiot, to Tennyson, the singing philosopher; from a jaw-bone rattled by a savage to a great organ played by Mendelssohn: such is the blue reach and overspan of the sky of music.

Music defies calculation, it baffles prophecy, it vanishes during analysis. It has more avatars than Vishnu, more metamorphoses than Jupiter, more transmigrations than Pythagoras's soul. It is, at one and the same time, an angel and a devil; a muse and a fury; a tarantula and an anodyne; a free Proteus and a Prometheus bound. It is a spiritual analogue to carbon; which appears one moment as charcoal, the next moment as rose-leaf, and the next as diamond. Yonder, as drum and horn, music marches at the head of armies like a General; here, as voice or lute, it sings by the cradles of children like a mother. In the cathedral it is chanting *Laudamus* for the birth of a king; in the graveyard it is chief mourner at the burial of a beggar. Last night in slippers and spangles it led a dance; to-day in sober black it leads a church-service. It conducts virtue along the aisle to the marriage-altar; it inflames vice to unholy embrace in the brothel. In the music-room it is a piano, in the forest it is a whistling bird, in the heavens it is a groaning wind, in the firmament it is a whirling star, and in the soul it is like a serene fire.

Why does not our age, which claims to be a Prospero of eras, subject and tame this singular spirit, Music, which is at once an Ariel and a Caliban, and will indifferently girdle the earth or chop firewood for us?

To the soul, music combines in itself the power of steam, the agility of electricity and the fidelity of printing-type. It is a civilization in a conch-shell.

Love is a vast lily whose petals gleam faintly just under the wave of life, and sometimes sway and float out above it. Up from this lily, then, arises an odor: it is Music.

"The orator," said Quintilian, "should know everything." How much more should the musician understand all things! For the true musician is as much higher than the orator as love is higher than law. The Greeks did well therefore when they made their word *Mousiké* signify a symmetrical and harmonious education of all the powers of a man.

And now (to turn from love to philosophy again), let us see how music has etherealized. At first glance, appearances do not seem propitious to the theory.* For there is in this country an institution which, under the guise of a devotee of music, has done music more injury than all its open enemies. This institution is the Italian Opera, *as at present rendered*—an important limitation, for it is by no means wished to attack those noble *chefs-d'œuvre* of some fine musicians, but only the present method of getting these works before the public. Out of the long catalogue of crimes committed by this Italian Opera, let us choose two, in the discussion of which our theory will perhaps be confirmed.

First: let it be known to those wholly unacquainted with the science, that if the tone E (for instance) be made upon the A string of the violin with the bow, and at the same time the open E string be gently and repeatedly touched with the little finger of the left hand, then the open string will repeat the tone of the string upon which the bow is drawn, producing a vibratory effect which is like a thrill, and is very powerful in suitable passages. This vibratory effect is a mere increase and decrease of the volume of the tone, which remains pure E all the time. Now in endeavoring to imitate this effect with the voice, the opera-people have allowed themselves to fall into a monstrous mistake, which, ridiculous as it is, has by excessive and monotonous repetition so habituated them and most of their hearers to it that, as bitter tobacco has became essential to men, so

* [MS B begins its attack on the Italian opera in an apostrophe to music: "And now, Thou beautiful Fury, thou fierce Flower, thou Tiger-Lily of matter as Love is of spirit,—while I am paying lover's-compliments to thee, . . . some knight . . . would join battle upon my challenge. . . . I believe he is thine enemy." For the possible relation of the opening words to the title *Tiger-Lilies* see Introduction, pp. xviii-xix.—ED.]

terrible discord has become essential to the opera. For instead of really imitating the violin effect—an imitation which even if perfectly accomplished should be used only in rare cases of peculiar expression—instead of really keeping the identical tone E, as the violin does, and alternately increasing and diminishing its volume, the opera-singers increase and diminish the *pitch* of their tone, and make a sort of up and down trill, from E, for instance, to E sharp above and E flat below: a mistake which besides rendering a wavering sound incapable of harmonizing with the purer instrumental tones of the orchestra, further produces in itself a horrible discord. To prove all this: let any one hear (for a common example) that pretty trio of Verdi's in *Attila* played by three pure horns, or flutes, or violoncellos, and the hearer will thank God for the gift of his ears; but let him hear the same trio as commonly rendered by the opera-people, and, unless his ears be long and villainous hairy ears, he will pray Heaven to close them up, for the discords are really unendurable save to those whose musical sense has been so battered that it is a question whether Bully Bottom's tongs and bones would not frantically delight them, if only the said tongs and bones should call themselves Tongoni and Bonetti.*

And, secondly: look! thou audience in white gloves and marvellous coiffure,—here comes out one on the stage to sing the tenor part in this opera. One—what? Is it a man? How it ogles, smirks, leers, strains, wiggles its moustache, and throws its whole artistic soul into the pose of its beautiful divine leg! "What a leg! what a calf!" we say, when it has finished perhaps the sweetest aria of Bellini.

Why, this singing *tertium quid* is not a man: it is only a calf of a leg, with appurtenances and machinery (such as soul, mind, stomach, and the like) for preserving the same in order and condition. Must we fall down and worship this calf (of a leg), set up in the temple of music by the heathen? It is not even a golden calf; nay, to crown this infinite blasphemous joke, it is not always a flesh calf, but oftentimes a mere counter-

* [MS A gives as a contrast to the Italian opera rendition by voices "the serenade and Miserere in *Trovatore* . . ., which is a fine, natural piece of music,—played upon instruments." The same passage continues: "It is . . . with delight that I hear one can go to Theo. Thomas' concerts . . ., besides to rapidly-multiplying Quartette and Quintette clubs, and hear good music presented by fresh unvibratory voices and by violins which are not insane."—Ed.]

feit, concocted of meal-bran and springs and flesh-colored tights!

Ah, *tenori* who adore your own calves; ah, *bassi* who pamper your tons of flesh, ye are but wretched human *confetti:* ye are not even the sweet-meats of men that you would be—bad enough, if genuine; but ye are only made of flour-paste without any sugar or spices at all,—mere *confetti* such as your countrymen throw at each other in the Carnival-days! What have these pastry-figures to do with music? What know they of the poverties, of the struggles, of the passions, of the blacknesses, of the weaknesses, of the yearnings, of the sister's-tendernesses, of the mother's-agonies, of the home-storms, of the rare purities of life? Are these the preachers by whom the beautiful evangel of music is to be unfolded to sinful men and women? Are these the men who can make our souls see the Titanic up-reaching of Beethoven; the glittering sparkle of Rossini; the tender purity of Bellini; the quiet, deep smiles of Mendelssohn; the intense heart of Chopin, which in breaking exhaled music as a crushed flower exhales fragrance; the night-worship of Schumann and Döhler; the pellucid depths of Ernst; the wailing unsatisfaction of Gottschalk, whose music stands over his life as over a grave stands the marble image of the dead man beneath; the quaint alternation of loneliness and ethereal cheerfulness of Gounod, in whose music Scotch echoes recur amid German beauties, as if heather-bells grew amid the vines of Rhineland; and all the thousand sweetnesses of the thousand other modern writers for piano or flute, or violin or voice?

Why do we not worship devoutly in the opera-house as in a church; why do not all the artists, as was said of Bach, transform with their music every place of performance into a church; why do we not have inspiration and instruction and conversion from this stage-pulpit where the preacher is life and his voice is music, with its force, its thrill, its persuasion, its healing, its wounding, its pure condemnation, its upward pointing?

Now this, as was said, at first looks bad for our theory of the progress of music; but it is really the proof of it. For opera-houses *do not pay*; and will not until the managers shall give us an opera with violins that are not insane, with singers that are men, with voices that are pure and unvibratory, with propriety of costume and scene, and with a *mise en scène* that is altogether quiet, pure, and dewy with the emotions of the morning, rather than loud, hot, and lustful with the dark-red passions of the evening. And so, when one speaks of music now-a-days, one, if he be any lover of music, has no reference whatever to the Italian Opera, one means Schubert's and Mendelssohn's and Chopin's music, as fresh young girls and pure men render it in private, the number of whom is now immense and rapidly increasing. For the Italian Opera has abandoned music in favor of legs; and music, with strict justice, has abandoned the Italian Opera.

In purifying herself of this very material and sensual element, music has etherealized, and, like painting, has floated away freely into all homes over the whole land. More than any art, music is *in omnium manibus*; and steadily improves in purity, in refined spiritual strength, in universality. The perfection of the piano, which has arisen out of the old spinet like a beautiful soul out of a deformed body; and the recent development of the flute into a pure solo instrument (for which, however, no adequate music has yet been written), together with the new creations of Chopin, of Mendelssohn, and of Wagner, which have each added a new continent to the old world of music (though Wagner's is, it must be confessed, as yet a barbarous continent); all these things show how music spiritualizes, how she strengthens with the strength of the spirit. At once purify and strengthen thyself, O Beloved, Beloved! for thou who compared with all art now seemest but as a dove by the side of the great bird Roc, thou wilt yet upon thy two dove's-wings bear a whole world-full of people to Heaven! *

To discover the process of spiritualization which poetry has undergone, one has only to compare Tennyson with Milton. One will immediately observe that both are powerful, but different in the method of it. Milton is strong rather from the

* [Regarding changes in the realm of music MS A adds: "Beethoven is become Chopin and Luther has changed into Schuberth [*sic*] or Mendellsohn [*sic*], Rossini has made way for Verdi (whom the world will recognize in a few years) and Mozart for Gottschalk." And in MS B Lanier inserts this autobiographical paragraph by way of transition: "From my boyhood, even when I have been upon the gravest errands, I could never pass a place where music was toward, without lingering too long: a habit which, as the reader has already doubtless observed, still clings to me."—Ed.]

main force of physical vastness and the unwieldly pressure of colossal matters; Tennyson is strong by virtue of the calm, collected, intense potential momentum of steady spiritual enthusiasm. Milton's is the strength of the sea in its rage; Tennyson's is the potential force of the sea in its repose: and inasmuch as calm control is better, is more spirit-like, is more ethereal than indiscriminate violence, however powerful, in just so much is Tennyson's poetry more spiritual than Milton's, and to-day's poetry more ethereal than that of the past times.

Observe, too, how many purely material accessories of Milton's poetry are well gotten rid of and purified away in Tennyson's. The elisions, the apostrophic shortenings, the involutions, the anaconda conceits which in mere kindness wind about us and crush us to death: these are gone. Full words, direct arrangements of clauses, terse phrases, Saxon roots, light airy metaphors, three-word conceits: these display themselves in Tennyson. Dainty flowers have sprouted where the gigantic ferns died. The sesquipedalion hollowness and clumsiness of the classic metres, the chilling shocks of the "poetic license," the comic *inevitableness* of the four-footed iambics rhyming though the heavens fall for it, and lashed in distichs like well-matched hounds in couples—all these iron manacles on the wrists of poetry have been stricken off by a magic touch, the walls of the prison have opened, and the bound apostle may now preach in the market-place.

Like the *Sänger* of Goethe, the modern poet sings as the bird sings. He need not wait for the fine frenzy: he is possessed by the unflickering flame of an enthusiasm that nor wanes nor dies; and we now get poems o' week-days as well as Sundays. Precisely as music freed itself from the serpentine cadenzas and mazy complexities and endless fugues of the last century, has poetry also freed itself from the hampering limitations of that era. Indeed poetry has in some notable cases of late so completely transfigured its external address that it must needs go under an alias. Several times recently poetry has put off the purple.* Porphyrogenitus has donned the sober dress of the

* [MS A adds: "Poetry . . . has, in many cases, entirely shaken off the shackles of verse or rhythmic construction, . . . no one dreams of thinking that Rhythm is more than the merest accessory of Poetry." Cf. *The Science of English Verse* (II, *passim,* of the present edition).—Ed.]

citizen, that he might go *incog.* into many places otherwise inaccessible to royalty. His alias is "Prose"; and how he becomes it! Look at Hugo; look at Richter, at Ruskin, at Carlyle, at De Guérin, at Hawthorne, at Poe! * Here is Poetry escaped from his palace, bathing, crazy with delight, in the sea and the air and the sunshine, darting into hovels that he never saw before, and relieving poverties that he never had suspected. What a man, a right, true, god-like man is this; who is as exemplary in citizenship as he was magnificent in royalty, so that men know not whether to love him better as the freeholder Prose or as the king Poetry!

Some years ago Elizabeth Browning** noticed that the drama now no longer employs the huge mask wherewith the player

> Was wont to ape the front of Themis' son,

nor the brazen trumpet which lent a terrific sonorousness to the voice, nor the thick sole which increased his stature to more than mortal height. The drama has outgrown these mere physical aids. Men's souls get taller, and do not have to be propped up so to see over the bars of matter into the ideal field beyond. And so poetry, wielding its kingly power with the light airiness of prose—a knight fighting in his scarf, still invulnerable, and all the better that his limbs are unshackled by the cumbrous armor which he has thrown off—is perhaps the most striking instance of the process which has been so often alluded to, the process of etherealizing, of lightening, of freeing things from the limitations of time and space. Time and space have long been our Giants Grim. Now their power doth wane and wane. It is well. They were tyrants: let them fall.

How tempting is it to pursue this idea of etherealization into extremes that might with justice be called fantastic! For even all those material forces which men once employed in the mechanic arts to fufill the stern exactions of space and time have undergone a precisely analoguous modification to that of art. For instance, the ancients did hew and whack each other with hard tangible stone and steel, while we propel our bullets with an elastic gas. And whereas the gross muscles of men and

* [Here MS B adds O. W. Holmes to the list.—Ed.]

** [MS A supplies an appositive, "regal Queen Bess of all women-poets."—Ed.]

beasts formerly did the world's work; now, on the contrary, the invisible vapor, steam, does it. Moreover, once the world talked between distances by carrier-pigeons and couriers; now, however, viewless electricity, which is so ethereal that some have even declared it to be a spirit, conveys our messages.

But, leaving these fancies to some quieter moment than this busy daybreak of a new epoch, it was asserted that politics and religion, as well as nature and art, spiritualize themselves through the ages. Politics and religion were called the body and soul of life. This expression, then used as metaphor, is here to be considered a rigorously literal truth. Let us get at the root of the matter.

1st. In the last analysis, politics has regard only to the physical sense of man; 2d. In the last analysis, religion has regard only to the spiritual love of man. For, first, politics regards only those new conditions in a man's life resulting from his contact with other men. Now this word " contact " is itself a proof of the first proposition. Contact is a touching; contact is only possible through the physical sense; the communication of spirit with spirit must of necessity be embodied into some physical shape or other. One can receive from his fellow no possible right or wrong which one has not previously seen, heard, tasted, touched, or smelled, in some physical form; and it is at the moment of this embodiment in physical form, and only at this moment, that politics takes cognizance of wrong.

But, secondly, religion regards only the spiritual love of man. " Love " is the term we apply to that peculiar activity which is the province of the soul. And there yet remain many people in the world who do not very clearly distinguish between the signification of soul and of intellect. As between soul and sense, intellect is surely a common ground, so different from either as to be entirely incomparable with them except by some remote symbolization or other. For instance, intellect is a debatable land full of powerful yeomen, who are without predilections or prejudices or loyalties, and who fight indifferently for soul or for sense, as careless whether one or the other as a steel-pen is careless whether truth or falsehood write with it. Such is intellect: but soul is the radical energy of man, namely, man's love, that strange divinity, in its thousand avatars of love of self, and love of one's fellow; of appetite and disgust; of desire and aversion; of faith, or love for the higher; and of charity, or love for the lower. Whenever the soul wishes to walk in the open air of the world, intellect, like a Grand Usher, must throw open the door of sense; and whenever the sense wishes to get into the fine air of the spiritual world, then intellect, like a Grand Vizier, must present his petition to the Sultan Soul. Here, then, is our old soul-and-sense idea recurring upon us in quite a new form, and suggesting certain relations between politics and religion which perhaps have not been clearly noticed by philosophers.

In their essential nature, politics and religion are at deadly variance with each other; and the perfection of either is the annihilation, by merging or by destruction, of the other. Certainly religion, if perfect, would destroy politics; for he who loved all things would injure no thing. And as surely would politics, if perfect, destroy religion; for the absolute confining of men's bad actions to themselves would convert the general soul into an irremediable hell. The best politics, therefore, is that which secures the most unlimited intercourse between fellow-men together with the least possible wrong therein; and the best religion is that which loves all things well and each thing adequately. And so politics, if it have followed the etherealizing course of nature and of art, will be found to have reduced, or at least to be reducing, to that minimum consistent with the least wrong-doing, the purely physical tenures it possessed upon men's actions: and these abandoned tenures will be found to have converted themselves into their spiritual analogues, namely, religious tenures. And religion, if it also have followed the course of nature and art, should be found to have purified itself as far as possible of all physical necessities for its support, and to have largely expanded the range of the objects of man's love.

Let us see. At intervals, and far more frequently of late days than formerly, there arises in the breasts of men a certain law-breaking temper which appears to be rather an electric instinct than any intellectual persuasion, and which busies itself in shivering to pieces all sorts of political restrictions. It never stops short of the thing demanded; and frequently, ignorant of what it does demand, goes far beyond its original hope. What is this, which is here called the law-breaking temper, except the grand idea of etherealization, descending in some new avatar and dwelling among men, whereby they find themselves driven straight forward to some high consummation which they do not know at the beginning, which they do not even recognize at the ending till they have drawn breath from the fighting and the labor and wiped their eyes and looked behind them and before them?

Like the buds in a forest of mulberry-trees, bursting in quick succession and each emitting its own little puff of vapor, have the events of the last fifty year opened about us and sent up clouds towards heaven. Until very recently the world had two dark closets of corpses. They were China and Japan. Now, curious commerce, like Blue-Beard's last wife, has thrust her sweet face in at their door, though forbidden to do so upon peril of her life. In Russia the serfs have been freed. Germany, once said Richter, has for a long time been the *Bois de Boulogne* of Europe, to which, whenever two powers became angry, they immediately repaired in order to fight out their terrific duel on its sward. But Count Bismarck has changed all that; and if Count Bismarck is a tyrant, he is surely not such a tyrant as two mad nations inflamed by war; which last is itself a greater tyrant than all others. In France, the revolution has burst and liberated its cloud. In England, John Bright is forcing his mulberry-bud, and it will open; violently, if a more skilful arboriculturist be not put in charge. In South America the lately-created republics continue to perfect themselves. In Mexico, President Juarez astonishes the world by subduing a coalition of church prerogative and foreign tyranny which at first seemed irresistible. In the Southern portion of the United States, the last five years have witnessed the extinction of negro slavery. In Brazil, the Emperor has set free the slaves of the Government. While this is written the Chinese insurgents make headway, and the Christian rebels in Candia defeat the Turks.

But there are some circumstances attendant upon the conclusion of the late war in the United States which notably exhibit how many physical bonds of restraint politics has found itself able to dispense with in these later days.

At the close of that war, three armies which had been fighting on the Southern side, and which numbered probably forty thousand men, were disbanded. These men had for four years been subjected to the unfamiliar and galling restrictions of military discipline, and to the most maddening privations. The exigencies of unsuccessful combat had wholly deprived them of any means of subsistence beyond what was available through manual labor. At the same time, four millions of slaves, without provisions and without prospect of labor in a land where employers were impoverished, were liberated. "Half a man's virtue," says Dr. Arnold, "is gone when he becomes a slave; and the other half goes when he becomes *a slave broken loose*."

The reign of law, at this thrilling time, was at an end. The civil powers of the States were dead. The military power of the conquerors was not yet organized for civil purposes. The railroad and the telegraph, those most efficient sheriffs of modern times, had fallen in the shock of war. All possible opportunities presented themselves to each man who chose to injure his neighbor with impunity. The country was sparsely settled, the country roads were intricate, the forests were extensive and dense, the hiding-places were numerous and secure, the witnesses were few and ignorant. Never had crime such fair weather for his carnival.

Serious apprehensions had been long entertained by the Southern citizens that in the event of a disastrous termination of the war, the whole army would be frenzied to convert itself after disintegration into forty thousand highwaymen, who would take advantage of the annihilation of the civil war to prey upon the numerous unfortunates who would be compelled to travel the country roads on errands necessitated by the needs of fallen fortunes, by yearnings for long-separated kindred, and by the demands of hard existence. Moreover, the feuds between master and slave, alleged by the Northern parties in the contest to have been long smouldering in the South, would seize this opportunity to flame out and redress themselves. Altogether, regarding humanity from the old point of view, there appeared to many wise citizens a clear prospect of dwelling in midst of a furious pandemonium for several years after an unfavorable termination of the war.

But was this prospect realized? Where were the highway

robberies, the bloody vengeances, the arsons, the rapine, the murders, the outrages, the insults? They *were* not anywhere. With great calmness the soldier cast behind him the memory of all wrongs and hardships and reckless habits of the war, embraced his wife, patched his cabin-roof, and proceeded to mingle the dust of recent battles yet lingering on his feet with the peaceful clods of his corn-field.*

What restrained these men? Was it fear? The word cannot be spoken. Was he who had breasted the storms of Gettysburg and Perryville to shrink from the puny arm of a civil law that was more powerless than the shrunken muscle of Justice Shallow? And what could the negro fear when his belief and assurance were that a conquering nation stood ready to support him in his wildest demand? It was the spirit of the time that brought about these things. Politics in a couple of hundred years past has learned to dispense with many iron bands wherewith it formerly restrained men from wrong-doing; and silken bands have taken the places of the iron ones, bands which rather attract men towards the good than rudely repel them from the bad. Many political restraints have been spiritualized into religious ones which appear not upon the statute-books, but are unconscious records on the heart.

In the view of philosophy, a thousand Atlantic cables and Pacific Railroads would not have contributed cause for so earnest self-gratulation as was afforded by this one feature in our recent political convulsion. Who will find words to express his sorrowful surprise at that total absence of philosophic insight into the age which has resulted in those hundreds of laws recently promulgated by the reigning body in the United States; laws which, if from no other cause at least from sheer multiplicity, are wholly at variance with the genius of the time and of the people, laws which have resulted in such a mass of crime and hatred and bitterness as even the four terrible years of war had entirely failed to bring about?

And so, to return from this digression, politics has really spiritualized itself, has lost many of its physical complexities,

* [MS B adds: "With heartfelt rejoicing, surprisingly tempered into a manly and extravagant self-congratulation, the negro thanked God for his freedom and straightway signed his cross-mark to the written contract between him and his former master for the continuance of his labor."—ED.]

and has etherealized. Let politics now purge itself of war. This is a material prop. Politics does not need it. Politics is at variance with the genius of the age until an international court of some sort is established. Some small but cheerful signs exist that this will be so, and that war will die. It was a strange circumstance that only two days ago the *London Times*, which has long been a mouthpiece through which a people has sounded the praise of its pluck, avowed itself uncompromisingly opposed to a war which certainly had more color of right than any war in which England ever engaged, and proceeded to refer not even angrily but only sorrowfully to the taunts which a previous expression of such peaceful opinion had elicited from foreign journals. And, in Germany, Richter swears that war is the relic of barbarism. And here and there are the Quakers. And perhaps, after two thousand years of coquettish blindness, the world will at length open its eyes and read what Christ said and did anent war.

It is time now, lastly, to speak of religion. Here one finds a wonderful etherealizing process. See how the Church has purified itself of the State, for instance. The union of Church and State threw both of them into the falsest of attitudes; it puffed up the State with a dignity far above its deserving, and it degraded the Church to a station utterly beneath it—necessarily, in order to bring them upon common ground, where they might unite. Any compromise between these two is simply ruinous to both. And so it is well that the Church has lost, or is losing, all temporal dominions and powers, whether these appear as territorial appanages of a Pope, as livings in the gift of a bishop, as Spanish Inquisitions, as Puritanical burnings of witches, as physical crusades in behalf of whatever religious order. Every time that religion has shaken itself free of an inquisition, of a persecution, of an intolerance, of any such material irrelevancy, she has signalized the event by rising and floating, and shining splendidly and expanding gloriously.

If this theory which has been enunciated be true, if material things constantly tend to spiritualize themselves into analogous forms, then will political changes tend to convert themselves quickly into their spiritual analogues, religious changes. And this after so much of retrospect, brings me to devote some small space to prospect.

The French revolution, along with a thousand spiritual changes, exhibits a *Vie de Jésus*; the English revolution proceeds, accompanied by an *Ecce Homo*; * the American revolution leaves a religion so unsettled as to be called Mormonism, Free Love, Oneida-ism, Spiritualism, English Church Catholicism, and a thousand other names denoting a thousand other disintegrated parts of the Church. What do these things, as events so small, as indications so great, signify? Are they not the little hissing lightnings out of a great and as yet unseen cloud? In a word, as the era just now closed was an era of political revolution, will not the era just now opening be an era of religious revolution?

* [Renan's work was published in 1863; J. R. Seeley's in 1865.—ED.]

NATURE-METAPHORS *

METAPHORS COME of love rather than of thought. They arise in the heart as vapors; they gather themselves together in the brain as shapes; they then emerge, from lip, from pen, from brush, from chisel, from violin, as full works, as creations, as Art.

Love—a term here used to signify the general underlying principle of all emotion, the τὸ ὑποχείμενον of all passion—originates metaphors by reason of its essential duality. Like Novalis' "Pupil," love "can see nothing alone." It exists upon a necessary hypothesis of two parties, one loving and one beloved. As between these two parties, the overwhelming desire of love is always union. Marriage, indeed, is a large term. For all loves, human, divine, friendly, social, political, ethnical; and certain other loves for which we have yet no name, since man has but recently come into the full possession and exercise of them: all these primarily and immediately demand some sort of union, some sort of marriage, between the two parties.

It is the last-named kind of these loves—the kind for which we have yet no name—that specially concerns us in this writing, for the unions or marriages produced by this kind of love are what I have called nature-metaphors.

I speak of the love of man for physical nature, and of that strange and manifold transfusing of human nature into physical nature which has developed the most interesting phasis of modern culture and which constitutes the most striking characteristic of modern art.

In a certain sense—which will appear in what follows—this humanization of physical nature is not only a striking but also a

* [First published in the *Southern Magazine,* X, 172-182 (Feb., 1872), from which the present text is taken; reprinted in *Music and Poetry* (New York, 1898), pp. 95-114, with trivial variants. A few obvious typographical errors and mechanical irregularities have been corrected. The only MS that survives is a rough pencil draft apparently written about 1868 in Lanier's Ledger, pp. 546-572 (Henry W. Lanier Collection, Johns Hopkins University; the revised MS of 1872 has not been found). This MS approximates the print version, except in the stylistic differences incident to a first draft and in a few short insignificant amplifications which Lanier omitted in his revision. Other isolated passages in the Ledger, pp. 38, 47-48, 275, and 465, relate to the subject of metaphors.—ED.]

distinctive characteristic of modern as opposed to ancient art. To transfer actions, thoughts, and feelings to natural objects and phenomena; to represent these as existing and occurring, if not consciously, at least by the will and pleasure of inhabiting divinities; nay, to completely transform these so that they were recognized and alluded to as beings, loving, fighting, working, planning: it is true that even in the ancient times this was a quite common procedure of that old instinct in man which draws him into blind love and reverence for the sun-risings, the star-gatherings, the seas, the storms, the trees, the mountains; and these old metaphors of the first poets reappear to us sometimes in the strangest guises. We find them becoming, after the lapse of years, fair religions which govern the hearts and control the souls of great peoples for long ages. Recent comparative philology, examining the mythologies of Greece, of Persia, of Egypt, of India, of Scandinavia, assures us with much show of truth that these systems which once, while in their primary purity, commanded the loving respect of men, derive their origin in great measure from stocks of metaphorical names applied by the old poets to natural objects and occurrences, especially to the sun and his doings.

But nature-metaphors, after having in the ancient days played so important a part—of giving a faith to the otherwise untutored and uncontrollable soul of the young world—continue in far other fashion to exert their fine influences upon men in these later days. Yet even now the nature-metaphor finds among us a recognition which, though universal and unequivocal, is still inexplicit and undefined to such a degree that by a large class of very intelligent critics the reproach of metaphor-mongering has been cast upon poets whose hold on the popular heart is impregnable. Nor is this all. Of the many people whose lives are daily refreshed by those good streams of subjective and domestic poetry which flow so freely of late days, few enjoy the pure and serene delight of metaphors without feeling a certain sense of shame in deriving pleasure from what is explicitly regarded as not the highest in art, or without endeavoring to find underneath the mere beauty some didactic truth or wholesome aphorism to chaperone their young delight, to protect it from light company, and to shed dignity upon it.

These persons cannot free themselves from the haunting recollection that the ascendant criticism of the day regards nature-metaphors rather in the light of "fancies," and calls vociferously for something solid to underlie all beautiful expressions of that sort.

This inconsistency between our instinctive taste—which undoubtedly loves nature-metaphors—and our critical education—which undoubtedly is a little afraid of them—leads one to go behind it, to inquire what after all *is* precisely the nature-metaphor, how does it as a poetic form consist with the modern *modus* of thought, and what is its importance to the interests of modern culture.

It has been before remarked that the metaphor is always a union of two objects. The nature-metaphor is a union of human nature with physical nature. Clay informed with a soul, this is a type of the nature-metaphor. Man himself precisely answers these conditions. Man is clay informed with a soul. It is therefore only a seeming stretch of language to say that man is the first metaphor. In this union of the physical and the spiritual, such as man himself presents, there is a most taking sweetness, since the parties to it are the two most widely differing forms in the universe. Matter is in itself dead. Traditions prove it to have been so regarded by all nations in all times. Even the heathen find themselves under the necessity of inventing deities to preside over all its movements, over the thunder, over the growing of the grass, over the moving of the winds and seas, over the flowing of the rivers. In all the mythologies these things go on by virtue of divinities within, never by virtue of themselves.

Spirit, on the other hand, lives, and by some name or another is recognized everywhere and at all times as the converse of matter in this respect.

When, therefore, these two come together and a beautiful One is formed; when, that is, a nature-metaphor is made, in which soul gives life to matter and matter gives Antæan solidity to soul, each complementing the other's significance, each *meaning* the other in such will-o'-wisp transfigurations as the mind cannot easily analyse—one must confess that here is something more than a mere "frothy fancy," however light may be the apparent weight of the ideas employed. One must see that each metaphor of this kind is noble by divine lineage, since God has decreed the correlative intersignificance of man and man's earth: noble by long pedigree, since the youngest nations of known time found their delight and their faith in the wildest of metaphors, and since all the highest love-songs, the *Song of Solomon*, the *Gita-Govinda*, the *Æneid*, all, down to our most loving poetry of to-day, are burdened with metaphoric sweetness; and lastly, noble by virtue of innate greatness and goodness and captivating loveliness, for all men respond to metaphor, all hearts open to give it place, and all souls in their inmost confessions acknowledge its power. One must believe that the poet who has uttered a beautiful metaphor is conscious of having beautifully re-created himself *in petto*. Fair Protean Nature, fair Protean Soul, I have married you again, I have given you another honeymoon!—must be the happy cry of the artist.

Essentially, then, the first of the questions proposed is now answered. Our nature-metaphor is a beautiful eternal bridal of spirit and matter, in which the immortality of the former gains the *form* of the latter, and the form of the latter gains the immortality of the former; each being transfused with the other like the souls of true man and wife, and both having given without losing and acquired without taking away.

How, then, does this so intrinsically noble form of expression consist with the modern mode of thought? And what, first, *is* the modern mode of thought?

This last question cannot be better answered than by observing the difference between the genius of modern language and the genius of ancient language; for these physical forms of thought exhibit a very rigid parallelism with, and indeed mould themselves by, thought itself. To illustrate more moderate differences by an extreme one, let us compare, in only a few prominent particulars, the English tongue with the Greek.

One notices at first view that the English performs the work —or more than the work—of the Greek with far less cumbersome machinery. In the Greek, for instance, one finds, as regards the nouns, three methods of declension, each with its five forms of inflection, terminating differently in singular, dual, and plural numbers. Three of these forms, the genitive, dative, and accusative, sustain complicated relations to the verbs and the prepositions. The adjectives, in all their degrees, which are themselves of complex form, have also their quintuple inflections, which again vary among *themselves* according to the gender. Still more cumbrous complexities present themselves in the numerous tense-forms, voice-forms, and mood-forms of the verbs.

Opposed to this, one finds in English nouns but a single inflection; while English prepositions and verbs are as precise and as plastic as Greek prepositions and verbs aided by manifold changes of termination.

So to the Greek adjective, varied by five cases differing as the adjective is masculine, feminine, or neuter, differing further as the adjective is singular, dual, or plural, and still further as positive, comparative, or superlative, the English adjective opposes its form uninflected as to case, unchanged for gender or number, and varying mostly by simple laws only for degrees of comparison.

In the same way one finds that the English verb (excluding irregular verbs common to both languages) with a few simple changes of form expresses, by the not complex machinery of the auxiliary verbs, all the shades of meaning possible to the Greek verb.

No less is the prosodial machinery of the Greek language embarrassed by intricacies which do not appear in the English. One can scarcely imagine a circumstance, aside from fundamental structural harshness, more unfavorable to melody of poetic expression than those very rules of rigid "quantity" which have been supposed by modern insane Grecians to conduce to music. An English poem written in the metre, or rather the metres, of the *Prometheus Bound*, would be far less rhythmical and far less melodious than many pages selected at random from the prose-writings of English authors who could be named.

When to all these complexities of the Greek tongue one adds the varying position and number of the accents, and the changes in the sound of the same word produced by the occurrence of long or short vowels in the oblique cases, together with the lawless superposition of the accent in the nominative case, one cannot fail to conclude that the English has in a wonderful degree at once simplified the machinery and extended the possible range of language as a working instrument in prose and as a singing instrument in poetry.

Now these characteristic differences between the English and Greek languages will be found to be at bottom the characteristic differences also between modern and ancient thought. The change from ancient to modern modes of thought and language is quite parallel with and is well illustrated by that which has occurred in military tactics and organizations. The heavy infantry of only a few years ago, with its straight lines, its angular movements, and its prescribed slow gait, is gone: in its place we have the light-armed troops who move either in right lines, curved lines, or oblique lines; who walk, trot, run, kneel, lie down, who load and fire at will or command, who separate at five paces and rally by fours or by regiment, as occasion requires.

Ancient thought was strong: modern thought has retained this strength and added to it a wonderful agility. Ancient thought was a huge Genie: modern thought is a Genie or a lightsome Ariel at will.

These then being the peculiarities of modern thought, how does the nature-metaphor fulfil the requirements of this modern intellectual *modus*, which is so simple and so wide-spanning, so domestic and so daring?

Truly, the two seem made for each other. The metaphor by its very constitution demands of the artist the utmost simplicity of construction, and rewards the artist with the widest range of application and significance. For instance, the most meagre description of Napoleon and Washington will have instantly acquired, so far as the poetic impression upon the mind of the reader is concerned, a force and beauty unattainable by any amount of detail, when the writer finishes it with: "Napoleon was lightning, Washington was sunlight." Here in a simple sextiole of words are bound up the most prominent characteristics of the men, to be unfolded at the reader's leisure. But now the idea of lightning, though so conjoined with the name of the great soldier, is by no means limited to this association;

for in the next moment the poet may sing, without fear of confusion, of the lightning in a lady's eye, and so on to eternity.

True, however, as is this consonance of the nature-metaphor with modern intellectual processes, this truth is yet not the gravest one in this connection, and does not lie at the root of the matter. For—if one did not fear to write too much about love lest one (alas, the times!) be suspected of lightness—the question might have been asked, how does the nature-metaphor suit the tendency of modern *love,* rather than of modern *thought?* This indeed would have been the appropriate inquiry; for wherever society locates its love (that is, its want, its desire), there she sends intellect to work in its service; and if one wish to discover whither the thought of a time is flying, one must discover first whither the love (or want, or desire) of the time has flown.

Now, nothing strikes the thoughtful observer of modern literature more quickly or more forcibly than the great yearning therein displayed for intimate companionship with nature. And this yearning, mark, justifies itself upon far other authority than that which one finds in (for example) the Greek nature-seeking. Granted the instinctive reverence for nature common to both parties: the Greek believed the stream to be inhabited by a nymph, and the stream was wonderful to him because of this nymph; but the modern man believes no such thing. One has appeared who continually cried love, love, love—love God, love *neighbors;* and these "neighbors" have come to be not only men-neighbors, but tree-neighbors, river-neighbors, star-neighbors. The stream—to carry on the Greek parallel—has acquired so much individuality independent of any inhabiting nymph, that men may love it, may be neighbors to it and neighbored by it, and may live life with it in the finest harmony.

Here, then, it is seen how nature, which before depended on mere blind reverence and on imagined indwelling deities for its hold on man's soul, has now become so far able to dispense with these as to claim a genuine love from man on its own individual account. How infinite is the field so added to the range of man's love! How beautiful and how numerous the unions of human emotion and physical phenomena made possible in virtue of this wholly new and sweet relation between humanity and nature!

This way, then, society has now sent its love—towards nature;

and the manifold relation between society and nature, demanding expression, finds it in the nature-metaphor, and revels in this with the finest and completest of satisfactions.

It must be remarked that one finds in the Hindu character a far nearer approach to this modern view of nature than in the Greek and Roman. Let us see by actual experiment how differently the hearts of the Hindu, of the Roman, and of the Englishman framed their nature-metaphors. Hear the poet Jayadeva, in the *Gita-Govinda:*

The gale that has wantoned around the beautiful clove-plant breathes from the hill of Malaya. . . .

The Tamála, with leaves dark and fragrant, claims a tribute from the Musk, which it vanquishes. . . .

The tender blossom of the Caruna smiles to see the whole world laying sham aside. . . .

The fresh Malica seduces with rich perfume even the hearts of hermits, while the Amra-tree with blooming tresses is embraced by the gay creeper Atimucta. . . .

Another stands meditating on the Lotus of his face. . . .

Whose mantle gleams like a dark-blue cloud illumined with rainbows. . . .

Lips brilliant and soft as a dewy leaf. . . .

Her face, with eyebrows contracting themselves through a just resentment, resembles a fresh Lotus over which two black bees are fluttering. . . .

Her face is like a water-lily veiled in the dew of tears. . . .

Her sighs are flames of fire kindled in a thicket; herself is a timid roe, and love is the tiger who springs on her like Yama, the genius of death. . . .

Her eyes, like blue water-lilies, with broken stalks dropping lucid streams. . . .

Long has she been heated with sandal-wood, moonlight and water-lilies, with which others are cooled. . . .

Many a flower points his extended petals to pierce the bosoms of separated lovers. . . .

The breeze which has kissed thy cheek. . . .

A mind languid as a drooping wing, feeble as a trembling leaf. . . .

O thou who sparklest like lightning! . . .

He is a blue gem on the forehead of the three worlds. . . .

Drowned in a sea of rapturous imaginations. . . .

The moon spread a net of beams over the groves of Vrindavan, and looked like a drop of liquid sandal on the face of the sky, which smiled like a beautiful damsel.

Flowers are indeed the arrows of love, and he plays with them cruelly. . . .

Her face, like the moon, is graced with clouds of dark hair. . . .

She floats on the waves of desire. . . .

He fixes white blossoms on her dark locks, where they gleam like flashes of lightning among the curled clouds. . . .

Her arms graceful as the stalks of the water-lily, and adorned with hands glowing like the petals of that flower. . . .

Whose wanton eyes resemble blue water-lilies, agitated by the breeze. . . .

His azure breast glittered with pearls of unblemished lustre, like the full bed of the cerulean Yamuna interspersed with curls of white foam. . . .

Liquid bliss. . . .

The fire of separation. . . .

These are nearly all the metaphorical expressions in the *Gita-Govinda.*

Hear now the Hindu's opposite, Virgil. One will notice in passing how the multitudinous imagery of the Hindu, devoted to some phase of love, is contrasted with the monotonous figures of the Roman used for the same purpose. These are mostly variations of some idea connected with fire; it is always *urit* (" she burns "), *amore incensus* (" inflamed with love ") : this, too, in spite of the fact that Virgil approaches nearer the passion-unfolding poets of later days than most ancient writers. The following are nearly all the metaphorical expressions in the first two hundred lines of the Fourth Book of the *Æneid*; in which book it might be supposed that the climax of Dido's hot indecision would be revealed in the strongest forms of expression known to the poet. These strongest forms are almost always nature-metaphors. The translation is, of course, for such a purpose, literal:

She fosters the wound in her veins, and is consumed with hidden fire.

The following Aurora was lighting the lands with Phœbean lamp, and had removed the humid shadow from the sky.

Tossed [*jactatus*] * by the fates [*sc.* as by the waves of the sea].

I recognize the marks of the old flame [of love].

But would that the earth might gape for me to the bottom, would that the omnipotent father might hurl me with lightning to the shades, the pallid shades, of Erebus and to profound night.

* [The bracketed interpolations are Lanier's.—Ed.]

O dearer to thy sister than life [*luce,* light] shalt thou alone, sad, through thy whole youth be wasted [*carpêre:* be plucked, as a flower which therefore dies].

With these words she inflamed a soul already burning with love.

Winter and watery Orion grew fierce upon the sea.

Meanwhile the soft flame eats her marrow.

Unhappy Dido burns. . . . . As an arrow-pierced doe among the woods of Crete, whom incautious some pursuing shepherd has shot and ignorantly left wounded, wanders in flight through woods and groves Dictæan.

The obscure moon by turns conceals her light and the setting stars invite sleep.

When to-morrow's sun [Titan] shall have netted the earth with his beams.

Meantime, the Morning, arising, left the ocean.

First Tellus and Juno, the marriage-goddess, give sign: lightnings glittered, and the air conscious of the nuptials, and from the summit of the peak chanted the nymphs.

Inflames his mind with words.

And now the master. How he makes all nature alive in *The Tempest:*

Blow [addressing the storm] till thou burst thy wind, if room enough!

Boats.—You do assist the storm.

Gon.—Nay, good, be patient.

Boats.—When the sea is. Hence! What care these roarers for the name of King?

He'll be hanged yet, though every drop of water swear against it, and gape at wid'st to glut him.

The sky, it seems, would pour down stinking pitch,
But that the sea, mounting to the welkin's cheek,
Dashes the fire out.

The very minute bids thee ope thine ear.

He was
The ivy which had hid my princely trunk
And sucked the verdure out on't.

I' the dead of darkness.

To cry to the sea that roared to us: to sigh
To the winds, whose pity, sighing back again,
Did us but loving wrong.

Our sea-sorrow.

In the veins o' the earth.

His bold waves.

It was mine art
That made gape
The pine, and let thee out.

I will rend an oak
And peg thee in his knotty entrails.

Wicked dew.

Come unto these yellow sands,
And there take hands.
Curtsied when you have, and kissed
(The wild waves whist),
Foot it featly here and there,
And, sweet sprites, the burden bear.
Hark, hark!
[Burden] Bowgh, wowgh,
The watch-dogs bark.
[Burden] Bowgh, wowgh.
Hark! hark! I hear
The strain of strutting Chanticlere
Cry, Cock-a-doodle-doo.

Most sure, the goddess
On whom these airs attend.

Mine eyes, ne'er since at ebb.

I saw him beat the surges under him
And ride upon their backs: he trod the water
Whose enmity he flung aside:
. . . his bold head
'Bove the contentious waves, and oared
Himself with his good arms in lusty stroke
To the shore that o'er his wave-worn basis bow'd,
As stooping to relieve him.

It is foul weather in us all, good sir,
When you are cloudy.

That from Naples
Can have no note unless the sun were post
(The man in the moon's too slow).

'T is fresh morning with me
When you are by at night.

Whom destiny . . .
The never surfeited sea,
Hath cause to belch up.

Exposed unto the sea, which hath requit it,
Him and his innocent child.

For which foul deed
The powers . . . have
Incensed the seas and shores.

The billows spoke and told me of it:
The winds did sing it to me.

Night, kept chained below.

Virgin snow.

Thy banks with peonied and lilied brims,
Which spungy April at thy hest betrims.

Spring come to you at farthest
In the very hand of harvest.

They smote the air
For breathing in their faces; beat the ground
For kissing of their feet.

His tears ran down his beard like winter's drops
From eaves of reeds.

Called forth the mutinous winds,
And 'twixt the green sea and the azure vault
Set roaring war.

And as the morning steals upon the night,
Melting the darkness, so their rising senses
Begin to chase the ignorant fumes that mantle
Their clearer reason.

Though the seas threaten, they are merciful.

These specimens of nature-metaphors exhibit very clearly the differing relations of the ancient and of the modern poet to nature. The ancient is rigorously restricted in his use of those rich materials which nature affords for the expression of beauty and passion. He is not only restricted in the use, but in the material itself: nature does not furnish so much to him as to his later brother. At best, nature comes to him in the person of the deities and half-deities which inhabit it; these divinities have each an appointed office and a conventional significance, and to these pre-appointments and conventionalities he is limited in his employment of nature for poetic purposes. Thus, when Virgil has brought Dido and Æneas to the same cave on the mountain-side, with the instinct of a poet he makes resort to nature for the purpose of strengthening and heightening the climactic situation. He cites *Tellus,* and *pronuba Juno,* and *ignes* and *conscius Æther,* and the ululating nymphs. But how limited his use of these! What an intense climax of human passion, long fought against, now conquering, brought to reach of its burning satisfaction amid rain-rivers rushing from the mountains (*ruunt amnes de montibus*), cloud with hail intermingled (*commixta grandine nimbus*), and all those fearful accessories of the storm which beat out the outer world and for the time annihilate the whole universe except these two passionate hearts that now come together for the first time! How gloriously might this have been told by a modern poet, to whom nature, instead of being a few rigidly-defined personalities, means all things, and helps him to say all things, according only as his soul has power to grasp and wield what is offered him.

In the Hindu poet one finds nature a little more freed from constraint, yet still limited. The principal parts she plays are mostly drawn either from love or from war, and only the most prominent characteristics of natural objects—such as the foam of the water, the color and shape of the leaf and the flower, and the like—are employed. Here are none of those inexhaustible resources which lie in such *details* of natural appearances as, although less prominent, are yet quickly recalled to the recollection of the most cursory observer of nature. In George Eliot's *Spanish Gypsy,* for instance, the successive gradations of light in a Spanish sunset are made to do noble work; each changing tint, from the glitter of the first glories to the gray twilight, comes thronged with marvellous-sweet images and meanings to which the ancient poet was a stranger. The ancient poet would have dismissed the sunset as a single scene, a glory which subsided and was not.

And this brings us to the *Tempest* images, in which one sees nature still personal, it is true, but so far from being definitely personified, nature is here one person, or all persons, or any person, or any passionate phase of any person. And herein lies the gist of the matter. Nature is like music. The meanings of the tones are not—as in language—preconcerted among men; each tone is free to mean all things, depending on its situation; nay, further, each hearing soul may translate the same tone differently for itself, may bend the music to its own particular need, as the humor strikes. And so with nature. Its objects and its phenomena are at the will and pleasure of the poet, to be informed with whatever spiritual phasis he may choose to perpetuate. No caprice of the poet's but he may find some nature-form to put it in.

And this, of caprice, introduces another peculiarity of the modern nature-metaphor as opposed to the ancient. In regarding these peculiarities, especially as exhibited by our greatest poets, one cannot help being struck with such forms of expression as occur in the song above quoted from *The Tempest.* Ariel is singing to the sprites, while he hovers over Ferdinand's head:—

Come unto these yellow sands,
And then take hands.
Curtsied when you have, and kissed
(The wild waves whist),
Foot it featly here and there,
And, sweet sprites, the burden bear.
Hark, hark.

—and suddenly, by an apparently immeasurable and unaccountable transition of thought, occurs—

Bowgh, wowgh,
The watch-dogs bark.
Bowgh, wowgh.
Hark! hark! I hear
The strain of strutting Chanticlere
Cry, Cock-a-doodle-doo.

Now—and this is far from being Shakspere-worship, since many similar instances are adducible out of other writers—surely no delicately-tuned poetic soul but must find in this *bizarre* introduction of watch-dog and chanticlere a rare exquisite pleasure. The secret of this pleasure, however, and the principle upon which the apparently so irrelevant idea of watch-dogs and crowing cocks is thrust into a song of sprites, are not so easy to discover. It is under the impression that these are genuine metaphorical expressions, in which the link between the primary and the conferred significations is referable to intangible and quickly-vanishing trains of thought, that they are cited in this place. For this impression strong grounds are not wanting. Who that has gazed upon a barking dog has not had come over him somewhat of that evanescent out-world sensation which arises when one (for instance) repeats a familiar word many times until it grows unfamiliar and wholly mysterious? Who has not begun to dream of the weird powers of nature that float, rather in suggestion than in person, in the strange eye of the animal? Who has not shivered at the evil secrets which seem to dwell in the red-rimmed eye of the crowing cock, secrets which somehow seem to link themselves on the one hand with that wild moment in which a cock announced to the unseen ears of the thronged night the treachery of Peter, and on the other hand with those fascinating tales which among all nations reveal a suspicion of inner meanings in animal-cries,—such, for instance, as the tale of the female magicians in the *Arabian Nights* who learn the language of animals and gather strange news and prophecies from them? This—if indeed my words convey any trace of those ideas which are so intangible that they cannot be directly imparted but only chance-awakened by some happy suggestion—is the *conferred* meaning which, in the song alluded to, gives to the ideas of dog and cock their metaphorical character.

Such instances are not found in the ancient poets. They require a delicacy of organization both in writer and reader not likely to be found in earlier ages than this. In old poets one finds rather strength than delicacy, rather power than beauty. And this is the order of nature. In art, as in all things, Jupiter conquers Saturn, beauty supplants strength; or—a better fable—strength dies and is born again as beauty.

If we come now, in accordance with the procedure suggested, to inquire lastly what is the importance of the nature-metaphor to the interests of modern culture, we are, it is hoped, already prepared to declare that it is great, almost transcendent. In spite of the cries of distressed theologians who dream that their large cities constitute the world, and who proclaim with much lamentation that the said world is given over to materialism, the open-eyed observer of our era must decide that all those important institutions of society which depend for their well-being on spiritual strength and knowledge and loving sympathy, are now far in advance of the best olden times. Any one who will compare the idea of marriage, for instance, as developed in Plato's *Republic*, with the idea of marriage as developed in Tennyson's *Princess*, will satisfy himself on this point. The age which proceeded on Plato's idea must have been at bottom a barbarous age, no matter what products of intellectual culture may have sprung from it. The age, on the other hand, in which Tennyson's idea is so universally diffused that no penny-a-liner in the country newspapers but turns it daily into intolerable verse, must be a hopeful age, no matter what vices flaunt in its avenues. Indeed, the cries of theologians in favor of idealism are based upon a mistaken notion, and are full of a harm which it will be the province of our nature-metaphors in some measure to counteract. For idealism, as a sole theory of life, is no better than materialism, and each is bad if dissociated from the other. Why shall men sunder the spirit of man from nature, which God hath joined together? The soul and the body work, in harmony well, in enmity ill. The metaphoric "flesh" of Scripture, which is to be mortified, has not stronger reference to the body than to the soul; for as many of the sins comprehended under that term are spiritual as are physical, and are so enumerated in the Bible.

This harmonious union of soul and body, of spirit and nature, of essence and form, is promoted by the nature-metaphor, which reveals with wonderful force how these two, united from of old, still have new points of sweet and thrilling contact, and still adorn and complement each other. Spirit needs form, and finds it in nature, which is formal; nature needs life, and finds it in spirit, which is life-giving. Never be these two sundered! Forever may the nature-metaphor stand a mild priest, and marry them, and marry them, and marry them again, and loose them to the free air as mated doves that nestle and build and bring forth mildnesses and meeknesses and Christ-loves in men's hearts!

PAUL H. HAYNE'S POETRY *

AT A TIME when the war of secession had left the South in a condition which appeared to render an exclusively literary life a hopeless impossibility, Mr. Hayne immured himself in the woods of Georgia, and gave himself wholly to his pen. Perhaps this was the most convincing method he could have adopted of testifying by acts to his poetic *nascitur*, for it was striking an audacious challenge-blow on the very shield of Fate, and probably none but a poet would have dared it. Doubtless, the struggle which succeeded was passionate, fierce, often bitter, sometimes despairing; one finds traces of all this along the music of these verses. It is pleasant now to open *Legends and Lyrics* with the knowledge that the darkest of his conflict is over, and that in the growing light of appreciation his by-past shadow will show only like a dark calyx through which the poet's rose of fame is bursting.

We wish to ease our mind in the beginning of the only material quarrel we have to pick with Mr. Hayne; and, for the double purpose of setting forth our *casus belli,* and of showing the reader what manner of work Mr. Hayne can do in the most difficult of poetic forms, we quote the sonnet addressed

TO WILLIAM MORRIS

In some fair realm unbound of time or space,
Where souls of all dead May-times, with their play
Of blissful winds, soft showers and bird-notes gay,
Make mystic music in the flower-bright place,
Yea, there, O poets! radiant face to face,
Keen heart to heart, beneath the enchanted day
Ye met, each hearkening to the other's lay
With rapt, sweet eyes, and thoughts of Old-World grace.

* [First published in the *Southern Magazine,* XVI, 40-48 (Jan., 1875); reprinted, with minor changes, in *Music and Poetry* (New York, 1898), pp. 197-211. The text adopted is that of the *Southern Magazine,* with several obvious typographical errors corrected and occasional alterations in punctuation and spelling to conform with Lanier's usual practice. Beginning in the spring of 1872 with the intention of reviewing Hayne's recently published volume, *Legends and Lyrics,* Lanier continued to work on his article for nearly three years, finally expanding it into a critique of Hayne's poetry as a whole (see letters to Hayne, Mar. 2, 1872; May 23, 1874). No MS has been found.—ED.]

"Son," saith the elder bard, "when thou wert born,
So yearned toward thine my spirit's fervency,
Flamelike its warmth on thy deep soul was shed;
Hence the ripe blood of England's lustier morn
Of song burns through thee; hence alone on thee
Fall the rich bays which bloomed round Chaucer's head!"

This sonnet was written on reading the *L'Envoy* in the third volume of Morris's *Earthly Paradise*. Now—though Mr. Hayne is by no means the only person who has likened William Morris to Geoffrey Chaucer—the enthusiastic belief that the spirit of the older poet has come to shine again in the later one, has never been more tenderly and reverently embodied than in this lovely sonnet; but, protesting that we owe some keen delights to Mr. Morris, we totally dissent from the opinion that there is at bottom any such resemblance betwixt him and Chaucer as to entitle him to any sonship or heirship of the latter. Moreover, we believe that this theory involves far more than a mere critical estimate of the likeness or unlikeness of two poets; nay, we are sure that Mr. Hayne and all modern poets would do well to drink much of Chaucer and little of Morris. For—to indicate briefly some points of contrast—how does the spire of hope spring and upbound into the infinite in Chaucer; while, on the other hand, how blank, world-bound, and wearying is the stone *façade* of hopelessness which rears itself uncompromisingly behind the gayest pictures of William Morris! Chaucer is eager, expectant. To-day is *so* beautiful, perhaps to-morrow will be more beautiful: life is young, who knows?—he seems to cry, with splendid immeasurable confidence in the reserved powers of nature and of man. But Morris does not hope: there is, there will be, nothing new under the sun. To-morrow? that may not come; if it does it will be merely to-day revamped; therefore let us amuse ourselves with the daintiest that art and culture can give: this is his essential utterance.

Again, how openly joyful is Chaucer; how secretly melancholy is Morris! Both, it is true, are full of sunshine; but Chaucer's is spring-sunshine, Morris's is autumn. Chaucer's falls upon bold mountain sides where are rocks, lithe grasses, and trees with big lusty boughs and juicy leaves; where the wild motions of nature, from spring-winds to leaping fawns, are artlessly free and unspeakably blissful; and yet where all other forms, whether of monstrous, terrible or wicked, are truly revealed. Morris's, on the other hand, is a late, pleasant, golden-tinted light (with just the faintest hint of a coming chill of twilight in it), falling upon an exquisitely wrought marble which lies half-buried in the sand, and which, Greek as it is, dainty as it is, marvellous as it is, is nevertheless a fragment of a ruin. Chaucer rejoices as only those can who know the bound of good red blood through unobstructed veins, and the thrilling tingle of nerve and sinew at amity; and who can transport this healthy animalism into their unburdened minds, and spiritualize it so that the mere drawing of breath is at once a keen delight and an inwardly-felt practical act of praise to the God of a strong and beautiful world. Morris too has his sensuous element, but it is utterly unlike Chaucer's; it is *dilettante,* it is amateur sensualism; it is not strong, though sometimes excessive, and it is nervously afraid of that satiety which is at once its chief temptation and its most awful doom.

Again, Chaucer lives: Morris dreams. Chaucer, for all the old-world tales he tells, yet tells them with the mouths and manners of his living time, and so gives us a picture of it like life itself. Morris stands between his people and his readers, interpreting his characters, who all advance to the same spot on the stage, communicate *per* him in the same language, the same dialect, the same tone, then glide away with the same dreamy mechanism. The *Canterbury Tales* is simply a drama with somewhat more of stage direction than is common; but the *Earthly Paradise* is a reverie, which would hate nothing so much as to be broken by any collision with that rude actual life which Chaucer portrays.

And finally—for the limits of this paper forbid more than the merest indication of a few of the many points of contrast between these two—note the faith that shines in Chaucer and the doubt that darkens in Morris. Has there been any man since St. John so lovable as " the Persoune "? or any sermon since that on the Mount so keenly analytical, so pathetic, so deep, so pitiful, so charitable, so brotherly, so pure, so manly, so faithful, so hopeful, so sprightly, so terrible, so childlike, so winning, so utterly loving, as *The Persoune's Tale?* But where (it is enough to ask the question in such a connection) in all that William Morris has written may one find, not indeed anything like the

Persoune and his tale, for that would be too much to ask—there is no man since Shakspere who has been at all capable of *that*—but anything even indicating the conception of the possibility of such a being as the Persoune? To this height, to this depth, neither William Morris nor any other man has reached since Dan Chaucer wrote. Let us Shakspere-worshippers not forget that Chaucer lived two centuries earlier than Shakspere, and had to deal with a crude poetic language which Shakspere found a magnificent song-instrument, all in tune and ready to his hand. Let us not forget that Shakspere is first poet and Chaucer second poet, and that these two repose alone, apart, far, far above any spot where later climbers have sunk to rest. And this adjuration is here made with a particular and unequivocal solemnity, because of the conviction that we expressed in the outset of this subject, that the estimate of these two poets which would have them like enough to be father and son, involves deeper matter than mere criticism. For if it be true that William Morris is Chaucer in modern guise; if it be true that by virtue of this nineteenth-century dress, Chaucer, the glowing, actual man and lover and poet and priest and man's brother, is changed into Morris, the aimless sunset-dreamer of old beautiful dreams; if Chaucer's hope is in five hundred years darkened to Morris's thin-veiled despair, Chaucer's joy to Morris's melancholy, Chaucer's faith to Morris's blank, Chaucer's religion to Morris's love-vagueness; if, we say, it be possible that five centuries have wrought Chaucer, that is life, into Morris, that is a dream-of-the-past: then, in God's name, with all reverence, what will five more centuries do to us? A true Hindu life-weariness (to use one of Novalis' marvellous phrases) is really the atmosphere which produces the exquisite haze of Morris's pictures. Can any poet—and we respectfully beg Mr. Hayne to think upon this view of the matter, being emboldened to do so by our regard for his devotion to letters and for his achievements in that behalf—can any poet, we say, shoot his soul's arrow to its best height, when at once bow and string and muscle and nerve are slackened in this vaporous and relaxing air, that comes up out of the old dreams of fates that were false and of passions that were not pure?

In convincing testimony that this question must be answered in the negative, any careful reader of *Legends and Lyrics* will observe that it is precisely when Mr. Hayne escapes out of this influence that he is at his best. Compare for example Mr. Hayne's treatment of the *Wife of Brittany* with the unnamed sonnet on page 55, which we shall presently quote. The *Wife of Brittany* is a legend founded upon the plot of the *Frankeleine's Tale* of Chaucer. Now in Chaucer's time this was a practical poem; many men had not really settled in their minds whether it was right to break even a criminal oath, made in folly. But the plot is only conceivable as a thing of the past, it belongs to the curiosities of history; and although Mr. Hayne has told the story with a thousand tender imaginings, with many charming graces of versification, with rare strokes of pathos, and with a final flow of lucid and silvery melody, yet the poem as a whole never reaches the artistic height attained by the sonnet to the mocking-bird. In the *Wife of Brittany* and in all similar artistic ventures Mr. Hayne will write under the disadvantage of feeling at the bottom of his heart that the passion of the poem is amateur passion, the terror of it amateur terror, and the whole business little more than a dainty titillation of the unreal. But in the sonnet how different! Here the yellow-jessamine, the bird, the vine-clumps, the odor, the bird-song, all are real; they doubtless exist in their actual, lovely entities around Mr. Hayne's home in the forest, and they have taken hold upon him so fairly that he has turned them into a poem meriting his own description of the mocking bird's song:

A star of music in a fiery cloud.

Having thus spoken in the genuine hope of suggesting to Mr. Hayne's mind a train of thought which might be serviceable to his genius, we proceed to remark that in *Legends and Lyrics* we find no polemical discussion, no "science," no "progress," no "Comtism," * no rugged-termed philosophies, no devotionalism, no religiosity of any sort. Mindful only of grand phenomena which no one doubts—of fear, hope, love, patriotism, heaven, wife, child, mother, clouds, sunlight, flowers, water—these poems tinkle along like Coleridge's

* [Lanier at first intended for his review to emphasize the freedom of Hayne's poetry from the evil spirit and influence of Trade (see Introduction, p. lii). This statement, however, is the closest actual approach to the topic.—ED.]

——hidden brook
In the leafy month of June,
That to the sleeping woods all night
Singeth a gentle tune.*

This last word indeed hints at what is one of the distinctive characteristics of all Mr. Hayne's poetry. It is essentially, thoroughly, and charmingly tuneful. In a time when popular poetry is either smug and pretty, or philosophically obscure and rhythmically rugged, this quality becomes almost unique. There is indeed nearly the same difference between poetry and culture-poetry that exists between music and counterpoint-music. Culture-poetry, like counterpoint-music, is scarcely ever *satisfactory* to the ear; it is not captivating with that indescribable music which can come out of the rudest heart, but which cannot come out of the most cultivated head. This feature alone would suffice to separate the book before us from the great mass of utterances which polished people who are not poets are daily pouring upon the air.

We should like to illustrate Mr. Hayne's faculty by quoting entire his *Fire Pictures*, a poem which in point of variety and delicacy of fancy is quite the best of this collection, and in point of pure music should be placed beside Edgar Poe's *Bells*. Of course, to one who has warmed his winters by nothing more glorious than coal; to one who has never sate in dreamful mood and watched the progress of a great hickory fire from the fitful fuliginous beginning thereof, through the white brilliance of its prime and the red glory of its decline, unto the ashen-gray death of the same, this poem is unintelligible; but to one who has, its fancies and its music will come home with a thousand hearty influences. We regret that it is too long to quote here. It is a poem to be read aloud; a true *recitativo*. The energy of its movements, the melody of its metres, the changes of its rhythm, the variety of its fancies, the artistic advance to its climax, particularly the management of its close, where at one and the same time, by the devices of onomatopeia and of rhythmical imitation, are doubly interpreted the sob of a man and the flicker of a flame so perfectly that sob, flicker, word, rhythm, each appears to represent the other, and to be used

* ["The Ancient Mariner."—Ed.]

convertibly with the other in such will-o'-wisp transfigurations as quite vanish in mere description; all these elements require for full enjoyment that the actual music of the poem should fall upon the ear.

Some of the changes of rhythm above referred to merit especial mention, and start some considerations which we regret the limits of this paper will not allow us to pursue. Suffice it here to remark that whenever an English-speaking person grows unusually solemn or intense he instinctively resorts to the iambic rhythm for expression. Note, for instance, how in number II at the close the change from the trochees to the two *iambi* " aspire! aspire! " at once represents the intensity of the situation and the broken fitfulness of the struggling flame; or, again, in that fine scene of number IV, where the *iambi* " dark-red like blood " give the reader a sudden wrench from the trochaic flow as if they plucked him by the sleeve to compel him to stop a second on the thought; or, again, most notable of all, in number VI, where from the words " a stir, a murmur deep " to the close of the picture the *iambi* present the agony and the glory of the martyr. With these three exceptions the entire poem is in trochees, and is an admirable example of the music which can be made with those elements. Return to number IX of this poem, from

> Like a rivulet rippling deep,
> Through the meadow-lands of sleep,

to its close is, in point of pure trochaic music, of rare excellence. We desire, however, to call Mr. Hayne's attention to a fault of tone which occurs in this picture, and in another of the poems of this book. Where the lines run:

> Though the lotos swings its stem
> With a lulling stir of *leaves,*
> Though the lady-lily *laves*
> Coy feet in the crystal *waves,*
> And a silvery undertune
> From some mystic wind-song *grieves,*

" leaves " of course is intended to rhyme with " grieves," four lines down, and " laves " with " waves; " but " laves " is the next rhyme-tone to " leaves," and this proximity renders it obnoxious to two objections. One is, that it leaves the reader for a moment in doubt whether "laves" is really intended to rhyme with "leaves"—a doubt which interferes with the reader's enjoyment as long as it lasts. The other and stronger objection is, that the immediate juxtaposition of the slightly-varying rhyme-tones "leaves" and "laves" gives the ear the same displeasure which the eye suffers from two shades of the same color in a lady's dress—both tones seem faded.

The faults of *Fire Pictures* are faults which we detect in all Mr. Hayne's poetry; and as they are remediable, we call his attention to them with all the more vigor. They are of two classes. First, we observe a frequently-recurring *lapsus* of thought, in which Mr. Hayne falls into trite similes, worn collocations of words and commonplace sentiments. To have these hackneyed couples of words and ideas continually popping in upon us out of Mr. Hayne's beautiful things, is to suffer the chagrin and the anguish of that hapless man who in the hot summer rushes afar from toil and trouble across the ocean into a distant land, and there in the heavenly weather, while idly wandering down some wild and lovely glen, given up to all tender meditations, suddenly, on pushing aside a great frond of fern, comes bump upon the smug familiar faces of Smith, Jones and Brown, whom he had left amid the hot grind of the street, and whose presence immediately transports him back to the sweaty moil of stocks, bacon and dry-goods. Such expressions are: "changing like a wizard-thought," or "like a charmed thought," or "like a Protean thought," and others in *Fire Pictures.* More notable still in this respect is the poem *Renewed.* The first four lines of this poem are so entirely commonplace that they are quite sufficient to throw any reader off the scent and cause him to abandon the piece; yet the very next four are exceedingly beautiful, with all the clear and limpid music of Mr. Hayne's style, and with a bright change in the rhythm which is full of happy effects. Witness:

RENEWED

Welcome, rippling sunshine!
Welcome, joyous air!
Like a demon-shadow
Flies the gaunt Despair!

Heaven through heights of happy calm
Its heart of hearts uncloses,
To win earth's answering love, in balm,
Her blushing thanks, in roses!—&c.

The second fault to which we wish to call Mr. Hayne's attention is diffuseness, principally originating in a lavishness and looseness of adjectives. Whatever may be said of Edgar Poe's theory of the impossibility of a long poem, or that all long poems are merely series of short poems connected by something that is not poetry, it may at least with safety be asserted that in a time when trade has lengthened life by shortening leisure, the ideal of the lyric poem is a brief, sweet, intense, electric flashing of the lyric idea in upon the hurrying intelligence of men, so that the vivid truth may attack even an unwilling retina, and perpetuate itself thereupon even after the hasty eyelid has closed to shut out the sight. Now, either a free or an inexact use of adjectives is a departure from this ideal, not only because it impairs the strength of the articulate idea, but because it so far cumbers the whole poem as, if the fault extends throughout, to render it too long to be readable by many of those whom all true poets desire to reach. Notable instances of Mr. Hayne's dereliction in this regard may be found in his frequent and often inexact employment of the words "cordial," "weird," and "fairy" in these poems. One can easily trace the manner in which this vice escapes the poet's attention. Busied with some central idea, and hurried by the passion of creating, he will not hesitate for a descriptive in some minor phrase, but dashes down the first term that occurs, if it will but answer tolerably, so that presently, from habit, a certain favored few adjectives come to understand, as it were, that this duty is expected of them, and get trained to stand by and help whenever the poet's mind is fatigued or hurried.

Perhaps the nearest approaches to the ideal of lyric poetry in this book are the invocation to the wife with which it commences—as it were, grace before meat—and the poem called *A Summer Mood*, based on a line from Thomas Heywood: "Now, by my faith, a gruesome mood for summer." From the latter we quote a line out of the third verse and the last three verses:

The sunshine mocks the tears it may not dry,

. . . .

The field-birds seem to twit us as they pass,
With their small blisses, piped so clear and loud:
The cricket triumphs o'er us in the grass;
And the lark glancing beam-like up the cloud,

Sings us to scorn with his keen rhapsodies:
Small things and great unconscious tauntings bring
To edge our cares, whilst we, the proud and wise,
Envy the insect's joy, the birdling's wing!

And thus for evermore, till time shall cease,
Man's soul and Nature's—each a separate sphere—
Revolves, the one in discord, one in peace,
—And who shall make the solemn mystery clear?

The stanza of this poem in which " the field-birds twit us as they pass, with their small blisses," is a genuine snatch caught from out the sedges of a Southern field, where we doubt not Mr. Hayne has often strolled or lain, companioned only by the small crooked-flighted sparrow, whose whistle, so keen that it amounts to a hiss, seems to have suggested the very sibillations of the s's so frequently occurring.

In *In Utroque Fidelis* is beautifully blended a tone of tranquil description with that of a passionate love-song. A lover about to be off to the wars has stolen at midnight to snatch a farewell glance at the home of his beloved. The following four verses show something of the art of the poem:

I waft a sigh from this fond soul to thine,
A little sigh, yet honey-laden, dear,
With fairy freightage of such hopes divine
As fain would flutter gently at thine ear,
        And entering find their way
Down to the heart so veiled from me by day.

In dreams, in dreams, perchance thou are not coy;
And one keen hope more bold than all the rest
May touch thy spirit with a tremulous joy,
And stir an answering softness in thy breast.
        O sleep, O blest eclipse!
What murmured word is faltering at her lips?

. . . .

Still, breathless still! No voice in earth or air:
I only know my delicate darling lies,
A twilight lustre glimmering in her hair,
And dews of peace within her languid eyes:
Yea, only know that I
Am called from love and dreams perhaps to die,

Die when the heavens are thick with scarlet rain,
And every time-throb's fated: even there
Her face would shine through mists of mortal pain,
And sweeten death like some incarnate prayer.
Hark! 'Tis the trumpet's swell!
O love, O dreams, farewell, farewell, farewell!

In the particular of tranquil description, however, some good work occurs in the ode to *Sleep.* Witness the following extracts, which form the beginning and the end of the poem:

Beyond the sunset and the amber sea,
To the lone depths of ether, cold and bare,
Thy influence, soul of all tranquillity,
Hallows the earth and awes the reverent air.

. . . .

Then woo me here amid these flowery charms;
Breathe on my eyelids, press thine odorous lips
Close to mine own, enfold me in thine arms,
And cloud my spirit with thy sweet eclipse;
And while from waning depth to depth I fall,
Down-lapsing to the utmost depths of all,
Till wan forgetfulness, obscurely stealing,
Creeps like an incantation on the soul,—
And o'er the slow ebb of my conscious life
Dies the thin flush of the last conscious feeling,—
And, like abortive thunder, the dull roll
Of sullen passions ebbs far, far away,—
O Angel! loose the chords which cling to strife,
Sever the gossamer bondage of my breath,
And let me pass, gently as winds in May,
From the dim realm which owns thy shadowy sway,
To thy diviner sleep, O sacred Death!

We would like to praise *Glaucus* for the fine spirit-of-green-leaves, which makes the poem so dainty and shady and cool. We would like, too, to discuss with Mr. Hayne whether the climacteric point in the tale of the *Wife of Brittany,*—which is the moment when the Wife meets Aurelian for the purpose of performing her dreadful promise—does not need a more dramatic accentuation to relieve it from the danger of anti-climax to which this wonderfully smooth narrative is liable at that point. We could wish further to commend the admirably harmonized tone of *Prexaspes,* where the words seem at once hot, wan, cruel, and wicked; and the elegant rendering of *Aëthra,* which is quite the most artistically told tale in the book; and the reverent piety which shines in the final offering to the poet's mother; and many other things. But this paper has already reached its limit. We may be permitted in closing it to observe that already since the publication of *Legends and Lyrics,* other poems of Mr. Hayne's have appeared, as for example the two *Forest Pictures* in the *Atlantic Monthly,* which exhibit a growing strength and more vigorous realism in his poetic faculty; and we venture to express the hope that his pen may yet embody the pretty fancy of his poem called

THE NEST

At the poet's life-core lying,
  Is a sheltered and sacred nest,
Where, as yet unfledged for flying,
  His callow fancies rest—

Fancies and thoughts and feelings
  Which the mother Psyche breeds,
And passions whose dim revealings
  But torture their hungry needs.

Yet there cometh a summer splendor
  When the golden brood wax strong,
And, with voices grand or tender,
  They rise to the heaven of song.

THE NEW SOUTH *

IT WOULD seem that facts may now be arrayed which leave no doubt that upon the general cycle of American advance the South has described such an epicycle of individual growth that no profitable discussion of that region is possible at present which does not clearly define at the outset whether it is to be a discussion of the old South or the new South. Although the movement here called by the latter name is originally neither political, social, moral, nor æsthetic, yet the term in the present instance connotes all these with surprising completeness. The New South means small farming.

What Southern small farming really signifies, and how it has come to involve and determine the whole compass of civilization in that part of the republic, this paper proposes to show, (1) by briefly pointing out its true relation, in its last or (what one may call, its) poetic outcome, to the " large farming " now so imminent in the North-west; (2) by presenting some statistics of the remarkable increase in the number of Southern small farms from 1860 to 1870, together with some details of the actual cultures and special conditions thereof; and (3) by contrasting with it a picture of large farming in England three hundred years ago. Indeed, one has only to recall how the connection between marriage and the price of corn is but a crude and partial statement of the intimate relation between politics, social

* [First published in *Scribner's Monthly,* XX, 840-51 (Oct., 1880); reprinted, with minor changes, in *Retrospects and Prospects* (New York, 1899), pp. 104-135. The *Scribner's Monthly* article is the basis of the present text, with a few mechanical irregularities corrected; a corrected galley, apparently set up for this article but struck out in the printing, is here given in a footnote. Three fragmentary MSS have been preserved (Charles D. Lanier Collection, Johns Hopkins University): MSS A and B were each originally of more than 60 note-paper pages; the single page of MS C suggests that it is from an abridged version of B. A is confined to a comparison of small farming in the South with large farming in the Northwest, B with large farming in England 300 years earlier; B refers to " the last paper " comparing Southern with Northwestern farming, and an explicit statement in a letter by Lanier (Jan. 25, 1880) bears out this implication that he originally had not one comprehensive article but two or more consecutive pieces. Both A and B supply more details and name more individuals, towns, and periodicals than the corresponding passages in the *Scribner's Monthly* text, and they contain still further matter (some of it rather irrelevant) which the *Scribner's Monthly* text omits. Preserved with the MSS are a considerable number of clippings on the South besides those Lanier incorporated in his article.—ED.]

life, morality, art, on the one hand, and the bread-giver earth on the other; one has only to remember that, particularly here in America, whatever crop we hope to reap in the future,—whether it be a crop of poems, of paintings, of symphonies, of constitutional safeguards, of virtuous behaviors, of religious exaltations,—we have got to bring it out of the ground with palpable plows and with plain farmer's forethought: in order to see that a vital revolution in the farming economy of the South, if it is actually occurring, is necessarily carrying with it all future Southern politics and Southern social relations and Southern art, and that, therefore, such an agricultural change is the one substantial fact upon which any really new South can be predicated.

Approached from this direction, the quiet rise of the small farmer in the Southern States during the last twenty years becomes the notable circumstance of the period, in comparison with which noisier events signify nothing.

I

As just now hinted, small farming in the South becomes clear in its remoter bearings when seen over against the precisely opposite tendency toward large farming in the West. Doubtless recent reports of this tendency have been sometimes exaggerated. In reading them, one has been obliged to remember that small minds love to bring large news, and, failing a load, will make one. But certainly enough appears, if only in the single apparently well-authenticated item of the tempting profits realized by some of the great north-western planters, to authorize the inference that the tendency to cultivate wheat on enormous farms, where the economies possible only to corporation-management can secure the greatest yield with the least expense, is a growing one.

And, this being so, the most rapid glance along the peculiar details of the north-western large farm opens before us a path of thought which quickly passes beyond wheat-raising, and leads among all those other means of life which appertain to this complex creature who cannot live by bread alone. For instance, classify, as a social and moral factor, a farm like the Grandin place, near Fargo, where 4,855 acres are sown in wheat; where five hands do all the work during the six winter months, while as many as two hundred and fifty must be employed in midsummer; where the day's work is nearly thirteen hours; where, out of the numerous structures for farm purposes, but two have any direct relation to man—one a residence for the superintendent and foreman, the other a boarding-house for the hands; where no women, children, nor poultry are to be seen; where the economies are such as are wholly out of the power of the small wheat-raisers, insomuch that even the railways can give special rates for grain coming in such convenient large quantities; where the steam machine, the telephone and the telegraph are brought to the last degree of skilful service; where, finally, the net profits for the current year are $52,239.[1]

It appears plainly enough from these details that, looked upon from the midst of all those associations which cluster about the idea of the farm, large farming is not farming at all. It is mining for wheat.

Or a slight change in the point of view presents it as a manufacturing business, in which clods are fed to the mill, and grain appears in car-loads at Chicago. And perhaps the most exact relations of this large farming to society in general are to be drawn by considering such farmers as corporations, their laborers as mill-operatives for six months in each year and tramps for the other six, their farms as mills where nature mainly turns the wheel, their investment as beyond the reach of strikes or fires, foreign distress their friend, and the world's hunger their steady customer.

It appears further that, while such agricultural communities are so merely in name and are manufacturing communities in fact, they are manufacturing communities only as to the sterner features of that guild,—the order, the machine, the minimum of expense, the maximum of product,—and not as to those pleasanter features, the school-house, the church, the little working-men's library, the sewing-class, the cookery-class, the line of promotion, the rise of the bright boy and the steady workman—all the gentler matters which will spring up, out of the dust-heaps, about any spot where men have the rudest abiding-place. On the large farm is no abiding-place; the laborer must move on; life cannot stand still, to settle and clarify.

[1] According to an anonymous writer in *The Atlantic Monthly,* January, 1880.

It would not seem necessary to disclaim any design to inveigh against the owners of these great factory-farms, if indignation had not been already expressed in such a way as to oblige one to declare that no obligations can be cited, as between them and their laborers, which would not equally apply to every manufacturer. If it is wrong to discharge all but ten laborers when only ten are needed, then the mill-owners of Massachusetts must be held bound to run day and night when the market is over-stocked *because* they ran so when it was booming; and if it is criminal to pay the large-farm hands no more than will hardly support them for thirteen hours' work, every mill-company in the world which pays market rates for work is *particeps*. But, with the coast thus cleared of personality; with the large farm thus classed as a manufacturing company in all its important incidents; and recognizing in the fullest manner that, if wheat can be made most cheaply in this way, it must be so made: a very brief train of thought brings us upon a situation, as between the small farmer on the one hand and the corporation on the other, which reveals them as embodying two tendencies in the republic at this moment whose relations it is the business of statesmanship and of citizenship to understand with the utmost clearness, since we are bound to foster both of them.

For, if we stop our ears to the noisy child's-play of current politics, and remember (1) that in all ages and countries two spirits, or motives, or tendencies exist which are essentially opposed to each other, but both of which are necessary to the state; (2) that the problem of any given period or society is to recognize the special forms in which these two tendencies are then and there embodying themselves, and to keep them in such relations that neither shall crush, while each shall healthily check, the other; (3) that these tendencies may be called the spirit of control and the spirit of independence, and that they are so intimately connected with the two undeniable facts which lie at the bottom of moral behavior—namely, the facts of influence from without, on the one hand, and free will on the other—that the questions of morals and of politics coalesce at their roots; (4) that these two tendencies are now most tangibly embodied among us in the corporation and the small farmer—the corporation representing the spirit of control, and the small farmer representing, in many curious ways, the spirit of independence; (5) that our republic vitally needs the corporation for the mighty works which only the corporation can do, while it as vitally needs the small farmer for the pure substance of individual and self-reliant manhood which he digs out of the ground, and which, the experience of all peoples would seem to show, must primarily come that way and no other: we are bound to conclude that the practical affair in the United States at the present juncture is to discover how we may cherish at once the corporation and the small farmer into the highest state of competitive activity, less by constitution-straining laws which forbid the corporation to do this and that, or which coddle the small farmer with sop and privilege, than by affording free scope for both to adjust themselves, and by persistently holding sound moral principles to guide the adjustment.

When, therefore, we behold the large farm as a defection from the farm-party in general—which represents individuality in the state—over to the corporation-party, whose existence is necessarily based upon such relations to employees as impair their individuality, we regard with all the more interest the rise of the small farmer, now occurring in an opposite direction so opportunely as to seem as if nature herself were balancing the North-west [1] with the South-east.

II

The phrase " small farming," used of the South, crops out in directions curious enough to one unacquainted with the special economies and relations of existence in that part of our country. While large farming in the South means exclusive cotton-growing,—as it means in the West exclusive wheat-growing or exclusive corn-growing—small farming means *diversified farm-products*; and a special result of the Southern conditions of agriculture has brought about a still more special sense of the word, so that in Georgia, for example, the term " small farmer " brings up to every native mind the idea of a farmer who, besides his cotton crop, raises corn enough to " do " him. But again,

[1] Always with the saving clause: if the North-west is really tending, on the whole, toward large farming; which certainly seems true, yet is not sufficiently clear to be argued upon, save with prudent reservations.

the incidents hinging upon this apparently simple matter of making corn enough to do him are so numerous as, in turn, to render *them* the distinctive feature of small farming. Small farming means, in short, meat and bread for which there are no notes in bank; pigs fed with home-made corn, and growing of themselves while the corn and cotton were being tended; yarn spun, stockings knit, butter made and sold (instead of bought); eggs, chickens, peaches, water-melons, the four extra sheep and a little wool, two calves and a beef,—all to sell every year, besides a colt who is now suddenly become, all of himself, a good, serviceable horse; the four oxen, who are as good as gifts made by the grass; and a hundred other items, all representing income from a hundred sources to the small farmer, which equally represent outgo to the large farmer,—items, too, scarcely appearing at all on the expense side of the strictest account-book, because they are either products of odd moments which, if not so applied, would not have been at all applied, or products of natural animal growth, and grass at nothing a ton. All these ideas are inseparably connected with that of the small farmer in the South.

The extent of this diversity of product possible upon a single small farm in Georgia, for instance, and the certain process by which we find these diversified products presently creating demands for the village library, the neighborhood farmers'-club, the amateur Thespian society, the improvement of the public schools, the village orchestra, all manner of betterments and gentilities and openings out into the universe: show significantly, and even picturesquely, in a mass of clippings which I began to make a couple of years ago, from a number of country papers in Georgia, upon the idea that these unconsidered trifles of mere farmers' neighborhood news, with no politics behind them and no argumentative coloring in front of them, would form the best possible picture of actual small-farm life in the South—that is, of the New South.

To read these simple and homely scraps is indeed much like a drive among the farms themselves with the ideal automaton guide, who confines himself to telling you that this field is sugar-cane, that one yonder is cotton, the other is rice, and so on, without troubling you for responsive exclamations or other burdensome commentary.

Rambling among these cuttings, one sees growing side by side, possibly upon a single small farm, corn, wheat, rice, sugar-cane, cotton, peaches, plums, apples, pears, figs, water-melons, cantaloupes, musk-melons, cherries, strawberries, raspberries, blackberries, Catawba grapes, Isabellas, Scuppernongs, peas, snap-beans, butter-beans, okra, squash, beets, oyster-plant, mustard, cress, cabbage, turnips, tomatoes, cauliflower, asparagus, potatoes, onions; one does not fail, too, to catch a glimpse of pigs sauntering about, chickens singing, colts flinging their heels at you and off down the pasture, calves likewise, cows caring not for these things, sheep on the rising ground, geese and turkeys *passim*, perhaps the green-gray moss—surely designed by nature to pack vegetables in and send them " North," —a very bed of dew for many days after cutting, and the roses and morning-glories everywhere for a benison.

The first clipping which comes to hand is a cunning commentary, expressed in facts, upon the diversified-culture aspect of small farming. Perhaps every one who has heard the results of premium awards read out at county fairs will have noticed how often a single name will recur in the same list as premium taker: For the best corn—John Smith; for the best sample of oats—John Smith; for the best lot of pigs—John Smith; for the finest colt—John Smith; and so on. The relation of cause and effect, as between small farming and such success, is direct. Small farming makes so many edges cut at once that many things are obliged to result. And so one is not surprised to see, in this item concerning the fair of the Marshallville Agricultural Society (Marshallville is in what is known as south-western Georgia, a cotton-growing portion of the State), the name of Mr. J. M. coming up in many varied connections; nor is one surprised to find, upon inquiry, that the same gentleman is a small farmer, who commenced work after the war with his own hands, not a dollar in his pocket, and now owns his plantation, has it well stocked, no mortgage or debt of any kind on it, and a little money to lend.

The attendance was very large, [says the clipping]. . . . Number of . . . exhibitors much larger than last year. . . .

PREMIUMS AWARDED

For the largest and best display of field crops and garden products by single planter—J. M.

For the largest and best display of stock by a single planter—J. M.

For the best display of old home-raised side meat and hams, old home-raised corn and fodder, home-raised flour, corn meal, syrup, and one quart ley hominy made of old corn—J. M.

Special mention is made of the fact that M. J. M. had on exhibition one hundred different articles.

And then we are given the " honorable mention " of " field-crops," which without taking up space with names of successful exhibitors may be cited here, so far as the crops are concerned, as partly indicating the diversified products customary in one narrow neighborhood of small farmers. Thus, a premium (" honorable mention ") was given to the

best corn, . . . best stalk of cotton, . . . best upland rice, . . . best cleaned wheat, . . . best cleaned oats, . . . best cleaned barley, . . . best cleaned rye, . . . best ribbon sugar-cane, . . . best golden-rod cane, . . . best chufas, . . . best ground peas (peanuts), . . . best field-peas.

And so, looking along through this batch of items,—which surely never dreamed of finding themselves together,—one gathers a great number of circumstances illustrating the small farm of Georgia from various points of view. One hears, for instance, how the people of Thomas County (southern Georgia) are now busy gathering, packing and forwarding the sand pear to Boston and New York (the sand pear, or Le Conte pear, is a luscious variety which has recently been pushed with great success among the sandy lands of lower Georgia; the entire stock is said to have come from one tree on the Le Conte plantation in Liberty County—the same farm which sent out a further notable product in the persons of the two illustrious professors John and Joseph Le Conte, now of the University of California); how last week thirty bushels of pears were obtained from the old tree mentioned in the preceding clause; how southern Georgia is making sugar-cane a leading crop; how Mr. Anthony (in Bibb County, middle Georgia) has twenty-eight varieties of grapes growing on a few acres, and has just introduced a new variety; how Bartow County (above Atlanta) shipped 225,000 pounds of dried apples and peaches last season; how over 15,000 pounds of wool have been received during the last four days at one warehouse in Albany (south-west Georgia), while in Quitman (same portion) our streets are constantly thronged with carts laden with wool from Colquitt and Berrien and Lowndes counties—this wool being, it should be added, the product of small farmers who " raise " many other things; how the common sheep is an extremely profitable beast, it being but a sorry specimen which will not furnish one lamb and two and a half pounds of wool per annum, which lamb will sell for two dollars while the wool will bring nearly another dollar, and all for no tendance except a little rice-straw and cotton-seed during the yeaning season, together with careful folding at night; how—and here the connection with small farming is only apparently remote—a library society is being organized in Milledgeville, while in another town the *Advertiser* is making a vigorous call for a library, and in a third the library has recently received many additions of books, and in a fourth an amateur Thespian corps has just been formed, consisting of five ladies and fourteen gentlemen, whose first performance is to be early in July; how there are curious correlations between sheep, whiskey, public schools and dogs—the State school commissioner vigorously advocating the Moffett bell-punch system of tax on liquor and a tax on dogs (of which, I find from another slip, there are 99,414 in the State, destroying annually 28,625 of the small farmers' sheep), for the purpose of increasing the school fund to a million dollars annually; how, at the Atlanta University for colored people, which is endowed by the State, the progress of the pupils, the clearness of their recitations, their excellent behavior, and the remarkable neatness of their schoolrooms altogether convince " your committee that the colored race . . . are capable of receiving the education usually given at such institutions "; how last Thursday a neighborhood club of small farmers, on Walnut Creek (near Macon), celebrated the fifth anniversary of the club by meeting under the trees, with their wives and children, recounting in turn how many acres each had in cotton, how many in corn, how many in potatoes, how many in peas, etc., and discussing these matters and a barbecue, a sub-committee bringing in a joking report with shrewd hits at the behindhand members,—as that we found on Mr. W.'s farm the best gourd-crop, and on Mr. R.'s some acres of very remarkable "bumble-bee cotton," the peculiarity of which cotton is that the bee can sit upon the ground and "exultantly sip from the tallest cotton-bloom on the plant"; how at a somewhat similar gathering the yeomen brought out the great Jones County soup pot, the same being an eighty-gallon syrup kettle, in which the soup began to boil on the night before and was served next day, marvellous rich and toothsome, to the company; how the single item of water-melons has brought nearly $100,000 into Richmond County this season, and how Mr. J., of Baker County—in quite another part of the State,—has just raised ten water-melons weighing together five hundred and fifty pounds; how Mr. R., of Schley County (in cotton-raising south-western Georgia), has made five hundred and fifty-six bushels of oats on a five-acre patch; how the writer has just seen a six-acre crop of upland rice which will yield thirty bushels to the acre; how a party of two hundred and fifty colored excursionists came up to town yesterday, and the colored brass band played about the streets; or, in another slip a column long, how Governor Colquitt reviews seven colored companies of Georgia soldiery in full uniform, who afterward contest in a prize drill, and at night are entertained with parties, balls and the like, by the Union Lincoln Guards, of Savannah, and the Lincoln Guards, of Macon; how (this is headed *Agriculture Advancing*) the last few years has witnessed a very decided improvement in Georgia farming: moon-planting and other vulgar superstitions are exploding, the intelligent farmer is deriving more assistance from the philosopher, the naturalist and the chemist, and he who is succeeding best is he who has plenty of horses, cattle, sheep, hogs and poultry of his own raising, together with good-sized barns and meat-houses filled from his own fields instead of from the West,—in short, the small farmer.

Fortunately, we have means for reducing to very definite figures the growth of small farming in the South * since the war, and thus of measuring the substance of the New South. A row of columns in the eighth and ninth census reports of the United States is devoted to enumerations of the number of farms in each State and county of given sizes; and a proper comparison

* [MS A states (p. 66) that "the day of big farms, liens on crops and stock for bacon and corn and mules and wheat is fast passing away."—ED.]

thereof yields us facts of great significance to the present inquiry. For example, taking the State of Georgia: we find that, while in 1860 it had but 906 farms of under ten acres, in 1870 it had 3,527 such farms; in 1860, but 2,803 farms of over ten and under twenty acres,—in 1870, 6,942 such farms; in 1860, but 13,644 farms of over twenty and under fifty acres,—in 1870, 21,971 such farms; in 1860, but 14,129 farms of over fifty and under one hundred acres,—in 1870, 18,371 such farms. Making a total of all these subclasses, considered as small farms in general, and subtracting that for 1860 from that for 1870, we reach the instructive fact that, in some five years preceding 1870, the increase in the number of small farms in the State of Georgia was 19,329.

In the State of Mississippi the increase is in some particulars more striking than that in Georgia. By the census report, Mississippi had in 1860 only 563 farms of over three but under ten acres, 2,516 of over ten but under twenty, 10,967 of between twenty and fifty, and 9,204 of between fifty and one hundred; while in 1870 it had 11,003 farms of the first-mentioned size, 8,981 of the second, 26,048 of the third, and 11,967 of the fourth; in short, a total gain of 34,749 small farms between 1860 and 1870.

The political significance of these figures is great. To a large extent—exactly how large I have in vain sought means to estimate—they represent the transition of the negro from his attitude as negro to an attitude as small farmer,—an attitude in which his interests, his hopes, and consequently his politics, become identical with those of all other small farmers, whether white or black.

Nothing seems more sure than that an entirely new direction of cleavage in the structure of Southern polity must come with the wholly different aggregation of particles implied in this development of small farming.

In the identical aims of the small-farmer class, whatever now remains of the color-line must surely disappear out of the Southern political situation. This class, consisting as it already does of black small-farmers and white small-farmers, must necessarily be a body of persons whose privileges, needs and relations are *not* those which exist as between the black man on the one hand and the white man on the other, but those which exist as between the small farmer on the one hand and whatever affects small farming on the other. For here—as cannot be too often said—the relation of politics to agriculture is that of the turnip-top to the turnip.*

* [A surviving proofsheet of "The New South" contains a passage written and corrected by Lanier, but not included in the print version, as follows:

"And in this reflection we find an instructive commentary upon the liability of statesmanship to error from the unconscious habit of looking upon man as primarily a political being, and as only secondarily anything else, instead of regarding all politics as the secondary outgrowth of circumstances which are primarily either physical needs or moral results of such struggles with nature or with man as are involved in the satisfaction of physical needs. One cannot but believe, in the midst of one's sincere admiration of Mr. Gladstone's great aims and honest pursuit of them, that that statesman has allowed undue weight to political over cereal considerations in a recent article of his relating to this country. The utterance now referred to is certainly not one of the chief points of his paper, and is, indeed, merely *obiter*; but, perhaps all the more clearly for this, it reveals the tendency so common among our own statesman and, therefore, surely, all the more pardonable in a foreigner,—and it almost seems as if Englishmen were nowadays, in many particulars, more foreign to us than Frenchmen or Germans or Italians,—to forget that in the case of the South what is at the top politics is at the bottom agriculture. If a city-bred man, after a visit to Jones's great turnip-patch in the country, should return and describe turnips to his tea-table as green leaves which grow in bunches near the ground, he would be no more upon the surface of matters than those who believe that—at least for a long time to come—any movements in the South besides agricultural ones are of permanent account as factors in the future politics of that region. For there politics must sit upon agriculture no otherwise than the turnip-top upon the turnip.

"These are the considerations which do not seem to have had due weight in the utterance of Mr. Gladstone referred to, where he alludes to 'the very curious influences which are shaping the politics of the negroes and the South,' and affirms that those influences are merely 'corollaries to the great slave question.' Surely, no; surely the small farmer began to rise before the slave began to sink; surely the freeing of the slave has added a most valuable accession to the ranks of the small farmer; and it is *because* it has done so, it is as a strengthening of this particular agricultural economy, that free labor is to be regarded a factor in Southern politics. It has just been shown that in such a political readjustment the important considerations will be not the relation of slave or freeman, not the relation of black to white, but the relation of the small farmer—the black small farmer and the white small farmer—to the interests or antagonisms of small farming.

"It seems worth noting in this connection that Mr. Gladstone is reported to have recently proposed to his own countrymen this same small-farming as a remedy for their agricultural distress, recommending that English 'farmers should turn their attention to raising fruits, vegetables, poultry, eggs and butter.' And it is curious to observe, finally, that, through the operation of causes which this paper has now grown too long even to outline, this political [1] attitude of white

[1] "The social relation of white and black in the South is a matter not here touched, and, indeed, at present beyond all definite opinion." [This appended footnote is Lanier's.—Ed.]

This obliteration of the color-line could be reduced to figures if we knew the actual proportion of the new small farms held by negroes. Though, as already remarked, data are here wanting, yet the matter emerges into great distinctness if we select certain counties where the negro population was very large in 1860, and compare the number of small farms in those counties for 1860 with the number for 1870.

This exhibit grows all the more close if we confine it to very small farms, such as the colored people have been able to acquire since the war by lease or purchase, and thus make it indicate—certainly in part—the accession to the number of small farmers from that source.

Consider, for example, the figures which stand opposite the name of Liberty County, Georgia, in Table VII of the census report for 1870, as compared with those for 1860, directing the attention to but two classes of farms—those over three but under ten acres, and those over ten but under twenty. Liberty, it may be remarked, was in 1860 a county producing mainly sea-island cotton and rice, from large farms inhabited or owned by many of the oldest and wealthiest families of the State. In the year 1860, according to the report, it had eighteen farms of over three but under ten acres, and thirty-five of over ten but under twenty. In 1870 we find these figures changed to 616 farms of over three but under ten acres, and 749 farms of over ten but under twenty acres. In Camden County—a county penetrated by the Satilla River through its whole length, and before the war mainly covered with great rice-plantations—the increase is nearly as striking, though the figures are smaller. Here, in 1860, were but three farms of over three and under ten acres, and but five of over ten and under twenty acres; while in 1870 the former class of farms had increased to 189, and the latter to 136. Chatham County—in which Savannah is situated—shows a similarly enormous increase, though here a number of the small farms represent an immigration of white "truck-farmers," raising vegetables for the North-

and black side by side as small farmers against all that threatens small farming must end in the precise result which Mr. Gladstone affirms, from different premises, to be 'very possible'—namely, that 'after a few years we may see most of the laborers, both in the Southern States and in England, actively addicted to the political support of that section of their countrymen who, to the last, had resisted their emancipation.' "—Ed.]

ern market—a business which has largely grown in that neighborhood since the war, with the increased facilities offered by fast and often-running steamers from Savannah to New York.

Considering the case of Liberty County: the 1,365 small farms of 1870 (that is, the total of both sizes of farms above mentioned) against the fifty-three of 1860 may be considered—so far as I know—largely representative of accessions of negroes to the ranks of the small farmer. For, though these colored farmers hire out at times, yet their own little patches of varied products are kept up, and they are—as is, indeed, complained of sadly enough by larger farmers in want of hands—independent of such hiring.

Here one of my slips, cut from a sea-coast paper while this article is being written—in February, 1880—gives a statement of affairs in Liberty County, which, coming ten years later than the 1870 census report last quoted from, is particularly helpful. After stating that a very large area of rice was planted last year, and a still larger area this year—that the price of rice is $1.15 a bushel, and the average yield thirty bushels to the acre, at which figures the farmers plant but little cotton—the writer adds:

> If the farmer of Liberty County could control the negro labor, she would soon become one of the richest counties of South Georgia; but there comes in the trouble. The negroes, most of them, have bought a small tract of land, ten acres or more, and they can make enough rice on it to be perfectly independent of the white man. If he hires one, he has to pay him his price, which is not less than fifty cents per day; but, with all that, the county seems to be thriving.

It does not seem possible to doubt, in the light of these considerations, that there is, in Georgia at least, a strong class of small farmers which powerfully tends to obliterate color from politics, in virtue of its merger of all conflicting elements into the common interest of a common agricultural pursuit.

I find my slips much occupied with a machine which, if promises hold, is to play an important part in the New South. This is the "Clement Attachment," which proposes not only to gin the cotton without breaking the fibre, but with the same motive-power spins it, thus at one process converting seed-cotton into cotton-yarn. The saving in such a process embraces a dozen methods of expense and waste by the old process, and would be no less than enormous.

But it is not only the product which comes out as cotton-yarn that is valuable. The cotton-seed are themselves, in various ways, sources of revenue. One of these ways—and one which has grown greatly in importance of late years—is referred to in the following slip:

> The cotton-seed oil factories in New Orleans are reaping this fall a golden harvest. . . . Every 450-pound bale of cotton, when ginned, yields about half a ton (1,100 pounds) of seed, which are sold to the factories at $15 per ton. Here the oil is expressed and the refuse is sold as oil-cake—chiefly exported to Europe for stock food, and used by the sugar planters as a fertilizer. Before expressing the seed, they are first linted and hulled. The lint extracted is sold to the white-paper factories, and the hulls are used for fuel and as fertilizers.

Of course, it remains to be seen whether all these fine things will be done by the Clement mills. Some of my slips show scepticism, a few, faith. It must be said that the stern experiences of the last fifteen years have inclined the New South to be, in general, doubtful of anything which holds out great promises at first. A cunning indication of such tendencies comes —upon the principle of like master, like man—in one of the cuttings before me (from the Atlanta *Constitution*), which records the practical views of Uncle Remus, a famous colored philosopher of Atlanta, who is a fiction so founded upon fact and so like it as to have passed into true citizenship and authority, along with Bottom and Autolycus. This is all the more worth giving since it is real negro-talk, and not that suppositititious negro-minstrel talk which so often goes for the original. It is as nearly perfect as any dialect can well be; and if one had only some system of notation by which to convey the *tunes* of the speaking voice in which Brer[1] Remus and Brer Ab would say these things, nothing could be at once more fine in humor and pointed in philosophy. Negroes on the corner can be heard any day engaged in talk that at least makes one think of Shakspere's clowns; but half the point and flavor is in the subtle tone of voice, the gesture, the glance, and these, unfortunately, cannot be read between the lines by any one who has not studied them in the living original.

[1] *Anglice,* Brother.

" Brer Remus, is you heern tell er deze doin's out here in de udder end er town? "

" W'at doin's is dat, Brer Ab? "

" Deze yer signs an' wunders whar dat cullud lady died day 'fo' yistiddy. Mighty quare goin's on out dar, Brer Remus, sho's you bawn."

" Sperrits? "

" Wuss'n dat, Brer Remus. Some say dat jedgment day ain't fur off, an' de folks is flockin' roun' de house, a-hollerin' an' a-shoutin' like dey wuz in er revival. In de winder-glass dar you kin see de flags a-flyin', an' Jacob's ladder is dar, an' dar's writin' on de pane what no man can't read—leastwise, dey ain't none read it yet."

" W'at kinder racket is dis youer givin' me now, Brer Ab? "

" I done bin dur, Brer Remus; I done seed um wid bofe my eyes. Cullud lady what was intranced done woke up an' say dey ain't much time fer ter tarry. She say she meet er angel in de road, an' he p'inted straight fur de mornin' star an' tell her fer ter prepar'. Hit look mighty cu'us, Brer Remus."

" Come down ter dat, Brer Ab," said Uncle Remus, wiping his spectacles carefully and re-adjusting them,—" cum down ter dat, an' dey ain't nuthin' that ain't cu'us. I ain't no 'spicious nigger myse'f, but I 'spizes fer ter hear dogs a-howlin' an' squinch owls havin' de ager out in de woods, an' w'en a bull goes a-bellerin' by de house, den my bones git cole an' my flesh commences for ter creep; but w'en it comes ter deze yer sines in de a'r an' deze yer sperrits in de woods, den I'm out—den I'm done. I is, fer a fac'. I been livin' yer more'n seventy year, an' I hear talk er niggers seein' ghos'es all times er night an' all times er day, but I ain't never seed none yit; an' deze yer flags and Jacob's lathers, I ain't seed dem, nudder."

" Dey er dar, Brer Remus."

" Hit's des like I tell you, Brer Ab. I ain't 'sputin' 'bout it, but I ain't seed um, an' I don't take no chances, deze days, on dat w'at I don't see, an' dat w'at I sees I gotter 'zamine mighty close. Lemme tell you dis, Brer Ab. Don't you let deze sines onsettle you. W'en ole man Gabrile toot his ho'n, he ain't gwinter hang no sine out in de winder-panes, an' w'en ole Fadder Jacob lets down dat lather er hisn you'll be mighty ap' fer ter hear de racket. An' don't you bodder wid jedgment-day. Jedgment-day is lierbul fer ter take keer un itse'f."

" Dat's so, Brer Remus."

" Hit's bleedzed ter be so, Brer Ab. Hit don't bodder me. Hit's done got so now dat w'en I gotter pone er bread, an' a rasher er bacon, an' nuff grease fer ter make gravy, I ain't keerin' much wedder folks sees ghos'es or no."

These concluding sentiments of Brer Remus would serve

very accurately as an expression of the attitude of the small farmer—not only in the South, but elsewhere—toward many of the signs and ghosts and judgment-days with which the careful politician must fight the possible loss of public attention. There may be signs of danger to the republic; there may be ghosts of dreadful portent stalking around the hustings and through the Capitol corridors; and Judgment-day may be coming,—to this or that representative or functionary; but meantime it is clear that we small farmers will have nothing to eat unless we go into the field and hoe the corn and feed the hogs. By the time this is done, night comes on, and, being too tired to sit up until twelve o'clock for a sight of the ghost, we go to bed soon after supper, and sleep without sign or dream till the sun calls us forth again to the corn and the hogs.

III

The evils just now alleged of large farming in the West were necessarily in the way of prophecy; but it is not difficult to show them as history. Early in the sixteenth century, England was seized with a passion for large farming such as perhaps no age can parallel; and it so happens that contemporary pictures place the results of it before us with quite extraordinary vividness.

After the fineness of English wool had been demonstrated, and had carried up the price of that commodity, the rage for sheep-raising became a mania like that of the South Sea speculation, and this one culture became the " large farming " of the period. Land-owners deliberately tore down farm-buildings and converted farms into sheep-walks; churches were demolished, or converted into sheep-houses; hamlets were turned to pasture; and rents were raised to such a rate as would drive off tenants holding leases, and enable the landlords to make sheep-walks of their holdings. Thus, bodies of productive glebe which had supported many farmers' families would be turned over to the occupation of a single shepherd. What must become of the farmers' families? Contemporary testimony is ample. They became beggars and criminals, and the world has rarely seen such sights of barbarous misery as are revealed by the writings, the sermons, the laws of this frightful period. A tract in

Lambeth Library, belonging to this time, is entitled *Certain Causes Gathered Together, wherein is showed the decay of England only by the great multitude of sheep, to the utter decay of household keeping, maintenance of men, dearth of corn, and other notable discommodities*; and, after estimating that 50,000 fewer ploughs are going than a short time before, declares that the families once fed by these ploughs " now have nothing but to go about in England from door to door, and ask their alms for God's sake "; and " some of them, because they will not beg, do steal, and then they be hanged. And thus the realm doth decay."

In that notable dialogue of Thomas Starkey's, recently published by the New Shakspere Society, purporting to be a conversation between Thomas Lupset, Oxford professor, and his friend, Cardinal Pole,—a work by no means an unworthy predecessor of Landor's *Imaginary Conversations*,—we have contemporary testimony to the same facts. " Who can be so blind or obstinate," cries Lupset, at a certain point, " to deny the great decay, faults and misorders of our common weal; . . . our cities, castles and towns of late days ruinate and fallen down "; and he laments the " ground so rude and waste, which hath been beforetime occupied and tilled "; declaring, in another place, that " this is sure, that in no country of Christendom you shall find so many beggars as be here in England," and inveighing against the " nourishing of sheep, which is a great decay of the tillage of this realm."

But here honest Hugh Latimer comes and nails his nail with lightning and thunder. In the first of those seven sturdy sermons which he preached before the young King Edward VI, in 1548, immediately after Henry VIII's death, describing the number of agricultural laborers who had been thrown out of possible employment by the sudden rage for sheep-raising, he exclaims:

> For wher as have bene a great many of householders and inhabitantes, ther is now but a shepherd and his dogge!
>
> My lordes and maisters, [proceeds Latimer,] I say also that all such procedynges . . . do intend plainly to make the yomanry slavery and the cleargye shavery.

And then we have a bright glimpse at better old days of small farming, in some personal recollections with which the old preacher was often fond of clinching an argument.

My father was a Yoman, and had no landes of his owne, onely he had a farme of iii or iiii pound by yere at the uttermost, and hereupon he tilled so much as kepte half a dozen men. He had walk for a hundred shepe, and my mother mylked xxx kyne. He was able and did find the king a harnesse, wyth hymselfe, and hys horsse, whyle he come to ye place that he should receyve the kynges wages. I can remembre yat I buckled hys harnes when he went unto Blackeheath felde. He kept me to schole, or elles I had not bene able to have preached before the kynges maiestie nowe. He maryed my systers with v pounde a pece. . . . He kept hospitalitie for his pore neighbours. And sum almess he gave to the poore, and all thys did he of the sayd farme. *When he that now hath it paieth XVI pounde by yere or more,* and is not able to do anything for his Prynce, for himselfe, nor for his children, or geve a cup of drincke to the pore.

Thus we learn, from the clause I have italicized, that within Hugh Latimer's personal recollection farm-rents had gone up more than three hundred per cent in consequence of the " inclosure " mania—" inclosure " being a term in many mouths during all this period, and always equivalent to " large farming."

It is inspiriting to observe the boldness with which Latimer charges home these evils upon the landlords, many of whom must have been sitting before him at the moment. These sermons were preached in the garden at Westminster, where the young king had caused a pulpit to be set up for Latimer in order to accommodate the crowd who desired to hear him. " You landlords," he cries, in another part of the same sermon,

you rent-raisers, I maye saye you step-lordes, you unnaturall lordes, you have for your possessions yerely to [too] much. Of thys to much, commeth this monsterous and portentious dearth . . . that poore menne . . . cannot wyth the sweate of their face have a livinge, all kinde of victales is so deare, pigges, gese, capons, chickens, egges, [etc.!]

But, worse again, in the large-farming mania, great landowners became land-grabbers of the most unscrupulous kind. In his second sermon, Latimer gives us a view of one of their methods:

I can not go to my boke, for pore folkes come unto me, desirynge me that I wyll speake that theyr matters maye be heard. [Occasionally he is at my lord of Canterbury's house,] and now and then I walke in the garden lokyng in my boke. . . . I am no soner in the garden and have red a whyle but by and by cometh there some or other knocking at the gate. Anon cometh my man and sayth, Syr, there is one at the gate would speake wyth you. When I come there then it is some or other . . . that hathe layne thys longe [time] at great costes and charges and can not once have hys matter come to the hearing; but among all other, one especially moved me at this time to speak. . . . A gentlewoman come to me and tolde me that a great man keepeth certaine landes of hyrs from hir, and wil be hyr tennante in the spite of hyr tethe. And that in a whole twelve moneth she coulde not gette but one day for the hearynge of hyr matter, and the same daye when the matter should be hearde, the greate manne broughte on hys syde a greate syghte of Lawyers for hys counsayle, the gentilwoman had but one man of lawe: and the great man shakes hym so that he can not tell what to do, so that when the matter came to the poynte, the Judge was a meane to the gentylwoman that she wold let the great man have a quietnes in hyr Lande.

But far more beautifully and comprehensively does that lucent soul Thomas More put the case, in the *Utopia*. Here, through the medium of another imaginary conversation, More is cunningly showing up affairs at home. He is talking with his supposititious traveller, Hythlodaye:

"I pray you, syr [quod I], have you ben in our countrey?"

"Yea, forsoth [quod he], and there I taried for the space of iiii or v monethes together. . . . It chaunced on a certayne daye, when I sate at the table of Archbishop John Morton, that a certain lawyer fell talking of thieves in England, rejoicing to see 'XX hanged together upon one gallowes,' and the like, wherto I replied:

"'It is to [too] extreame and cruel a punishment for thefte, . . . much rather provision should have been made that there were some means whereby they myght get their livyng, so that no man shoulde be dryven to this extreame necessitie, firste to steale and then to dye . . . [One cause of this is] as I suppose, proper and peculiar to you Englishmen alone.'

"'What is that,' quod the Cardinal.

"'Forsoth, my lorde [quod I], your shepe that were wont to be so meeke and tame and so smal eaters, now, as I heare say, be become so great devowerers, and so wylde that they eate up and swallow downe the very men themselves. They consume, destroye, and devoure whole fieldes, houses and cities. For looke in what partes of the realme doth growe the fynest, and therefore dearest woll [wool] these noblemen, and gentlemen, yea and certayn Abbottes, holy men, no doubt, leave no grounde for tillage, thei inclose al into pastures, thei throw downe houses, they plucke down townes, and leave nothing standynge but only the churche to be made a shepe-house, [so that] the husbandmen be thrust owte of their owne, or els either by coveyne fraude, or by violent oppression thei be put besyde it, or by wronges and injuries thei be so weried that they be compelled to sell all; . . . either by hooke or crooke thei must needs departe awaye, poore, selye, wretched soules, men, women, husbands, wives, fatherless children, widowes, wofull mothers with their yonge babes, and their whole household, smal in substance and muche in numbre, as husbandrye requireth many handes. Awaye thei trudge, I say . . . fyndynge no place to reste in. All their householde stuffe, . . . beeyng sodainely thruste oute, they be constryned to sell it for a thing of nought. And when they have wandred abrode tyll that be spent, what can they then els doo but steale, and then justly pardy be hanged, or els go about a-beggyng? . . . I praye you, what other thing do you then [than] makes theves, and then punish them?' "

It seems difficult to believe that towns were actually destroyed, and churches deliberately pulled down, to give room for sheep-pastures; yet, if anything were needed beyond the testimony already given, it is clinched beyond all doubt by many statutes of the reign of Henry VIII and Elizabeth. For example, the Preamble to the statute of Henry VIII, Chapter I, recites: *

The King, our Sovereign Lord, calling to his most blessed remembrance that whereas great inconvenience be and daily increase by . . . pulling down and destruction of houses and towns within his realm, and laying to pasture land which customably have been . . . occupied with tillage and husbandry . . . whereby husbandry is decayed, churches destroyed, [etc., etc., therefore enacted that such places] be re-edified, and such lands so turned into pasture be restored to tillage, [upon penalty of the king's seizing half the yearly profits to his own use until they should be so re-edified and restored.]

Eighteen years later I find *An Acte Concernyng Fermes and Shepe,* whose preamble yields some curious details of this large-farming rampant, and shows that Latimer's poor gentle-

* [MS B adds (pp. 35-36): "It may be that many of the evils recited in its Preamble will before long be filling the Preambles of American statutes; and the remedies here proposed, crude as they are, will not be unfamiliar to those who watch the legislative proceedings of many States in this Republic."—ED.]

woman, who had a great man for her tenant in spite of her teeth, was but one of many.

> For as much as divers and sundry persons of the king's subjects of this Realm . . . now of late . . . have daily studied and practiced . . . ways and means how they might accumulate and gather together into fewer hands as well great multitude of farms as great plenty of cattle and in especial sheep, putting such land as they can get to pasture and not to tillage, whereby they have not only pulled down churches and towns and enhanced the old rates of the rents . . . of this Realm . . . but have raised the prices of all manner of corn, cattle, wool, pigs, geese, hens, chickens, eggs, and such other, almost double . . . by reason whereof a marvelous multitude of the people of this Realm be not able to provide meat, etc., for themselves, their wives and children, but be so discouraged with misery and poverty that they fall daily to theft, robbing, etc., . . . or pitifully die for hunger and cold;

and as all this comes of large farming in sheep, whereby great herds are gathered into few hands; therefore enacted that hereafter no person shall have, of his own proper cattle, above two thousand head at a time; upon pain of three shillings and four pence—a heavy fine—for each surplus sheep.

And to similar intents I find act after act, running far into Elizabeth's reign.

But to no effect; for who can stop gambling? "We have good statutes," quoth Latimer, "as touching commoners,"—commoners being those who usurped commons for sheep-walks, in short, large-farmers,—"but there cometh nothing forth. . . . Let the preacher preach till his tongue be worn to the stumps, nothing is amended."

In a time when ballads were so plentiful that, as *Martin Marsixtus* (1552) hath it, "every red-nosed rhymester is an author," and "scarce a cat can look out of a gutter but out starts some penny chronicler, and presently a proper new ballad of a strange sight is indited," such matters as these could hardly fail to find their way into popular verse; and accordingly we find the story in such forms as:

> The towns go down, the land decays,
> Of corn-fields, plain leas;
> Great men maketh nowadays
> A sheep-cot of the church.
>
> . . . . . .

Poor folk for bread to cry and weep;
Towns pulled down to pasture sheep;
This is the new guise.*

How far this large farming, thus carried on, converted the most virtuous occupation of man—husbandry— into the most conscience-withering of all pursuits,—the gambler's,—and gave to the wildest speculation the factitious basis of a sort of real-estate transaction; how far it was connected with that national passion for dicing which Roger Ascham mourns, when he partly quotes the *Pardoner's Tale* of Chaucer, wishing that English

Lordes might finde them other maner of pleye
Honest ynough to drive the day awaye,

and concludes, so beautifully: "I suppose that there is no one thyng that chaungeth sooner the golden and sylver wyttes of men into copperye and brassye wayes than dicing"; how far it was of the same piece with that frightful knavery in public station against which we hear old Latimer thundering, "They all love bribes, and bribery is a princely kind of thieving," and telling them the story of Cambyses, who flayed a bribe-taking judge and covered the judge's chair with it, that all succeeding judges might sit in that wholesome reminder, and finally exclaiming, "a goodly syne, . . . I praye God we may see the signe of the skynne in England"; how far it was connected with gentle George Gascoigne's picture in *The Steel Glass,* of the clergyman who

will read the holy writ,
Which doth forbid all greedy usury,
And yet receive a shilling for a pound;
. . . will preach of patience,
And yet be found as angry as a wasp;
. . . reproveth vanity,
(While he himself, with hawk upon his fist
And hounds at heel, doth quite forget the text);
. . . corrects contentions
For trifling things, and yet will sue for tithes;

how far it had to do with Bernard Gilpin's rebuke, in his ser-

* [MS B (p. 48) adds from Crowley's *Epigrams* the story of two beggars who, unable to get work, keep their sores from healing in order to avoid imprisonment.—Ed.]

mon, of *Never so many gentlemen and so little gentleness*; and how far the past of large farming in England sheds light on the future of large farming in America: are questions beyond the limits of this paper.

Meantime, it seems like an omen to this brief sketch, that while it is being written the newspapers bring report how Mr. Gladstone has recently proposed small farming as a remedy for the present agricultural ills of England, and has recommended that "English farmers should turn their attention to raising fruits, vegetables, poultry, eggs, and butter."

In truth, I find a great man appealing to the small farmer a long time before Mr. Gladstone. Euripides praises him for not being a crazy democrat. It is these farmers, he declares, who stay at home and do not come to the public assembly, that save the country.*

It is impossible to end without adverting to a New South which exists in a far more literal sense than that of small farming. How much of this gracious land is yet new to all real cultivation, how much of it lies groaning for the muscle of man, and how doubly mournful is this newness, in view of the fair and fruitful conditions which here hold perpetual session, and press perpetual invitation upon all men to come and have plenty! Surely, along that ample stretch of generous soil, where the Appalachian ruggednesses calm themselves into pleasant hills before dying quite away into the sea-board levels, a man can find such temperances of heaven and earth—enough of struggle with nature to draw out manhood, with enough of bounty to sanction the struggle—that a more exquisite co-adaptation of all blessed circumstances for man's life need not be sought. It is with a part of that region that this writer is most familiar, and one cannot but remember that, as one stands at a certain spot thereof and looks off up and across the Ocmulgee River, the whole prospect seems distinctly to yearn for men.**

* [MS B (p. 55) places this incident at the time "when the Peloponnesian War has brought on a wild democratic rule." (Lanier was apparently thinking of the political chaos in the South during Reconstruction.) The allusion carries the mind more readily to Aristophanes' pictures of contemporary conditions than to any extended passage in Euripides.—Ed.]

** [MS B (pp. 57-58) defines this region most familiar to Lanier as "the middle ground . . . of . . . Georgia,—say, from above Marietta to below Macon, and from the Flint eastward across the Ocmulgee and Oconee rivers to the Savannah." And the vantage point for his view: "As one stands in the street of Vineville, a pleasant collection of residences suburban to Macon."—Ed.]

Everywhere the huge and gentle slopes kneel and pray for vineyards, for corn-fields, for cottages, for spires to rise up from beyond the oak-groves. It is a land where there is never a day of summer nor of winter when a man cannot do a full day's work in the open field; all the products meet there, as at nature's own agricultural fair; rice grows alongside of wheat, corn alongside of sugar-cane, cotton alongside of clover, apples alongside of peaches, so that a small farm may often miniature the whole United States in growth; the little valleys everywhere run with living waters, asking grasses and cattle and quiet grist-mills; all manner of timbers for economic uses and trees for finer arts cover the earth; in short, here is such a neighborly congregation of climates, soils, minerals and vegetables, that within the compass of many a hundred-acre farm a man may find wherewithal to build his house of stone, of brick, of oak, or of pine, to furnish it in woods that would delight the most curious eye, and to supply his family with all the necessaries, most of the comforts, and many of the luxuries, of the whole world. It is the country of homes.

And, as said, it is because these blissful ranges are still clamorous for human friendship; it is because many of them are actually virgin to plow, pillar, axe or mill-wheel, while others have known only the insulting and mean cultivation of the earlier immigrants, who scratched the surface for cotton a year or two, then carelessly abandoned all to sedge and sassafras, and sauntered on toward Texas: it is thus that these lands are, with sadder significance than that of small farming, also a New South.